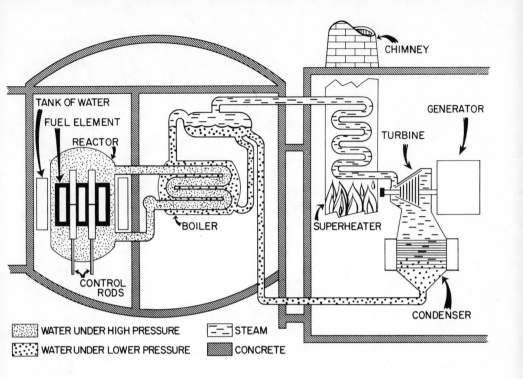

TANK OF WATER
FUEL ELEMENT
REACTOR
CONTROL RODS
BOILER
CHIMNEY
GENERATOR
TURBINE
SUPERHEATER
CONDENSER

WATER UNDER HIGH PRESSURE
WATER UNDER LOWER PRESSURE
STEAM
CONCRETE

Explanation of the Atomic Power Plant at Indian Point

In 1962 the Consolidated Edison nuclear electric plant located at Indian Point, N. Y., and pictured on the front cover of this book went into operation. At its peak performance this plant is expected to generate 275,000 kilowatts of electricity. The accompanying diagram indicates how the plant operates.

The fuel for the reactor consists of 2,420 pounds of uranium-235 oxide mixed with 37,800 pounds of thorium-232 oxide. This fuel, in pellet form, is encased in stainless steel tubes to form 120 fuel elements, each of which contains nearly 200 tubes. Water, under a pressure of 1,500 pounds per square inch, flows between the tubes and absorbs the heat produced in the core of the reactor. The steel tank of water surrounding the reactor is to prevent the escape of dangerous radiation. For further protection against radiation, the entire structure is enclosed in thick concrete.

Because of its great pressure, the water does not boil, even though it is heated to 519° F. The heated pressurized water, which is radioactive, is pumped through a series of U-shaped tubes in the evaporator section of the boiler. Water in the evaporator absorbs the heat of the pressurized water and turns to steam. Note that this water and steam are not radioactive.

The steam, at a temperature of 449° F and a pressure of 405 pounds per square inch, is collected in a separate part of the boiler called the drum. It then flows through the coils of the superheater, where it is heated to 1,000° F at a pressure of 355 pounds per square inch.

The superheated steam is piped to a steam turbine which drives an electric generator. Leaving the turbine, the steam is condensed back to water, which is pumped back to the boiler to be used again.

Cover photograph courtesy of Consolidated Edison Company of New York, Inc.

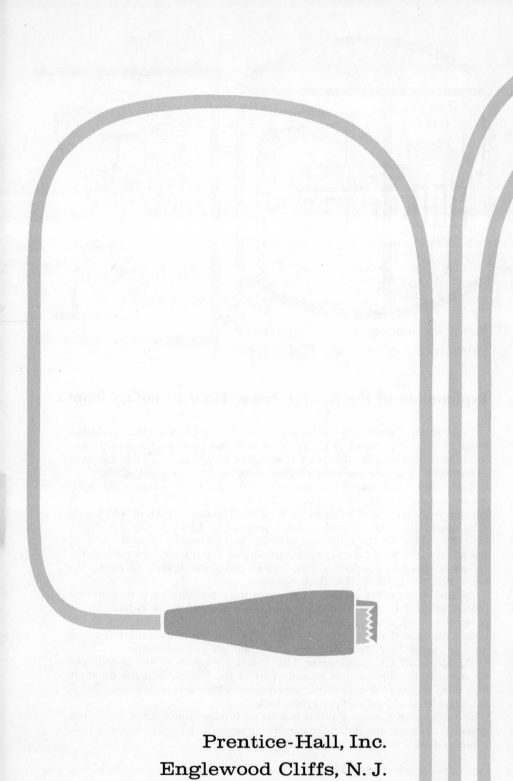

Prentice-Hall, Inc.
Englewood Cliffs, N. J.

2nd edition

Basic Electricity

Abraham Marcus

PRENTICE-HALL INDUSTRIAL ARTS SERIES

To Rebecca,

beloved wife and helpmate, without whose inspiration and patience this book could never have been written.

About This Book

A textbook is a teaching device. As such, it must pertain to specific subject matter. This book is a text on the fundamentals of electricity. A textbook must be intended for a specific type of student. This book is intended for beginners. It requires no prerequisite knowledge of physics or mathematics other than ordinary arithmetic.

And, above all, a textbook must be pedagogically sound. Proper organization is all-important. Whenever a new concept is presented to a student, the gap between this new material and what he already knows must not be too great. Rather, the new ideas must be a continuation and extension of his knowledge.

An advanced student can easily fit a new concept into his wide background. But a beginner has no such background. Unless the new material is not too far removed from what he has already learned, he may find himself unable to bridge the gap. A book for beginners must present a continuous story, proceeding from concept to concept, continually building upon that which has gone before.

With this in mind, this book was written. It is divided into six sections. The first, and introductory, section deals with the question, "What is electricity?" The second section deals with direct-current phenomena. Alternating current is discussed in the third section. The fourth section concerns itself with generators of electricity—mechanical, chemical, etc. Included here are some of the new and, as yet, experimental types of generators such as the solar and atomic types.

Practical applications of electricity are discussed in section five. A separate chapter is devoted to each type of application, based upon the various effects of the electric current, such as the thermal, luminous, chemical, and magnetic effects. The electric motor, both d-c and a-c types, rates a chapter of its own.

No book on electricity would be complete without mention of electronics. Section six deals with this subject. The electron tube and transistor are explained and practical applications in the fields of communication, industry, entertainment, radar, television, etc., are discussed.

Numerous drawings and photographs are included in this book.

These illustrations are an integral part of this text and must be studied as such. A set of questions will be found at the end of each chapter. These questions serve the dual purpose of summary and review of the chapter. As a summary the questions offer the obvious advantage that the student must first read the text. The appendixes contain various glossaries of electrical terms, units, abbreviations, formulas, and graphic symbols. Included, too, are wire and mathematical tables.

Contents

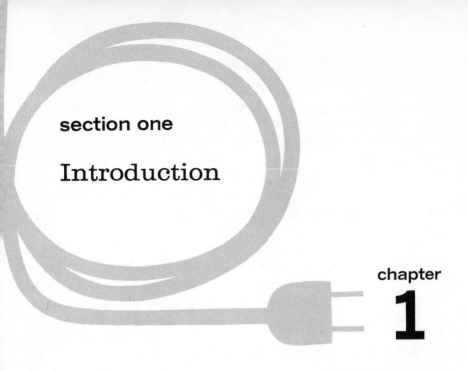

Introduction

What Is Electricity?

A. *Early theories*

The ancient people of the world had a magic. Digging in the earth, they sometimes turned up yellow, glasslike stones. When these stones were rubbed with a cloth, they mysteriously acquired the power of attracting small specks of dust, bits of straw, pieces of paper, and such. The ancients believed that these stones had a "soul" that attracted small particles of matter.

These stones were, in reality, *amber,* a fossilized form of resins that ooze from certain types of trees. As early as 600 B.C., a Greek philosopher, Thales of Miletus, wrote about experiments he conducted with amber, which the Greeks called "elektron." It is from this word that we get our modern term "electricity."

About 1600 A.D., William Gilbert, physicist and doctor to the English Queen Elizabeth I, discovered that other substances, such as sulfur, sealing wax, and glass, had properties similar to that of amber. The scientists of his time believed that such substances,

1

when rubbed, or *charged,* exuded a sort of fluid which attracted light objects. They called this "fluid" *electricity.*

Early in the eighteenth century, a French scientist, Charles du Fay, came to the conclusion that there were *two* types of "fluids," or electricity. One type he called "vitreous," the electricity present in charged glasslike substances. The other type he called "resinous," the electricity present when objects such as amber, wax, and rubber are charged.

Du Fay noted that charged vitreous substances attracted charged resinous substances, but repelled other charged vitreous substances. And he noted that charged resinous substances attracted charged vitreous substances, but repelled charged resinous substances.

About 1747, Benjamin Franklin, the American statesman and scientist, came to the conclusion that there was only one type of "fluid," or electricity. The "vitreous" and "resinous" charges, he believed, were only two opposite phases of the same phenomenon. He arbitrarily called the "vitreous" charge *positive* (+) and the "resinous" *negative* (−).

For the next one hundred and fifty years, though dissatisfied with the "fluid" theory of electricity, scientists could find no better explanation. But at the beginning of the twentieth century, while they were investigating the nature of matter in general, the outlines of a better and more rational theory began to take shape.

B. *Present-day theories*

1. THE STRUCTURE OF MATTER

Our world is full of a great many things that we call *matter,* by which we mean anything that has weight and takes up space. Let us consider one of these things—for example, water.

If we take some water and continue to divide it, we ultimately reach, theoretically, a speck of water so small that it no longer can be divided. But, small though it is, this speck of water has all the properties and tendencies of the original substance. This ultimate particle of a substance we call a *molecule.*

If an electric current passes through the molecule of water it breaks it down further into two gases, *oxygen* and *hydrogen.* Note, however, that these gases do not resemble the original water. The molecule seems to be made up of simpler substances.

A substance that can be broken down into two or more simpler substances is called a *compound*. If the substance cannot be broken down any further, it is called an *element*. Water is a compound; oxygen and hydrogen are elements. The smallest particle of a compound is a *molecule;* the smallest particle of an element is called an *atom.*

There are as many kinds of molecules as there are kinds of matter; but there are only 92 kinds of atoms.* Just as a few different kinds of bricks may be used to build a great many different types of buildings, so these relatively few kinds of atoms may be combined to form the enormous number of different molecules known to man.

In 1897, Joseph J. Thomson, an English scientist, announced he had definite proof that atoms, under certain conditions, shot out smaller particles of matter, which now are called *electrons.* The amazing thing about these electrons is that they are all alike, regardless of what substance emits them.

Once it was shown that the atom could be broken up, scientists delved deeper into its secrets. As a result, the *electron theory* † of the structure of matter was set forth. Most scientists today believe this theory to be true. But keep in mind that it is only a theory. It may be modified from time to time, and even, if proved to be false, discarded.

According to the electron theory, all matter is composed mainly of three types of particles. These are (1) the *electron,* a particle carrying a negative electrical charge; (2) the *proton,* a particle carrying a positive electrical charge; and (3) the *neutron,* a particle that carries no electrical charge. All atoms are composed of these particles;

---

* When scientists succeeded in unlocking the secret of nuclear energy, they also succeeded in changing elements from one type to another. At the same time a number of new elements were created in the laboratories. When we talk of the 92 kinds of atoms we mean those that were found in nature.

† When this theory was first stated it was believed that all atoms were made up of electrons and protons. Hence the name "electron theory." Today we know that the atom contains a number of other particles such as neutrons, mesons, positrons, neutrinos, anti-protons. Thus it no longer is strictly accurate to talk about the "electron theory of atomic structure." However, to avoid confusion between our present-day theory and the old atomistic theories, we will retain the term *electron theory.*

Except for the electrons, protons, and neutrons, the other particles that make up the atom do not exist normally. They are created and exist for an extremely short period of time as atoms break up. Accordingly, we will ignore these particles in this book. Also, the theories presented here must, of necessity, be in greatly simplified form.

the atoms differ from one another in the number of particles they contain and in the arrangement of these particles.

Niels Bohr, a Danish scientist, gave us a picture of atomic structure which, at that time, was widely accepted.* According to Bohr, the atom is composed of a central *nucleus,* which is surrounded by revolving *electrons,* somewhat as our sun is surrounded by revolving planets. In fact, the electrons that revolve around the nucleus are called *planetary* electrons. (See Figure 1-1.)

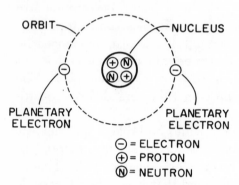

ORBIT — NUCLEUS

PLANETARY ELECTRON   PLANETARY ELECTRON

⊖ = ELECTRON
⊕ = PROTON
Ⓝ = NEUTRON

Fig. 1-1.

Theoretical structure of an atom. The nucleus here contains two protons and two neutrons. The two planetary electrons revolve around the nucleus in the orbit indicated. This is the helium atom.

The nucleus contains all the protons and neutrons. An atom of one element differs from an atom of any other in the number of protons contained in the nucleus. The number of protons in the nucleus is called the *atomic number* of the element and varies from 1, for the element *hydrogen,* to 92 for the element *uranium.* (The number is even higher for the new man-made elements.) The atomic number of helium, whose structure is shown in Figure 1-1, is 2.

The negative charge on the planetary electron is equal and opposite to the positive charge on the proton. Hence, these charges tend to neutralize each other. Since the nucleus contains all the protons, it carries a total positive charge that is equivalent to the number of protons present. Inasmuch as a normal atom is *neutral*— that is, it has no external electrical charge—the positive charge on the nucleus is exactly neutralized by the negative charges of the planetary electrons revolving about it.

---

* Although the picture of atomic structure originally presented by Niels Bohr has been considerably modified by the discovery of new facts, for the purposes of this book it may be better if we consider the earlier, and simpler, Bohr atomic structure.

It follows that the neutral atom has as many planetary electrons as there are protons in its nucleus. Consequently, the number of planetary electrons revolving around the nucleus varies from 1, for hydrogen, to 92, for uranium (and higher, for the man-made elements). Note that in the helium atom shown in Figure 1-1 there are two protons and two planetary electrons.

All atoms, except those of ordinary hydrogen, contain one or more neutrons in the nucleus. The helium atom (Figure 1-1) contains two neutrons; the uranium atom may contain 146 neutrons. The neutron carries no electrical charge and in some respects acts as though it were composed of a proton and electron combined, with the positive charge of the proton neutralized by the negative charge of the electron.

Although the opposite electrical charges carried by an electron and a proton are equal in magnitude, the *mass,* or weight, of the proton is about 1,840 times as great as the weight of the electron. The mass of the neutron is about equal to that of the proton. We can readily see that practically the entire mass, or weight, of the atom is contained in the nucleus.

The number of protons and neutrons in the nucleus of an atom determines its weight, or *mass number.* The mass number of atoms varies from 1 for ordinary hydrogen, which is the lightest of the elements (one proton and no neutrons in its nucleus), to 238 for uranium which, until recently, was the heaviest element (92 protons and 146 neutrons in its nucleus). The new and heavier elements have even greater mass numbers. The mass number for the helium atom shown in Figure 1-1 is 4 (two protons and two neutrons).

All of the atoms of an element contain the same number of protons in their nuclei, and the atoms of one element differ from those of all other elements in the number of protons so contained. For example, each hydrogen atom contains one proton in its nucleus and each uranium atom has 92 protons. But the atoms of one element may differ in mass number, owing to different numbers of neutrons in their nuclei.

For example, three different types of hydrogen atoms have been found. All of these atoms have the same atomic number of 1 (one proton in the nucleus). However, one of these atoms (the type most commonly found in nature) has a mass number of 1—that is, one proton and no neutron in its nucleus. A second type has a mass number of 2—one proton and one neutron in the nucleus. A third type has a mass number of 3—one proton and two neutrons. Except for the differences in weight, all three types of atoms have identical properties.

We call these different atoms of the same element *isotopes*. Most elements are known to have two or more isotopes. It is interesting to note that scientists have been able to produce artificial isotopes by bombarding the nuclei of atoms with neutrons. In this way, for example, an atom of uranium with a mass number of 238 (92 protons and 146 neutrons in its nucleus) sometimes captures a neutron, raising the mass number to 239 (92 protons, 147 neutrons).

So far, we have concentrated on the nucleus of the atom. Now let us turn our attention to the electrons revolving around the nucleus. As previously stated, the normal atom has one planetary electron for each proton in the nucleus. Thus, the number of such electrons will vary from 1, for hydrogen, to 92, for uranium (and higher for the new elements).

These electrons do not revolve around the nucleus in a disorderly fashion. Their orbits, or paths, form concentric shells, or layers, somewhat like the layers of an onion. There is a certain maximum number of electrons that each shell can contain. If this number is exceeded, the excess electrons arrange themselves in the next outer shell.

The shell nearest to the nucleus may contain up to two electrons. If there are more than two electrons, the excess form a second shell around the first. This second shell may hold up to eight electrons. Then a third shell will be formed which may hold up to 18 electrons. The fourth shell may hold up to 32 electrons, the fifth shell up to 50 electrons, and the sixth shell up to 72 electrons. However, in some of the more complicated atoms, electrons may be found in outer shells even before some of the inner ones have been filled up.

Look at Figure 1-2A. This is the theoretical picture of the structure of the helium atom. The nucleus contains two protons and two neutrons. The two planetary electrons revolve in a single shell around the nucleus.

In Figure 1-2B the structure of the carbon atom is shown. Around a nucleus containing six protons and six neutrons revolve six electrons. The first two electrons form the shell nearest to the nucleus. Since this shell can contain no more than two electrons, the remaining four electrons form themselves into a second shell outside the first. (The orbits generally are considered to be elliptical, although they are drawn circular here for convenience.)

In Figure 1-2C we see the structure of the lead atom. The 82 electrons are contained in six shells, or layers, around the nucleus.

Except for the electrons in the outermost shell, the particles of

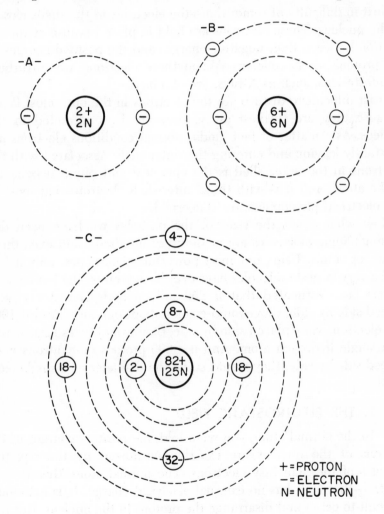

Fig. 1-2. Theoretical structures of atoms.
A. Helium atom.
B. Carbon atom.
C. Lead atom.

the atom are held together tightly, and relatively tremendous forces are required to pry them apart. Most difficult to disrupt is the nucleus. What holds the protons and neutrons together, we do not know, but when we do succeed in exploding the nucleus, as was accomplished in the atomic bomb, an enormous amount of energy is released.

Next in difficulty of removal are the electrons in the shells closest to the nucleus. These electrons are held in place because of the attraction between their negative charges and the positive charges of the protons of the nucleus. When these electrons are disturbed, manifestations, such as X-rays, are obtained.

Least difficult to disturb are the electrons in the outermost layer. Because they are furthest away, they are least attracted to the nucleus. As a matter of fact, under normal conditions electrons are constantly leaving and entering this outer shell. Associated with the electrons in the outer shell is the chemical and physical behavior of the atom. And it is with these outer-shell electrons that most of our electrical phenomena are concerned.

Now what about the sizes of the particles we have been discussing? Some molecules are made up of hundreds, and even thousands, of atoms. Using our most powerful microscopes, only a few of the very largest molecules have ever been seen by the human eye. It has been estimated that if 250 million hydrogen atoms were placed side by side, they would extend about one inch. And if 100,-000 electrons were placed side by side, they would be as large across as a single hydrogen atom. And if 1,800 protons or neutrons were placed side by side, they would equal the diameter of a single electron!

2. THE ELECTROSTATIC FIELD

In the normal atom, you were told, the positive charges of the protons of the nucleus are exactly neutralized by the negative charges of the planetary electrons. The normal atom, therefore, is neutral—that is, it has no external electrical charge. It is extremely difficult to get at and disarrange the protons in the nucleus. But it is quite easy to disturb the arrangement of the planetary electrons, especially those of the outermost shell.

Suppose we were to remove one or more of the outermost electrons from a neutral atom. Since there then would be more positive protons than negative electrons, the atom would no longer be neutral. Instead, it would show a positive charge. But should we add extra electrons to a neutral atom, the atom would show a negative charge.

We believe that a *field of force* exists around a charged body, somewhat like the gravitational field that surrounds all objects. This field of force, which is called the *electrostatic,* or *electric, field,* will cause oppositely charged objects to be attracted to each other. If the objects have similar charges, they will be repelled.

Now let us return to our piece of amber. When it is rubbed with a cloth, the amber atoms tear electrons away from the cloth. As a result, the amber receives a negative charge (excess of electrons) and the cloth receives a positive charge (deficiency of electrons). Because of these opposite charges, the amber and cloth will attract each other.

What determines which substance will seize electrons and which will lose them? The answer lies in the nature of the substance—that is, the number and arrangement of its outermost electrons. Some substances, such as cloth and glass, have their outermost electrons so arranged that they can lose them quite easily (and so obtain a positive charge). On the other hand, a piece of amber or hard rubber, for example, has its outermost electrons so arranged that, when it is rubbed, it will seize electrons from the material with which it is stroked, and it will accumulate an excess of electrons (negative charge).

Another question. A charged body will attract an oppositely charged body, but how does a charged body, such as amber, attract an uncharged body, such as a small piece of paper?

The answer is shown in Figure 1-3. By rubbing the piece of amber, we charge it negatively (excess of electrons). As this negatively

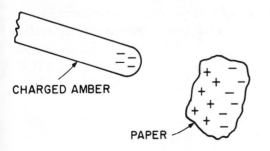

CHARGED AMBER

PAPER

Fig. 1-3.

How a charged body attracts an uncharged one.

charged body is placed near the uncharged paper, some of the electrons along the side of the paper nearest the amber are repelled and tend to move to the opposite side. This leaves the atoms of the paper nearest the amber with a deficiency of electrons (positive charge). We say that this nearer side is charged by *induction*. Because the attraction between the positively charged nearer side of the paper and the negatively charged amber is greater than the repulsion between the latter and the negatively charged farther side, the paper will be attracted to the amber.

There is another aspect of electricity to be considered. When a glass or hard rubber rod is being charged by losing or acquiring an excess of electrons, the action is local. That is, only the portion of the rod being rubbed is affected. If you take away or add electrons to one end of a hard rubber or glass rod, the atoms at the other end remain neutral and thus the rod at that end has no charge. We call such materials *insulators*. Examples are glass, hard rubber, wax, amber, sulfur, and paper.

On the other hand, there are certain substances, generally metals, whose outer electrons are held very loosely. As a matter of fact, a certain number of these outer electrons are constantly jumping from atom to atom, even without external influence. We call such moving electrons *free* electrons, and we call such substances *conductors*.

If an excess of electrons (negative charge) is placed at one end of a conductor, the repulsion between like charges will cause the loosely held electrons of neighboring atoms to move toward the other end. The movement of these electrons will cause a disturbance among electrons further away and, as a result, the excess of electrons quickly distributes itself throughout the entire conductor.

Similarly, if electrons are removed from one end of a conductor (positive charge), electrons from neighboring atoms are attracted to compensate for the deficiency. Again, all the atoms are affected and soon the deficiency is spread throughout the entire conductor. Thus a charge placed upon any portion of a conductor quickly spreads itself.

QUESTIONS

Wherever possible, diagrams should be used to clarify the answers to these questions. These diagrams need not be elaborate, but they should be drawn neatly with the significant portions clearly labeled.

1. Describe Bohr's theory of the structure of the atom.
2. What is meant by the *atomic number* of an atom? By its *mass number?*
3. In terms of the electron theory, how do atoms of one element differ from those of another?
4. What is meant by *isotopes?* How do isotopes of the same element differ from one another?
5. Draw the theoretical picture of an atom of *calcium* whose atomic number is 20 and whose mass number is 40.
6. What is meant when we say an atom is *neutral?* What is meant when we say that an object has a *positive charge?* A *negative charge?*
7. State the law of static attraction and repulsion. What is meant by the *electrostatic field of force?*
8. Explain how a charged piece of hard rubber can attract small scraps of paper.
9. In terms of the electron theory, explain what is meant by an *insulator;* a *conductor.*

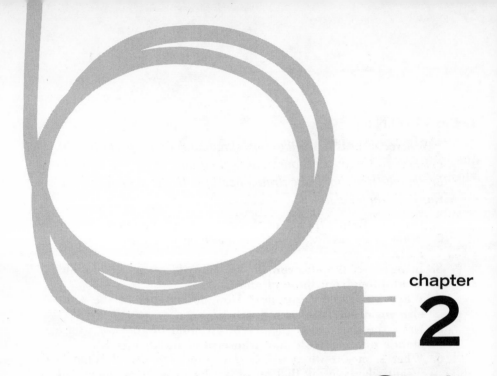

chapter

2

Static
Electricity

A. *Electrical pressure*

We now know that a field of force exists between two dissimi-larly charged objects. Another way of looking at this is to picture the excess electrons (negative charge) as straining to reach a point where there is a deficiency of electrons (positive charge).

If the two oppositely charged bodies are connected by a conductor, the excess electrons will have an easy path to the point of deficiency. The loosely held and free electrons of the conductor are repelled from the end that has the negative charge (excess of electrons). At the same time they are attracted to the end that has the positive charge (deficiency of electrons). As a result, a stream of electrons flows through the conductor from the end that has the excess of electrons to the end that has the deficiency. This flow continues un-til all the electrons are distributed uniformly throughout the con-ductor.

But if the two oppositely charged bodies are separated by an in-sulator, the picture is different. The insulator has few, if any, free electrons and the outermost electrons are tightly held to their orbits.

Accordingly, the excess electrons cannot move from the negative end of the insulator to satisfy the deficiency at the positive end.

As we continue to pile up an excess of electrons upon one end of the insulator and a proportionate deficiency at the other end, the electrostatic field of force increases. The stress, or *electrical pressure,* becomes quite great and, after a certain limit is reached, the insulator no longer can restrain the excess electrons and they rush across to the point of deficiency. This rush of electrons produces light and we see it in the form of a spark. At the same time, the air through which the electrons rush is heated and expands. We may hear the inrush of air that follows cooling in the form of a sharp, crackling sound, which accompanies the spark.

This rush of electrons, or spark, takes place in a small fraction of a second, and it might seem that the electrons merely jump from the point of excess to the point of deficiency. But closer examination indicates that the electrons jump back and forth between the two points many times (even millions of times) per second.

We may understand this better, perhaps, if we consider the behavior of a pendulum. Suspend a small weight from a string tied to a nail. The weight hangs straight down. Now lift the weight several inches to the right. The force of gravity tends to pull the weight back to its original position (that is, straight down). Release the weight. It swings toward its original position, but keeps right on going and now swings to the left. Again the force of gravity pulls it back, and once again it swings to the right. This process continues, each swing being a little less than before, until the weight comes to rest in its original position.

Similarly, electrons at a point that has a negative charge seek to satisfy the deficiency at the opposing point. When they rush over, more go than are needed to satisfy the deficiency. The two charges change places. The electrical pressure now is in the opposite direction and the electrons rush back. This to-and-fro surge of electrons continues until both points are neutral and the electrons are at rest once more.

B.   *Electricity and lightning*

The similarity between the electric spark and the flash of lightning led to the conclusion that they were identical. This identity was proved by Benjamin Franklin in 1752. Reasoning that lightning was the passage of electricity from the clouds to the earth, he set out to draw some of that electricity by means of a kite raised during a thunderstorm. Some of the electricity flowed down the wet string of the kite to a metal key attached at its end. By placing his knuckle near the key, he was able to draw a spark as the electricity jumped from the key to the ground through his body. He probably was unaware that he was risking his life by that experiment!

We now know that the lightning flash occurs because of a tremendous electrical pressure arising from opposite charges on the clouds and on the earth. How do these charges get on the clouds?

We are not sure, but we do know that thunder clouds are accompanied by a tremendous upward rush of warm air. We believe this upward rush of air tears apart the droplets of water of the cloud. The friction between the rushing air and the fragments of waterdrops generates an electrical charge. The positively charged particles generally are carried to the upper portion of the cloud, giving this upper portion a positive charge and leaving a negative charge on the lower portion of the cloud (Figure 2-1). By induction, the

Fig. 2-1.

Distribution of electrical charges on a cloud and on the earth beneath it. Sometimes the charges are reversed so that the underside of the cloud is positive and the ground is negative. Yet the result is the same whether the excess electrons start flowing from the cloud to the ground, or from the ground to the cloud.

ground beneath the cloud receives a positive charge. Since trees and houses in contact with the ground acquire the same charge, they, too, are charged positively.

When the electrical pressure becomes great enough, the excess electrons on the under portion of the cloud surge downward toward the earth in the form of a lightning flash. As was true of the spark, so in the lightning flash the electrons surge back and forth many times between the earth and the cloud. All this may take place in a few millionths of a second; that is why a lightning flash appears to be a single bolt.

Sometimes the charges are reversed so that the lower portion of the cloud becomes charged positively. The ground beneath the cloud then receives a negative charge by induction and the first rush of electrons may be up to the cloud. The effect is the same whether the lightning stroke first starts moving upwards or downwards.

So great are the electrical charges involved, that a lightning flash may extend five miles from cloud to earth. Most lightning flashes, however, are from cloud to cloud and such discharges may be up to ten miles long though, generally, they are much shorter. The clap of thunder that accompanies the flash is caused by inrushing air. The air that had been expanded by the passage of the hot lightning bolt has cooled and contracted, creating a partial vacuum. The surrounding air rushes into the low-pressure zone.

You see now why you should not stand under a tree during a lightning storm. Since the tree has the same charge as the ground and is closer to the cloud than the ground beneath it, there is a better chance that the lightning will strike the tree. So great is the force when this occurs, that the tree may be splintered and the heat of the flash may set it on fire.

It was the fact that lightning tends to strike the highest point that led Benjamin Franklin to invent the *lightning rod,* a device that protects buildings from lightning. It is a long, slender, metal rod extending above the roof of the building and connected to the earth by a heavy metal cable. Hence it presents an easier path to ground than the building, and any electrical charge it receives is carried away harmlessly through the cable directly to the ground.

The lightning rod protects the building in another way, also. If a charge is placed upon a spherical conductor, the mutual repulsion between like charges will cause the charge to be distributed uniformly over the sphere's surface. But if the conductor is eggshaped, the pointed end will become more highly charged than the rounded end. The greater charge causes a greater electrical pressure and, as a result, the charge will leak off into the air more readily from the pointed end than from the rounded one. By the same token, a pointed conductor will receive a charge from a nearby object more readily than will a rounded conductor.

For this reason, the upper end of the lightning rod is pointed and, consequently, its charge leaks off readily. Since the rod is attached to the building, the charge on the latter, too, will leak off through the sharp point of the lightning rod. Thus, the electrostatic field between the building and the cloud above it is lessened and the chances of the building's being struck by lightning are reduced.

C. *Practical applications of static electricity*

There are two ways in which we may put electricity to work. We may use the energy of the electrostatic field existing between two opposite charges. This is called *static* electricity. Or else we may use the energy of the movement of the electrons as they travel from a point of excess to a point of deficiency. This is called *current* electricity. For the remainder of this chapter we shall confine ourselves to practical applications of static electricity.

To further their studies of lightning, scientists sought to produce miniature flashes in the laboratory. Even on a smaller scale, a tremendous electrical pressure is required to cause electrons to jump, say, 20 feet of air from a negatively charged sphere to a positively charged one.

To obtain these tremendous electrical pressures, an American scientist, Robert Van de Graaff, in 1931 designed a machine that continuously placed small electrical charges into a large "container," thus building up the charge. Its action is somewhat similar to the manner in which an endless chain of buckets will bring water up from a well and fill a large tank on top of a building. A simplified version of the Van de Graaff generator is shown in Figure 2-2.

In essence, it consists of a large, hollow, metal ball set on a long tube. This metal ball, which may be ten or more feet in diameter, is the "container" for the electrical charge. The tube, which may be 30 or 40 feet long, supports the metal ball, and is made of some insulating material in order to prevent the charge stored in the ball from flowing to the ground. Inside this tube a long silk belt is made to pass rapidly over a set of pulley wheels. These wheels are insulated from the ground. Note the positions of the four eggshaped metal electrodes marked **A** and **B** (near the bottom of the belt) and C and D (near the top).

Let us suppose that a small positive charge is deposited on the righthand (descending) side of the silk belt. (This charge may be placed there by friction or by some other means.) As this charged portion of the belt comes opposite the point of electrode A, electrons are drawn from this electrode to compensate for the deficiency on the belt. This leaves **electrode A** with a positive charge.

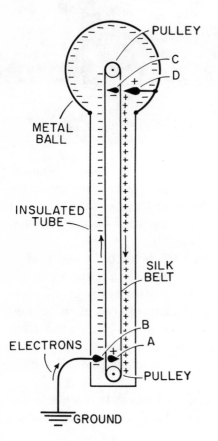

Fig. 2-2. Van de Graaff generator.

Fig. 2-3. External view of Van de Graaff generator.

Electrode B is connected to the ground. As electrode A becomes positive, it induces a negative charge on electrode B, whose excess electrons flow up from the ground. Some of these electrons leak off the pointed end of electrode B and are deposited on the silk belt, which rapidly carries them up the structure.

Near the top, the belt passes electrode C. Some of its excess electrons leak over, making this electrode negative. As a result, electrode D is made positive by induction. Hence, it attracts the excess electrons still remaining on the silk belt as the latter passes by its pointed end, and it deposits them on the metal ball to which it is connected. Having lost its electrons, the descending silk belt has a positive charge and is ready to repeat the cycle when it passes by electrode A.

The belt revolves at high speed and each revolution adds to the negative charge on the surface of the metal ball. Of course, the metal ball may be charged positively by starting the process with a negative charge on the descending side of the belt.

Tremendous charges may be built up in this way. When the electrical pressure becomes great enough, the sphere discharges to ground in the form of a miniature stroke of lightning. Sometimes two such generators, one creating a positive charge and the other a negative, are operated simultaneously. When the electrical pressure becomes great enough, a tremendous discharge, many feet in length, takes place between the two metal balls.

In addition to producing miniature lightning flashes, the Van de Graaff generator is used for other purposes where tremendous electrical pressures are required. For example, in atomic research, it is used to generate the large electrical pressure needed for the bombardment of nuclei of atoms.

Electrical charges can be used for other purposes. For example, in Figure 2-4 you see a device that is used to filter dust and soot that otherwise would go up a factory smokestack together with the hot gases. Not only is the surrounding air kept purer, but often valuable chemicals are recovered.

The operation of this device is extremely simple. The hot gases, dust, and soot pass through a metal chamber before entering the

Fig. 2-4.

How soot and dust are removed from factory exhaust gases.

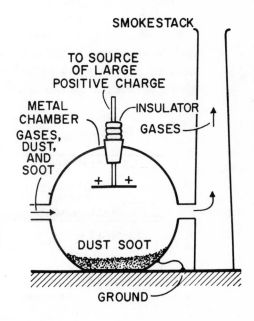

smokestack. A metal plate is mounted from an insulator near the top of the chamber. A large positive charge is placed upon this plate. As the particles of dust and soot pass beneath the charged plate, they are attracted to it. Once they touch the plate, the particles, too, acquire positive charges. As such, they are repelled from the charged plate and accumulate at the bottom of the chamber, which is grounded. The hot gases, cleaned of dust and soot, continue up the smokestack.

The electrostatic field is used, too, in the manufacture of sandpaper and similar abrasives. Ordinarily, a backing of paper or cloth is covered with an adhesive and the abrasive grains are spread over this adhesive and permitted to harden in place. In an improved method, however, the abrasive grains are dropped onto a belt, which carries them between two oppositely charged plates. The backing, coated with adhesive, is passed beneath the upper plate (Figure 2-5). As the abrasive grains enter the electrostatic field between the two charged plates, they acquire the same charge as the lower plate. They are repelled from this plate and fly up to the adhesive backing where, since all the grains have similar charges, they repel each other, spacing themselves uniformly. When the adhesive hardens, therefore, the abrasive grains are found to be standing on end and uniformly spaced. The result is a great improvement in the cutting quality of the abrasive.

A similar method is used in the manufacture of certain fabrics, such as simulated velvet or carpeting. The cloth backing is coated with an adhesive and passed beneath the upper of two charged plates. A belt carries tiny textile fibers over the lower plate. These

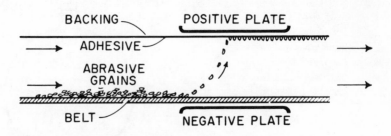

Fig. 2-5. How the electrostatic field is used in the manufacture of a better sandpaper.

fibers are repelled from the lower plate and are shot into the adhesive where they stand on end and are evenly spaced, often packed in at 250,000 fibers per square inch. Sometimes, instead of being spread uniformly, the adhesive is applied in the form of a design. The result, then, is a raised design where the tiny fibers stick to the adhesive.

So far we have dealt with stationary charges. The excess electrons deposited on a body have remained there, except for the brief interval when they have distributed themselves over a conductor or during an electrical discharge. It is for this reason that we have headed this chapter Static, or *stationary*, Electricity. In the following chapters, however, we shall study the electrons as they move from point to point under the influence of an electrical pressure. We shall, therefore, be considering *current*, or *flowing*, electricity.

QUESTIONS

Wherever possible, diagrams should be used to clarify the answers to these questions. These diagrams need not be elaborate, but they should be drawn neatly with the significant portions clearly labeled.

1. In terms of the electron theory, what is meant by *electrical pressure?*
2. Explain how lightning is produced.
3. Why is it unsafe to stand beneath a tree in an open field during a thunderstorm?
4. Explain how the lightning rod operates to protect a building from lightning.
5. Explain the operation of the Van de Graaff generator.
6. Explain how static electricity may be used to prevent dust and soot from polluting the air near a factory chimney.
7. Explain how static electricity may be used in the manufacture of sandpaper.
8. Explain how static electricity may be used in the manufacture of simulated velvet.
9. Explain the difference between *static* and *current* electricity.

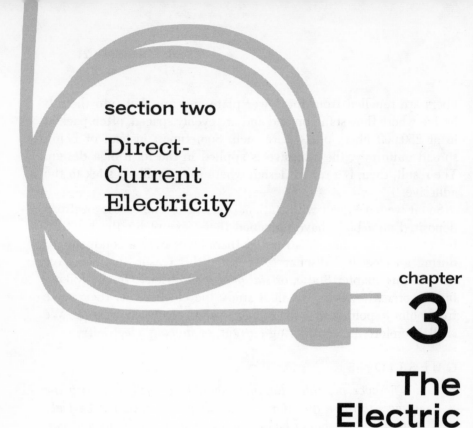

Direct-
Current
Electricity

The
Electric
Current

If an electron is removed from a neutral atom, the atom becomes *positively* charged. If an electron is added, the neutral atom becomes *negatively* charged. In the space between any two charged particles there exists a stress, or *field of force*. We call this field of force the *electric*, or *electrostatic, field*. Particles bearing like charges tend to repel one another, whereas particles bearing unlike charges tend to attract one another. The movement of charged particles arising from the presence of this field is called the *electric current*. This, of course, includes the movement of electrons, which are negatively charged particles.

A. *Three factors of an electric current*

1. ELECTROMOTIVE FORCE

Whenever an excess of electrons (negative charge) occurs at one end of a conductor and a deficiency (positive charge) at the other end, the electric field between the two ends will set up an electrical pressure that will cause the loosely held electrons from the outer shells of the atoms of the conductor to stream from the point of excess to the point of deficiency. Thus, an electric current will flow through the conductor from the negative end to the positive one.

To get an idea of *electrical pressure,* let us consider a simple analogy. Assume that we have a U-shaped tube with a valve or stopcock at the center (Figure 3-1). Assume that the valve is closed. We now pour water into arm A to a height represented by X. We pour water into arm B to a height represented by Y. If the valve now is opened, the water will flow from arm A to arm B until X and Y are equal.

What caused the water to flow? It was not *pressure* in arm A, because when X and Y are of equal length, no water flows even though the water in arm A still exerts pressure. It was the *difference in pressure* between the two arms that caused the water to flow. The flow continued until the pressures in the two arms were equal and the *difference in pressures* was zero.

So it is with electrons. If, at one end of a conductor, electrons are piled up, and at the other end, electrons are fewer in number or are

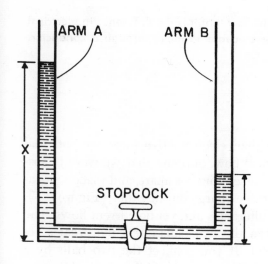

Fig. 3-1.

Diagram illustrating the fact that it is the **difference** in pressure which causes a fluid to flow through a tube.

being taken away, the excess electrons will flow toward the point of deficiency.

In Figure 3-1, the water in arm A can do no work until the valve is opened. Nevertheless, it represents a *potential* source of energy— that is, energy due to position. However, the actual work is not done by the potential energy of the water in arm A, but by the *difference in potential energy* between the water in A and the water in B.

Similarly, in Figure 3-2, it is not simply the potential energy of the excess electrons at one end of the conductor that causes the electrons to flow. It is the *difference* between the amounts of potential energy at the two ends of the conductor that does the work. We may say that electrons flow through a conductor (that is to say, an electric current flows) because of the difference in potential energy between the ends of the conductor. The force that moves the electrons from one point to another is known as the *potential difference,* or *electromotive (electron-moving) force.*

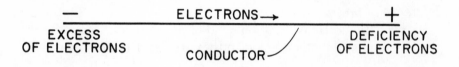

Fig. 3-2. Diagram illustrating the fact that it is the **difference** in electrical pressure which causes electrons to move through a conductor.

2. RESISTANCE

There is a factor other than electromotive force, or potential difference, that affects electrical flow. Suppose that we were to suspend two metallic balls in air several inches apart, and place a negative charge on one and a positive charge on the other (Figure 3-3).

Here we have a potential difference, and yet no current flows. The reason is that the air between the two balls offers too great a *resistance* to the flow of current. If you connect the two balls by a piece of metal, however, the electric current will flow from the negatively charged ball to the other one. The resistance of the metal strip is low enough so that the potential difference may send the electric current flowing through it.

But it is not necessary to connect the two balls with a metal strip to cause the electrons to flow from one to the other. All we need do is increase the charges. When the potential difference becomes great enough, the electrons will jump across through the air in the form of an electric spark. We conclude, therefore, that, *for electric current to flow, the potential difference must be great enough to overcome the resistance of the path.*

Different substances offer different resistances to the flow of electric current. Metals, generally, offer little resistance and are good conductors. Silver is the best conductor known, and copper is almost as good. Other substances, such as glass, rubber, sulfur, and the like, offer a very high resistance and are known as *insulators.* But all substances will permit the passage of some electric current, provided the potential difference is high enough.

3. CURRENT FLOW

For the third factor that affects electrical flow, refer back to Figure 3-1. We measure the flow of water from one arm to the other in terms of quantity per unit of time. We say so many gallons flow past a certain point in a minute. Similarly, we measure the flow of electricity by the number of electrons that flow past a point on a conductor in one second.

What determines the amount of water per unit of time that flows through the valve in Figure 3-1? Obviously, it is the difference be-

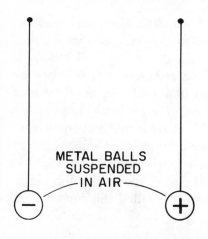

METAL BALLS
SUSPENDED
—IN AIR—

Fig. 3-3.

Two oppositely charged balls suspended far apart in air. Although there is a potential difference between them, no current flows because the resistance of the path between them is too great.

tween the amounts of potential energy of the water in the two arms of the tube, and it is also the size of the opening in the valve (that is, the resistance the valve offers to the flow of water).

In the case of the electric current, the quantity of electricity (the number of electrons per second) that flows in a conductor depends upon the potential difference and the resistance of the conductor. *The greater the potential difference, the larger the quantity of electricity that will flow; the greater the resistance, the smaller the quantity of electricity.*

B. *Units of measurement*

1. QUANTITY OF ELECTRIC CHARGE

Adding an electron to a neutral atom gives it a negative charge; taking an electron away from a neutral atom gives it a positive charge. Thus, the electrical charge of the electron is our basic unit.

Since the charge of one electron is very small, a *coulomb* is used as a practical unit for measuring the quantity of electric charge. A coulomb is equal to the combined charges of 6,280,000,000,000,-000,000 electrons. Of course, a figure this large is meaningless to the average person. It is stated here merely to emphasize the fact that the electrical charge on the electron is extremely small and that the combined charges of many electrons are employed to make up the coulomb.

2. ELECTRIC CURRENT

When we talk of electric current, we mean electrons in motion. When the electrons flow in one direction only, the current is called a *direct current* (abbreviated *dc*). In the discussion of electricity in this section we are speaking only of direct currents. It is important to know the number of electrons that flow past a given point on a conductor in a certain length of time. If a coulomb flows past a given point in one second, we call this amount one *ampere* of electric current. Hence, the unit of electric current is the ampere.

Aside from the fact that electrons are too small to be seen, we would find it impossible to count them as they flowed by. Fortunately, we have an electrical instrument, called the *ammeter* (to be described later), that indicates directly the amount of current flowing through it.

Where the ampere is too large a unit to be used, we may employ the *milliampere*, which is a thousandth (1/1,000) of an ampere, or the *microampere*, which is a millionth (1/1,000,000) of an ampere. In an electrical formula, the capital letter *I* stands for current.

3. RESISTANCE

A number of factors determine the resistance that a substance offers to the flow of electric current. First of all, there is the nature of the substance itself. The greater the number of free electrons present in the substance, the lower is its resistance.

Resistance is also affected by the length of the substance. The longer an object is, the greater its resistance. Another factor is the cross-sectional area of the substance, which is the area of the end exposed if we slice through the substance at right angles to its length. The greater the cross-sectional area, the less the resistance to current flow.

Resistance is also affected by the temperature of the substance. Metals generally offer higher resistance at higher temperatures. Certain nonmetallic substances, such as carbon, on the other hand, offer lower resistance at higher temperatures.

The unit of resistance is the *ohm*. By international agreement, the ohm is the resistance to the flow of electric current offered by a uniform column of mercury, 106.3 centimeters long, having a cross-sectional area of one square millimeter, at 0°C. Where the ohm is too small a unit, we may employ the *kilohm* (1,000 ohms) and the *megohm* (1,000,000 ohms). The symbol for the ohm is the capital Greek letter *omega* (Ω). In an electrical formula, the capital *R* stands for resistance.

All the substances offer a certain amount of resistance to the flow of current. There are times, however, when we wish deliberately to introduce definite amounts of resistance into the current path. To do so we use devices called *resistors*. Where the resistance required is not too great, the resistor may consist of *nichrome* wire, whose resistance is more than 50 times that of copper, of suitable length and thickness wound upon a ceramic tube. An insulating ceramic coating usually is applied over the winding. This is called a *fixed* resistor.

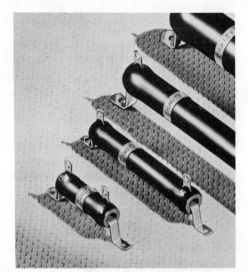

Fig. 3-4.

Fixed resistors.

Ohmite Mfg. Co.

(See Figure 3-4.) If the resistance is to be large, the resistor may consist of a thin coat of a carbon composition deposited on a ceramic tube and covered with some insulating material. Connections are made by means of wires attached to the ends of the resistor.

Where the resistor is to be variable, the wire is wound on a fiber strip which may be bent into a circular form. A metal arm or slider, manipulated by a knob, is made to move over the wire, thus making contact with any desired point. In this way the length of wire, and hence the resistance, between one end of the wire and the slider may be varied. Such variable resistors are called *rheostats* or *potentiometers*. (See Figure 3-5.) Where the resistance is to be large, a carbon composition deposited on the fiber strip may replace the coiled wire.

4. ELECTROMOTIVE FORCE

The electromotive force creates the electric pressure that causes the current to flow through a conductor. Another name for this force is *voltage*. We can measure the voltage between any two selected points on a conductor by means of an electrical instrument, called the *voltmeter* (to be described later).

The unit of measurement of electromotive force, or voltage, is called the *volt*. The volt is defined as *that electromotive force that is*

*necessary to cause one ampere of current to flow through a resistance
of one ohm.* Where the volt is too large a unit, we may use the
millivolt (1/1,000 of a volt) or the *microvolt* (1/1,000,000 of a volt).
Where the volt is too small a unit, we may use the *kilovolt* (1,000
volts). In an electrical formula, the capital letter *E* stands for
voltage.

5. ELECTRIC POWER AND ENERGY

A body at rest tends to remain in this condition or, if it is in
motion, it tends to continue this motion in a straight line. This property of the body is known as *inertia.* To overcome the effect of inertia,
force is required. Thus force may be considered as a push or a pull
and, in mechanics, it commonly is measured in units of *pound.*

Work is the product of the force and the distance through which
it acts and is measured in units of *foot-pound.* If a 1-pound weight
is lifted 1 foot, the work done is 1 foot-pound. If the weight is lifted
5 feet, the work done is 5 foot-pounds.

Power is the rate at which work is done. A child might lift the

Ohmite Mfg. Co.

Fig. 3-5.

Variable resistor.

weight 5 feet in 5 seconds. A more powerful adult might lift it the same distance in 1 second. The formula then may be

$$\text{Power} = \frac{\text{work done}}{\text{time}}.$$

The unit of power (for mechanics) is *foot-pound per second*. Thus, in the case of the child,

$$\text{Power} = \frac{1 \text{ pound} \times 5 \text{ feet}}{5 \text{ seconds}} = 1 \text{ foot-pound per second.}$$

In the case of the adult,

$$\text{Power} = \frac{1 \text{ pound} \times 5 \text{ feet}}{1 \text{ second}} = 5 \text{ foot-pounds per second.}$$

Five hundred and fifty foot-pounds per second, or 33,000 foot-pounds per minute, equal one *horsepower*.

In electricity, work is done as the electromotive force causes electrons to move through a conductor. The *electric power* (the rate of doing work) is the product of the electromotive force and the number of electrons set flowing per unit of time. But the number of electrons flowing per unit of time is the current (measured in units of ampere). Hence, the power, whose symbol is P, is the product of the electromotive force, in volts, and the current, in amperes. The unit of electric power is the *watt*. The formula for power thus becomes

$$P \text{ (watts)} = I \text{ (amperes)} \times E \text{ (volts)}.$$

Example. What is the power required to enable a dry cell whose electromotive force is 1.5 volts to cause a current of 2 amperes to flow through a conductor?

$$P = I \times E = 2 \text{ amperes} \times 1.5 \text{ volts} = 3 \text{ watts.} \quad \textit{Ans.}$$

The dry cell generates the power; the power is consumed as the current flows through the conductor.

Most electrical appliances carry labels stating the voltage at which the appliance is to operate and the power it consumes. Thus an electric lamp may bear a label indicating "60 watts, 120 volts." From this you can calculate that the filament of this lamp has 0.5 ampere of current flowing through it.

As previously stated, the unit of electric power is the *watt*, which is defined as the power used when an electromotive force of one volt causes a current of one ampere to flow through a conductor. Where the watt is too large a unit to be used conveniently, we employ the *milliwatt* (1/1,000 of a watt). Where the watt is too small a unit, we may use the *kilowatt* (1,000 watts).

The horsepower (33,000 foot-pounds per minute) is the unit of mechanical power. The kilowatt is the unit of electric power. Since mechanical energy can be converted to electric energy, and vice versa, the two units of power may be equated. Thus:

$$1 \text{ kilowatt} \quad = 1.34 \text{ horsepower}$$
$$1 \text{ horsepower} = 0.746 \text{ kilowatt}.$$

To measure the total *electrical energy* consumed by an appliance we must know how much power it uses (in watts) and the length of time (in seconds) it continues to consume this power. Thus, the unit of energy is the *wattsecond*, or *joule*—that is, one watt of power applied for one second. Since the wattsecond is a small unit, we frequently use the *watthour* (one watt applied for one hour) or the *kilowatthour* (1,000 watts applied for one hour).

It is on the basis of kilowatthours that we pay our electric bill. For example, how much would it cost to run five 60-watt lamps four hours a day for 30 days if we had to pay at the rate of $.05 per kilowatthour?

Each day we consume

$$5 \times 60 \text{ watts} \times 4 \text{ hours} = 1,200 \text{ watthours}.$$

In 30 days we consume
1,200 watthours $\times$ 30 = 36,000 watthours or 36 kilowatthours.
At $.05 per kilowatthour, our bill is $1.80.

C. Ohm's law

The relationship between the electromotive force, the current, and the resistance was discovered by a German scientist, George Simon Ohm, at the beginning of the nineteenth century. The unit of resistance was named in his honor.

This relationship, which is called *Ohm's law,* can be expressed mathematically by means of the following formula:

$$\text{Current} = \frac{\text{electromotive force}}{\text{resistance}} \quad \text{or} \quad I = \frac{E}{R},$$

where I is measured in amperes, E in volts, and R in ohms. This formula means that the greater the electromotive force is, the greater will be the current; and the greater the resistance, the smaller the current.

Let us try a problem. How much current will flow through a conductor whose resistance is 10 ohms, when the electromotive force is 100 volts? Using our formula $I = E/R$, we get $I = 100$ volts/10 ohms, or 10 amperes. *Ans.*

Our Ohm's law formula can be transposed as follows:

$$E = I \times R \qquad \text{and} \qquad R = \frac{E}{I}.$$

Example. How many volts are required to make a current of 5 amperes flow through a conductor whose resistance is 2 ohms?

Substituting our known values in the formula $E = I \times R$, we get $E = 5$ amperes $\times$ 2 ohms, or 10 volts. *Ans.*

Example. What is the resistance of a conductor if 100 volts are required to force 2 amperes of current through it?

$$\text{Since } R = \frac{E}{I}, \ R = \frac{100 \text{ volts}}{2 \text{ amperes}}, \text{ or 50 ohms.} \quad \textit{Ans.}$$

We also can use these formulas to show the relationship between power (in watts), current (in amperes), and resistance (in ohms). You will recall that

$$\text{Power} = \text{current} \times \text{voltage} \qquad \text{or} \qquad P = I \times E.$$

If we substitute for E its equivalent $(I \times R)$ we get

$$P = I \times I \times R \qquad \text{or} \qquad P = I^2 \times R.$$

Example. How much power will be required to force a current of 2 amperes to flow through a conductor whose resistance is 5 ohms?

Since $P = I^2 \times R$, substituting our values we get

$$P = (2)^2 \times 5 = 4 \times 5 = 20 \text{ watts.}\quad \textit{Ans.}$$

In a similar manner, we can show the relationship between power (in watts), electromotive force (in volts), and resistance (in ohms). Since $P = I \times E$, substituting for I its equivalent (E/R) we get:

$$P = \frac{E}{R} \times E \qquad \text{or} \qquad P = \frac{E^2}{R}.$$

Example. If the electrical pressure is 10 volts, how much power will be dissipated by a resistance of 20 ohms?

$$\text{Since } P = \frac{E^2}{R}, \text{ then } P = \frac{(10)^2}{20} = \frac{100}{20} = 5 \text{ watts.}\quad \textit{Ans.}$$

QUESTIONS

1. Explain what is meant by *electric current; direct current.* In what unit do we measure current?
2. Explain what is meant by *electromotive force.* What is its unit of measurement?
3. Explain what is meant by *resistance.* What is its unit of measurement?
4. Explain four factors affecting the resistance of a substance.
5. Explain Ohm's law.
6. How many volts are required to make a current of 5 milliamperes flow through a 1-megohm resistor?
7. If a voltage of 100 volts be applied to a 50-ohm resistor, how much current will flow through it?
8. What must be the resistance of a resistor if 60 volts will cause 3 amperes of current to flow through it?
9. Explain what is meant by *electric power.* What is its unit of measurement?
10. What is the power in an electrical circuit whose resistance is 4 ohms if the applied voltage is 10 volts?
11. How much power is consumed in a circuit where a current of 50 milliamperes flows through a conductor whose resistance is 1,000 ohms?
12. Explain what is meant by electric energy. What is its unit of measurement?
13. The resistance of the heating element of an electric stove operating on a 120-volt line is 12 ohms. How much would it cost to operate this stove for 5 hours if the power company charged $.04 per kilowatthour?

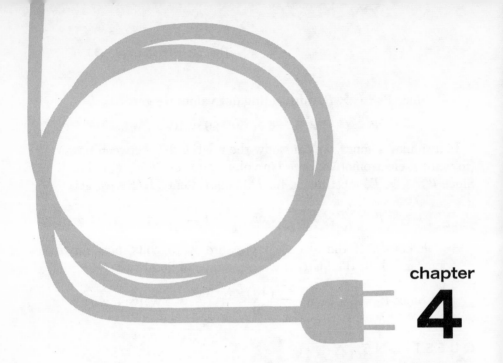

How Current Flows Through a Circuit

A. The electric current in solids

If èlectrons are added to one end of a solid conductor, such as a piece of copper wire, and some are taken away from the other end, an electric field is set up between the ends of the wire. This field tends to cause free electrons in the wire to move from the negative end to the positive one. As previously stated, this movement of electrons is an electric current.

The free electron moves comparatively slowly through the wire and travels but a short distance before it collides with an atom. This collision generally knocks an electron free from the atom, and this new free electron travels a short distance toward the positive end of the wire before it collides with another atom. Thus, there is a slow drift of electrons from the negative to the positive end of the wire.

But although the drift of electrons is comparatively slow, the disturbance that causes this drift travels through the wire at a speed that approaches the speed of light (approximately 186,000 miles per second). This action may be understood by visualizing a long, hollow tube completely filled with balls. (See Figure 4-1.) If a ball is

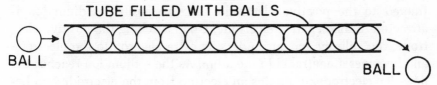

TUBE FILLED WITH BALLS

BALL

BALL

Fig. 4-1. Motion of electrons through a solid conductor.

added to one end of the tube, a ball at the other end is forced out immediately. Thus, although each ball moves slowly and for only a short distance, the disturbance is transmitted almost instantaneously through the entire tube.

Note that the electric current consists, essentially, of the movement of the electrons of the conductor itself. The device that furnishes the electromotive force may be considered as a sort of pump that removes electrons from one end of the conductor (thus creating a deficiency or positive charge at that end) and piles them up at the other end (creating an excess or negative charge).

B. *The electric current in liquids*

A molecule of ordinary table salt is made up of an atom of sodium and an atom of chloride. When these two atoms combine to form a molecule of salt (whose chemical name is *sodium chloride*) an electron from the sodium atom couples up with an electron from the chlorine atom to form a *bond*. If the salt molecule is dissolved in water, the bond is broken and the molecule breaks up into sodium and chlorine atoms once again.

However, as the bond breaks (we say the molecule *disassociates*), the chlorine atom seizes both of the electrons of the bond. Since it has an extra electron, the chlorine atom now has a negative charge. The sodium atom has lost an electron, so it has a positive charge.

A charged particle is called an *ion*. Thus when a molecule of salt disassociates it forms negative and positive ions.

If two metal plates (called *electrodes*) are set at opposite ends of the solution and a source of electromotive force is connected to these plates so that one becomes a positive (electron-deficient) electrode and the other a negative (electron-excess) electrode, an electric field is created between these two electrodes. (See Figure 4-2.)

Since opposite charges attract, the negative chlorine ion is attracted to the positive electrode and the positive sodium ion is attracted to the negative electrode. Upon reaching the positive electrode, the chlorine ion surrenders its extra electron to the electrode and becomes a neutral chlorine atom. As the sodium ion reaches the negative electrode, it obtains an electron from the electrode and becomes a neutral sodium atom.

The effect of the electromotive force, then, is to cause a movement of ions through the solution. The movement of charged particles constitutes an electric current and in this way the electric current flows through a liquid.

A liquid containing a substance that is able to disassociate into free ions is called an *electrolyte*. The resistance of an electrolyte depends upon the degree to which these ions are released (*ionization*). The greater the amount of ionization, the less is the resistance of the liquid. Thus, for a given electromotive force, the greater the ionization, the greater is the current transmitted by ions through the liquid.

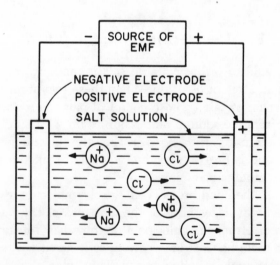

Fig. 4-2. Movement of ions through a liquid. The symbol Na^+ represents the positive sodium ion, Cl^- the negative chlorine ion.

C. *The electric current in gases*

The molecules of a gas are in a perpetual state of motion, constantly colliding with one another. These collisions knock off electrons, producing free electrons and converting the atoms that have lost electrons into positive ions. Since, by definition, a charged particle is called an ion, we may consider the free electrons as negative ions. Thus the gas contains positive and negative ions, just as an electrolyte does. If positive and negative electrodes are placed in the gas, the free electrons tend to travel to the positive electrode, and the positive ions to the negative electrode, thereby producing an electric current.

Normally, a positive or negative ion cannot travel very far in a gas before meeting an ion of opposite charge. This meeting would tend to produce neutralization and would result in neutral molecules. Since neutral molecules are not affected by the electric field between the two electrodes, the current would tend to cease flowing.

But if the gas is placed in a sealed container (such as a glass tube or bulb, with the two electrodes sealed in), and if most of the gas is pumped out, then the ions can travel considerable distances without being obstructed. The effect of the electric field is to accelerate, or speed up, the motion of the ions, so the farther they travel, the more velocity they attain. If a fast-moving ion collides with a neutral molecule, the ion tends to knock electrons off the neutral molecule, thereby creating more ions. This process is cumulative and tends to keep a constant stream of ions moving toward the electrodes. In this manner, an electric current flows through a gas.

When the positive ions reach the negative electrode, they acquire electrons to become neutral molecules once more. The negative ions (electrons) are attracted to the positive electrode. Then the entire process is repeated.

D. *The electric current in a vacuum*

If a free electron were in a vacuum within the electric field set up between positive and negative electrodes, the negatively charged electron would be attracted to the positive electrode. The movement of the electron would constitute a flow of electric current. It is upon this principle that the electron tubes used in our radio and television receivers operate.

We can construct an electron tube by sealing a pair of metal electrodes into opposite ends of a glass bulb and evacuating the air from within the bulb, leaving a vacuum. Connecting the electrodes to a source of electromotive force makes them positive and negative, respectively. (See Figure 4-3.) A question now arises. How can we get the free electron into the tube?

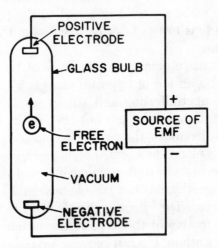

Fig. 4-3. Diagram illustrating the basic principle of the electron tube. The symbol ⓔ represents a free electron.

As previously described, there always is a disorderly movement of free electrons within all substances, especially metals. If the difference of potential between the two sealed-in electrodes be made great enough, some of the free electrons of the negative electrode will be attracted so strongly to the positive electrode, that they will leave the former and fly through the vacuum to the latter.

If a substance is heated, the movement of free electrons within that substance is increased. If the temperature is raised high enough, the movement of free electrons is increased to the point where some of the electrons actually fly off from the substance. We call this process *thermionic electron emission.*

In most electron tubes, the negative electrode is heated to the point where it emits electrons. These electrons are attracted to the positive electrode and constitute a one-way flow of electric current through a vacuum from the negative to the positive electrode.

Certain substances, such as sodium, potassium, and cesium, will emit electrons if they are exposed to light. This phenomenon is known as the *photoelectric effect*. If the negative electrode of the tube is made of such a material and light is permitted to fall on it, it will emit electrons that will be attracted to the positive electrode. Such a tube is called a *photoelectric cell*. We will delve deeper into the flow of current through gases and through a vacuum in the section on Electronics.

E. *Types of electric circuits*

Just as water flows downhill from a point of high potential energy to a point of low potential energy, so the electric current flows from a high-potential point (excess of electrons) to a low-potential point (deficiency of electrons). The path or paths followed by the current flow is called the *electric circuit*.

All circuits must contain a source of electromotive force to establish the difference of potential that makes possible the current flow. This source may be a dry cell, a mechanical generator, or any of the other devices that will be discussed later in the book. All paths of the circuit lead in closed loops from the high-potential (negative) end of the electromotive-force source to its low-potential (positive) end.

The current in a circuit may flow through solid conductors, liquids, gases, vacuums, or any combinations of these. Its path may include lamps, toasters, motors, or any of the thousand-and-one electrical devices available in this electrical age. But, regardless of the type of circuit and the devices through which the current flows, all circuits offer some resistance to the current.

This resistance may be high or low, depending upon the type of circuit and the devices employed. Sometimes this resistance is undesirable, as, for example, the resistance of the wires connecting the various devices in a circuit. Accordingly, we keep this resistance at a low level by using wires made of copper having a large cross-sectional area, and by keeping their lengths as short as possible. Sometimes, however, it is desirable to introduce concentrated, or lumped, resistances into the circuit. Such a lumped resistance is called a *resistor* and in electrical diagrams its symbol appears as —ᐯᐯᐯ— .

In this chapter we will consider three general types of circuits. One is the *series* circuit which offers a single, continuous, external path for current flow from the negative side of the electromotive-force source to the positive side. Another is the *parallel* circuit which offers two or more parallel paths for current flow from negative to positive. The third type is the *series-parallel* circuit, a combination of the other two.

1. THE SERIES CIRCUIT

The series circuit, we have stated, offers a single, continuous, external path for current flow from the negative side of the electro-motive-force source to the positive side. Such a circuit is illustrated in Figure 4-4. Electrons flow (as indicated by the symbol e →) from the negative side of the source, through resistors R_1 and R_2, and back to the positive side of the source.

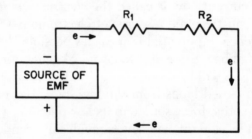

Fig. 4-4. Series circuit. The symbol e→ indicates current flow.

The total resistance of the series circuit is equal to the sum of all the individual resistances. Thus the total resistance of the series circuit shown in Figure 4-4 is equal to the sum of the resistance of R_1, the resistance of R_2, the resistance of the connecting wires, and the resistance of the electromotive-force source (all expressed in ohms). The total resistance of a series circuit may be determined by the following formula:

$$R_{total} = R_1 + R_2 + R_3 + R_4 +, \text{ and so forth.}$$

Example. In Figure 4-4, if the resistance of R_1 is 30 ohms and R_2 is 20 ohms, what is the total resistance of the circuit (neglecting the resistance of the source and the connecting wires)?

$R_{total} = R_1 + R_2 = 30$ ohms $+ 20$ ohms $= 50$ ohms.   *Ans.*

Since there is only one path over which the current may flow, the current flow is the same in all parts of the series circuit. This can be proven by inserting a current-measuring device, called an *ammeter*, in different portions of the circuit and noting that the reading is always the same. We may determine what this current will be if we know the electromotive force of the source (in volts) and the total resistance of the circuit (in ohms). Then, by applying Ohm's law ($I = E/R$) we can find the current (in amperes).

Example. In Figure 4-4, if R_1 is 30 ohms and R_2 is 20 ohms, and the electromotive force is 100 volts, what current will flow through the circuit (neglecting the resistance of the source and the connecting wires)?

$R_{total} = R_1 + R_2 = 30$ ohms $+ 20$ ohms $= 50$ ohms.

By Ohm's law, $I = \dfrac{E}{R} = \dfrac{100 \text{ volts}}{50 \text{ ohms}} = 2$ amperes.   *Ans.*

Although the current is the same in all portions of the series circuit, the electromotive force, or electrical pressure, is not. Starting with full pressure at the negative terminal of the source, the electrical pressure gradually diminishes as it is expended, driving the electrons against the resistances encountered in the circuit until it reaches zero at the positive terminal of the source.

Let us see how this applies to the circuit illustrated in Figure 4-4. We again assume that R_1 is 30 ohms, R_2 is 20 ohms, and the voltage of the source is 100 volts. We also know that the current is equal to 2 amperes. For the sake of simplicity we again neglect the resistances of the connecting wires and of the source.

We start at the negative terminal of the source with the full voltage of 100 volts. A certain amount of this voltage is required to force 2 amperes of current to flow through R_1 (30 ohms). This can be determined by Ohm's law ($E = I \times R$).

$E = I \times R = 2$ amperes $\times 30$ ohms $= 60$ volts.

Since 60 volts are required to force the current through R_1, only 40 volts are left to drive the electrons around the rest of the circuit.

At R_2 more of the voltage is lost forcing the current through that resistor. Again, by Ohm's law,

$$E = I \times R = 2 \text{ amperes} \times 20 \text{ ohms} = 40 \text{ volts.}$$

Thus the remaining 40 volts have been used up and the voltage has dropped to zero.

Note that the current flowing through it causes a difference of potential to appear between the ends of a resistor. This potential difference is equal to the voltage drop which, in turn, is equal to the product of the resistance (ohms) and the current (amperes). Hence the voltage drop across a resistor is called its *IR* drop. In a series circuit, the sum of all the *IR* drops is equal to the voltage of the source.

Note that the voltage drop across R_1 is 60 volts and the current flowing through it is 2 amperes. From the formula P (watts) $= E$ (volts) $\times I$ (amperes) we may determine the electric power dissipated by that resistor. Thus:

$P = I^2 R$ $$P = E \times I = 60 \text{ volts} \times 2 \text{ amperes} = 120 \text{ watts.}$$

This means that R_1 must be able to dissipate at least 120 watts without overheating or burning up. The voltage drop across R_2 is 40 volts and the current flowing through it is 2 amperes. Thus:

$$P = E \times I = 40 \text{ volts} \times 2 \text{ amperes} = 80 \text{ watts,}$$

and R_2 need dissipate only 80 watts.

The total power consumed by the entire circuit may be found by multiplying the voltage of the source by the total current. Thus:

$$P = E \times I = 100 \text{ volts} \times 2 \text{ amperes} = 200 \text{ watts.}$$

Note that this is equal to the sum of the power dissipated by R_1 and R_2.

(There is an interesting sidelight we may consider. Suppose that R_2 becomes defective, opening the circuit. Since the circuit is broken, no current flows. Hence there is no *IR* drop. However, since the ends of R_2 are still connected to the source, the full 100 volts appears across those ends.)

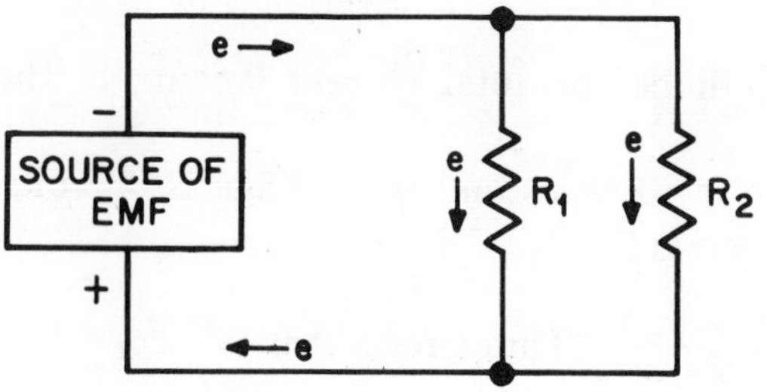

Fig. 4-5.

Parallel circuit.

2. THE PARALLEL CIRCUIT

The parallel circuit is illustrated in Figure 4-5. Note that the electromotive force across all components of such a circuit is the same. Current flows (as indicated by the symbol $e \rightarrow$) from the negative side of the source to the upper junction of resistors R_1 and R_2. Here it divides, part flowing through R_1 and part through R_2. At the lower junction of R_1 and R_2 both currents reunite and flow back to the positive side of the source.

[At this point, it might be well to mention a few facts concerning electrical circuit diagrams. Often, we must show two wires crossing each other. There are several methods of designation, but in this book, if two wires cross and connect with each other, this connection will be indicated by a dot at the point of crossover ($\dashv\!\!\!\bullet\!\!\!\vdash$). If there is no connection, a loop ($\cap$) will be used to indicate this fact.]

The total resistance of resistors connected in parallel may be expressed by the following formula:

$$\frac{1}{R_{\text{total}}} = \frac{1}{R_1} + \frac{1}{R_2} + \frac{1}{R_3} + \frac{1}{R_4} +, \text{ and so forth.}$$

Example. Assume, in Figure 4-5, that R_1 is 90 ohms and R_2 is 45 ohms. What is the total resistance of R_1 and R_2 in parallel?

$$\frac{1}{R_{\text{total}}} = \frac{1}{R_1} + \frac{1}{R_2} = \frac{1}{90 \text{ ohms}} + \frac{1}{45 \text{ ohms}} = \frac{3}{90}$$

$$R_{\text{total}} = \frac{90}{3} = 30 \text{ ohms.} \quad Ans.$$

Now let us carry our problem a step further. Assuming a voltage source of 90 volts, what will be the total current flowing in the circuit?

Since the total resistance is 30 ohms and the voltage is 90 volts, by Ohm's law $(I = E/R)$ we get

$$I = \frac{E}{R} = \frac{90 \text{ volts}}{30 \text{ ohms}} = 3 \text{ amperes.} \quad \textit{Ans.}$$

Knowing that a total of 3 amperes is flowing through the circuit, how much current flows through R_1 and through R_2? Note that the same voltage is applied across R_1 as R_2, that is, the IR drop across R_1 and R_2 is 90 volts. Again, by Ohm's law, we can determine the current flowing through each resistor. Thus, for R_1:

$$I = \frac{E}{R} = \frac{90 \text{ volts}}{90 \text{ ohms}} = 1 \text{ ampere.} \quad \textit{Ans.}$$

And for R_2:

$$I = \frac{E}{R} = \frac{90 \text{ volts}}{45 \text{ ohms}} = 2 \text{ amperes.} \quad \textit{Ans.}$$

Note that the greater current flows through the resistor with the lower resistance. And because R_2 has half the resistance of R_1, twice as much current flows through R_2 as through R_1.

Power dissipated by each resistor may be determined from the formula $P = E \times I$. For resistor R_1, E equals 90 volts and I equals 1 ampere. Hence the power is 90 watts. For resistor R_2, E equals 90 volts and I equals 2 amperes. Hence the power is 180 watts. The power consumed by the entire circuit may be found by multiplying the voltage of the source by the total current. Thus:

$$P = E \times I = 90 \text{ volts} \times 3 \text{ amperes} = 270 \text{ watts.}$$

Note that this is equal to the sum of the power dissipated by R_1 and R_2. Note, too, that in series circuits the total power dissipation is also equal to the sum of the power dissipated by each of the individual resistors.

3. THE SERIES-PARALLEL CIRCUIT

As its name implies, this circuit is a combination of the other two types. A simple example of such a circuit is illustrated in Figure

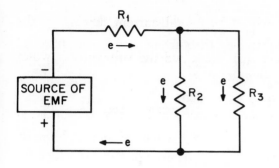

Fig. 4-6.

Series-parallel circuit.

4-6. Note that R_2 and R_3 are connected in parallel with each other and that both together are connected in series with R_1. To find the total resistance of this circuit, we first find the joint resistance of R_2 and R_3 in parallel and then add this joint resistance to that of R_1, as in any other series circuit.

Let us assume that the voltage of the source is 150 volts. Further assume R_1 is 20 ohms, R_2 is 90 ohms, and R_3 is 45 ohms. What is the total resistance of the circuit (neglecting the resistance of the connecting wires and of the source)?

First we find the joint resistance of R_2 and R_3 in parallel.

$$\frac{1}{R_{\text{joint}}} = \frac{1}{R_2} + \frac{1}{R_3} = \frac{1}{90 \text{ ohms}} + \frac{1}{45 \text{ ohms}} = \frac{3}{90}$$

$$R_{\text{joint}} = \frac{90}{3} = 30 \text{ ohms.}$$

Next, we find the total resistance of R_{joint} and R_1 in series.

$$R_{\text{total}} = R_{\text{joint}} + R_1 = 30 \text{ ohms} + 20 \text{ ohms} = 50 \text{ ohms.} \quad \textit{Ans.}$$

To find the current flowing through R_1, R_2, and R_3, first find the total current of the circuit. Knowing the voltage of the source and the total resistance, we may find the total current by Ohm's law. Thus:

$$I = \frac{E}{R} = \frac{150 \text{ volts}}{50 \text{ ohms}} = 3 \text{ amperes.}$$

Since R_1 is in series with the rest of the circuit, the total current flows through it. Thus the current flowing through R_1 is 3 amperes.

We can now calculate the voltage drop across R_1.

$$E = I \times R = 3 \text{ amperes} \times 20 \text{ ohms} = 60 \text{ volts.}$$

Since 60 volts are expended forcing the current through R_1, 90 volts are left for the rest of the circuit. Because R_2 and R_3 are connected in parallel, the same voltage is applied to each. Hence the voltage drops across R_2 and R_3 are 90 volts each.

Since the resistance of R_2 is 90 ohms and its voltage drop is 90 volts, then:

$$I = \frac{E}{R} = \frac{90 \text{ volts}}{90 \text{ ohms}} = 1 \text{ ampere flowing through } R_2.$$

Similarly, since R_3 is 45 ohms and its voltage drop, too, is 90 volts, then:

$$I = \frac{E}{R} = \frac{90 \text{ volts}}{45 \text{ ohms}} = 2 \text{ amperes flowing through } R_3.$$

To find the total power consumed by the circuit, multiply the total voltage (150 volts) by the total current (3 amperes). This comes to 450 watts. The power dissipated by R_1 may be found by multiplying its voltage drop (60 volts) by its current (3 amperes). This comes to 180 watts. To find the power dissipated by R_2, multiply its voltage drop (90 volts) by its current (1 ampere). This comes to 90 watts. To find the power dissipated by R_3, multiply its voltage drop (90 volts) by its current (2 amperes). This comes to 180 watts. If we add up the power dissipated by R_1, R_2, and R_3, it equals the total of 450 watts consumed by the entire circuit. Thus, regardless of the method of connection, the total power consumed by the circuit is equal to the sum of the power consumed by all of its parts.

Gustav Kirchhoff, a German physicist, noted several interesting facts about circuits. At any point in the circuit, he found, the current flowing towards the point is equal to the current flowing away from that point. Let us see how this applies to the circuit we have just discussed.

In Figure 4-7 you see this circuit upon which we have indicated the amount of current flowing through its various portions and the direction of current flow. Consider point A. Three amperes of current are flowing towards it. On the other hand, three amperes of current are flowing away from it—one ampere through R_2 and two amperes through R_3. Similarly, at point B, three amperes of current

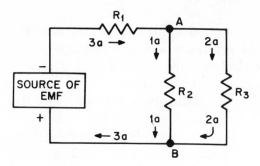

Fig. 4-7. Circuit diagram illustrating Kirchhoff's First Law.

are flowing towards it, and three amperes are flowing away from it.

Kirchhoff set his findings in a set of laws that bear his name. If current flowing towards a point is designated as plus $(+)$ and current flowing away from the point is designated as minus $(-)$, then the algebraic sum of all currents flowing to and away from a point in any type of circuit is equal to zero.

Kirchhoff formulated a second law, which deals with electromotive forces and voltage drops $(IR$ drops) in a circuit. He found that the algebraic sum of all the voltage drops and electromotive forces in any closed circuit, when taken with their proper signs, is equal to zero.

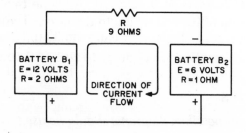

Fig. 4-8. Circuit diagram illustrating Kirchhoff's Second Law.

For example, look at Figure 4-8. Here are two sources of electromotive force (batteries B_1 and B_2) connected in a series circuit with a resistor (R). Battery B_1 has an electromotive force of 12 volts and an internal resistance of 2 ohms. Battery B_2 has an electromotive force of 6 volts and an internal resistance of 1 ohm. Note that the batteries are connected so that their electromotive forces oppose each other. The resistance of R is 9 ohms.

To add the electromotive forces of the batteries algebraically, we may call the direction of the electromotive force of one of the batteries (in this case, the direction of the one with the larger voltage, B_1) plus (+). Since the direction of the electromotive force of B_2 is in the opposite direction, we call this direction minus (−). To add the two voltages algebraically, we add + 12 volts and −6 volts, which gives a resultant of +6 volts. The total resistance of this series circuit (2 ohms + 9 ohms + 1 ohm) is 12 ohms. We may find the current flowing in this circuit by Ohm's law:

$$I = \frac{E}{R} = \frac{6 \text{ volts}}{12 \text{ ohms}} = 0.5 \text{ ampere.}$$

Now let us see how Kirchhoff's law applies. Start with the positive (+) terminal of battery B_1. Going from the positive to the negative pole of the battery, we encounter a *voltage increase* of 12 volts. At the same time, owing to the internal resistance of the battery, we suffer a *voltage drop* of 1 volt ($E = IR = 0.5$ amp $\times$ 2 ohms = 1 volt). Thus the electromotive force is +11 volts. Passing to resistor R we suffer another voltage drop of 4.5 volts (0.5 amp $\times$ 9 ohms = 4.5 volts), thus reducing the electromotive force to 6.5 volts. At battery B_2, because it is connected in opposition to battery B_1, we suffer a *voltage decrease* of 6 volts. At the same time, we have another voltage drop of 0.5 volt owing to the internal resistance of that battery (0.5 amp $\times$ 1 ohm = 0.5 volt). Thus the algebraic sum of the applied electromotive forces drops to zero (6.5 volts − 6.5 volts).

QUESTIONS

Wherever possible, diagrams should be used to clarify the answers to these questions. These diagrams need not be elaborate, but they should be drawn neatly with the significant portions clearly labeled.

1. **Explain how electric current flows through a solid conductor.**
2. **What is meant by an *ion*; an *electrolyte*?**
3. **Explain how electric current flows through a liquid.**
4. **Explain how electric current flows through a gas.**
5. **Explain how electric current flows through a vacuum.**

6. What is meant by an *electric circuit;* a *series circuit;* a *parallel circuit?*
7. Two resistors, one 40 ohms and the other 20 ohms, are connected in series across a 120-volt line.

   a) What is their total resistance?
   b) What is the total current flowing through the entire circuit?
   c) How much current will flow through each resistor?
   d) What will be the voltage drop across each resistor?
   e) What is the total power dissipated by the circuit?
   f) How much power is dissipated by each resistor? Check this answer against *e*) above.

8. Two resistors, one 60 ohms and the other 30 ohms, are connected in parallel across a 120-volt line.

   a) What is their total resistance?
   b) What is the total current flowing through the entire circuit?
   c) How much current will flow through each resistor?
   d) What will be the voltage drop across each resistor?
   e) What is the total power dissipated by the circuit?
   f) How much power is dissipated by each resistor? Check this answer against *e*) above.

9. Three resistors, one 30 ohms, one 40 ohms, and the other 60 ohms, are connected in a series-parallel circuit across a 120-volt line, as illustrated below.

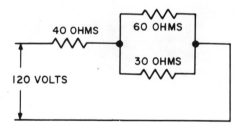

   a) What is their total resistance?
   b) What is the total current flowing through the circuit?
   c) How much current will flow through each resistor?
   d) What will be the voltage drop across each resistor?
   e) What is the total power dissipated by the circuit?
   f) How much power is dissipated by each resistor? Check this answer against *e*) above.

10. A portion of a circuit is shown below. It was found that 5 amperes were flowing through R_1 towards the junction of the three resistors and that 2 amperes were flowing through R_2 towards that junction. How much current is flowing through R_3 and is its direction towards or away from the junction?

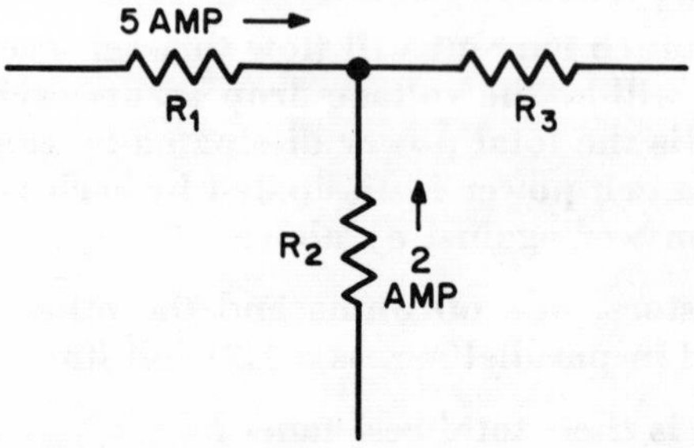

11. A battery whose electromotive force is 10 volts and whose internal resistance is 1 ohm, a battery with an electromotive force of 20 volts and an internal resistance of 2 ohms, and a resistor are connected in series. The batteries are connected so that their electromotive forces oppose each other. It is found that the current flowing in this circuit is 2 amperes. What is the resistance of the resistor?

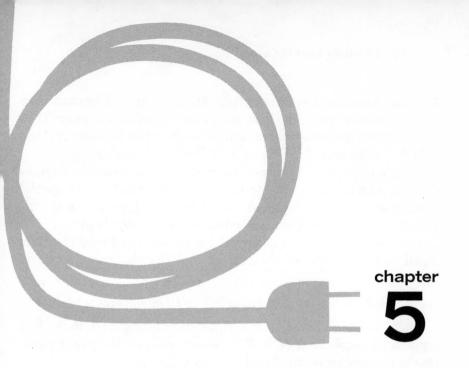

Effects of Electric Current

A. *Thermal effect*

When mechanical energy is applied to a machine, one of the losses it must overcome is a kind of "resistance," called *friction*. Mechanical power is "lost" overcoming this friction. However, it is not really lost since it shows up as heat at the point or points of friction. It has merely been changed from mechanical energy to heat energy.

Similarly, when electrical energy is applied to a conductor, the resulting current flow must overcome the resistance of the conductor. Electrical power is "lost" overcoming this resistance. As is true of the mechanical power, the electrical power is not really lost, but is converted to heat in the conductor. Some of the electrical energy has been changed to heat energy.

In many instances the heat so produced is undesirable and steps are taken to keep it at a minimum. For example, where large currents are to flow, conductors may be made of heavy copper bars to keep the resistance low. Where these steps are not sufficient to keep the heat at safe levels, the heat itself may be conducted away. Thus many motors are constructed with a built-in fan to blow cool air over the wires heated by the current flowing through them.

However, there are instances where the heat is desirable. Certain devices, such as toasters, heaters, irons, are constructed with special conductors made of alloys that offer a fairly high resistance to current flow. We will consider such devices later in the book.

You will recall that the electrical power consumed by a circuit is equal to the product of the current and the electromotive force. Thus,

$$P \text{ (in watts)} = E \text{ (in volts)} \times I \text{ (in amperes)}.$$

Since, by Ohm's law, $E = I \times R$, by substituting for E in the first equation its equivalent $(I \times R)$, we may indicate the power equation in terms of current (I) and resistance (R). Thus:

$$P = E \times I = (I \times R) \times I = I^2 \times R.$$

Similarly, since $I = E/R$, then

$$P = E \times I = E \times \frac{E}{R} = \frac{E^2}{R}.$$

Thus, if we wish to determine the power lost (in watts) as current flows through a resistor, we may multiply the current (in amperes) by the voltage drop across it (in volts). Of else we may multiply the square of that current by the resistance (in ohms) of the resistor. Still another method is to divide the square of the voltage drop by the resistance. All these methods produce the same result.

Since the voltage of a circuit usually is kept at a constant value, the two variables generally are the resistance of the resistor and the current flowing through it. Hence the power loss most frequently is expressed in terms of $I^2 \times R$. Since this power produces heat, the heating effect of an electric current often is called the I^2R loss.

B. *Luminous effect*

If we heat a substance, such as a metal wire, for example, the molecules of the substance are made to move faster. As we continue to add heat, the molecules move faster until a point is reached where light is emitted. (We believe the light is produced as a result of the rearrangement of the electrons around the nucleus. However, this matter is not within the scope of this book.)

You now know that as a current flows through a conductor, heat is produced as a result of the I^2R loss. If the current and resistance be large enough, the heat so produced may be great enough to make the conductor emit light. This is the principle of the *incandescent lamp,* invented by Thomas A. Edison in 1879.

To provide for a high enough resistance, Edison used a wire, or filament, made of carbon. However, if this filament be heated until it emits light—that is, to *incandescence*—it burns up in the air, which supports combustion. Accordingly, Edison sealed the carbon filament in a glass bulb from which he pumped out the air. (See Figure 5-1.)

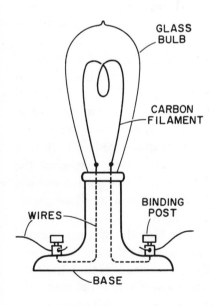

GLASS BULB

CARBON FILAMENT

WIRES

BINDING POST

BASE

Fig. 5-1.

Edison incandescent lamp.

The passage of an electric current may heat a gas, as well as a solid, to incandescence. This principle underlies the *carbon-arc light* which was used extensively for street lighting at the beginning of the twentieth century. In this type of street light, current is led to two carbon rods. (See Figure 5-2.) The tips of these rods are touched together and then slightly separated. As a result, a hot

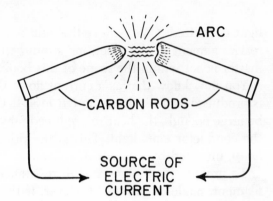

Fig. 5-2.

Carbon-arc light.

electric spark, or *arc,* jumps from tip to tip. The heat of this arc vaporizes some of the carbon, and the passage of current through this carbon vapor heats it to burning and incandescence. (The tips of the rods, too, are heated to incandescence, thus furnishing an additional source of light.)

So far, we have discussed light produced as a solid or a gas is heated to incandescence. There are other electrical methods for producing light without the necessity for heating a substance. You will recall that electric current flows through a gas by the movement of ions to oppositely charged electrodes sealed into opposite ends of a tube from which most of the gas has been evacuated (Chapter 4, Subdivision C). When the positively charged gas ion reaches the negative electrode, it receives an electron and becomes a neutral atom once more. As it does so, light is emitted (as a result of the rearrangement of the electrons of the gas atom).

It is not only at the negative electrode that the gas atom emits light. Anywhere in the tube, when a positive gas ion meets an electron, neutralization takes place and light is emitted. Hence the tube glows over its entire length. The process is continuous since the neutral atom soon is struck by a speeding ion and becomes an ion once more. Each type of gas produces light of characteristic color. Neon produces a reddish light. Helium produces a pinkish light; argon produces a bluish-white light; mercury vapor produces a greenish-blue light.

In addition to producing a visible greenish-blue light, mercury vapor produces an invisible ultraviolet light. When ultraviolet light strikes certain chemicals, called *phosphors,* these chemicals glow with a color that depends upon their composition. This is the principle upon which the fluorescent lamps so widely used today operate.

A long glass tube is coated on its inner surface with one of these phosphors. Within the tube, mercury is heated until it vaporizes and forms a mercury vapor. Current is passed through this mercury vapor, producing ultraviolet light. As the ultraviolet light strikes the phosphor, visible light is produced by the phosphor glow. (A discussion of the practical applications of the various luminous effects of the electric current will be found later in this book.)

C. Chemical effect

We touched upon the transformation of electrical energy into chemical energy when we discussed how the electric current broke the salt molecule into its component sodium and chlorine atoms (Chapter 4, Subdivision B). This type of energy transformation is used in a great number of industrial processes such as electroplating and the manufacture of aluminum. We shall consider this matter in greater detail later in this book.

D. Magnetic effect

1. MAGNETISM

The ancient people had a second magic to match the mysterious properties of rubbed amber. They found that certain stones could attract small pieces of iron. Also, if a bar of iron or steel were stroked with one of these stones, the bar would acquire the same mysterious power of attracting other pieces of iron. Further, if the stone, or the iron bar that was stroked by it, were suspended so that it could swing freely, the stone or bar would turn until one end faced north and the other south. In addition, if the north-facing end of one such stone or bar were to be brought near the north-facing end of another, the two stones or bars would be repelled. Similarly, if two south-facing ends were brought together, they also would repel each other. On the other hand, if a north-facing end were brought near a south-facing end, they would attract each other.

No wonder the ancients thought that these stones, which we now know to be a type of iron ore, had magical powers. A great many legends grew up about these stones, which were called *lodestones* or *magnets.* Of course, these legends, such as the ability of a magnet to cure disease, were false. Nevertheless, the ancient Chinese did invent an extremely useful navigation device, the *compass,* that made use of the north-facing property of the magnet.

Today, we know that a magnet can attract, not only pieces of iron, but also certain other metals, such as nickel and cobalt, although with less force. We call substances that can be attracted by a magnet *magnetic,* and the ability of a magnet to attract magnetic substances we call *magnetism.*

If a magnet is sprinkled with iron filings, we notice that these filings are not attracted uniformly to the whole surface, but rather tend to cluster at either end of the magnet. (See Figure 5-3.) It would seem that the magnetism is concentrated at these two ends of the magnet. We call these two ends of concentration the *poles* of the magnet. It has been found that the earth itself is a huge magnet with its two magnetic poles located in the Arctic region (near the north geographic pole) and in the Antarctic region (near the south geographic pole).

We have confirmed the fact that if a magnet is suspended so that it can swing freely, one pole will face towards the earth's north magnetic pole and the other towards its south magnetic pole. We call the pole of the magnet that turns to the earth's northern magnetic pole the *north-seeking pole,* or, more simply, the *north pole.* We gen-

MAGNET

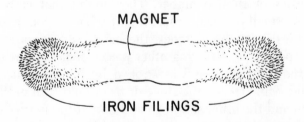

IRON FILINGS

Fig. 5-3. How iron filings cling to a magnet. Note concentration at both ends.

erally designate it by N. The pole that turns to the earth's southern magnetic pole is called the *south-seeking,* or *south, pole.* It is designated by S.

Thus, every magnet has a north pole and a south pole. We have confirmed the fact that like poles (that is, two north poles or two south poles) tend to repel each other. On the other hand, unlike poles tend to attract. It is for this reason that the north pole of the compass always turns to the earth's north magnetic pole (which, in reality, is a south magnetic pole, though misnamed.)

a. The magnetic field

This matter of attraction and repulsion between poles of magnets warrants close attention. It was found that the poles need not touch each other. Even if they are a distance apart, like poles will repel each other and unlike poles will attract each other. If a nonmagnetic substance is placed between the poles, their attraction or repulsion is unchanged. Thus, if a sheet of glass or copper is placed between two unlike magnetic poles, they continue to attract each other as though the glass or copper were not there.

We may understand this phenomenon a little more clearly if we consider gravitation. Here, too, you will find bodies acting upon each other through space since an attraction exists between any two bodies because of their masses. We say that a *gravitational force,* or *field,* exists between these bodies.

Similarly, two charged bodies may act upon each other through space. (Chapter 1, Subdivision B,2.) If the charges be similar, the two charged bodies tend to repel each other. If the charges be unlike, they attract each other. We say that an *electrostatic force,* or *field,* exists between these bodies.

It would appear, then, that a *magnetic force,* or *field,* exists between the two opposite poles of a magnet. We may find out more about this magnetic field by means of a simple experiment. Place a magnet on a wooden table. Over it, place a sheet of glass. Sprinkle iron filings on the glass and tap the glass lightly. The iron filings will assume a definite pattern on the glass sheet (Figure 5-4).

The iron filings are attracted to the magnet through the glass sheet. Although the glass prevents these iron filings from touching the magnet, nevertheless the filings will form a pattern which will show the form of the magnetic field. Note that the iron filings arrange

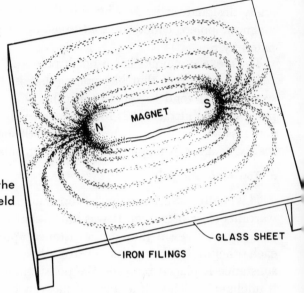

Fig. 5-4.

How iron filings show the form of the magnetic field around a magnet.

themselves in a series of closed loops outside the magnet that extend from pole to pole.

It is in this way that we visualize the magnetic field around a magnet. We say that the magnet acts as though *magnetic lines of force* surround it in the pattern formed by the iron filings. Of course, the pattern formed in Figure 5-4 represents the magnetic field only in the horizontal plane. To obtain a true picture, we should consider the magnetic field surrounding the magnet as existing in three dimensions, that is, over and under the magnet as well as on either side of it.

Note that the lines of force do not cross, but actually appear to repel each other. It would seem that these lines try to follow the shortest distance from pole to pole, at the same time repelling each other. It might help if we think of them as a bundle of stretched rubber bands. Thus they tend to shorten and, at the same time, push the others away sidewise.

A force must have a direction in which it acts. In the case of the electrostatic field we consider the force as acting from the point of negative charge to the point of positive charge. In the case of the magnetic field we arbitrarily assume the force acts from the north pole to the south pole. It is as if the lines of force "flowed" from the

north pole into the south pole. If, theoretically, we were to place a
small north pole in the magnetic field, it would be repelled from
the north pole of the magnet and move along the path of a line of
force until it reached the south pole.

We can see now why like poles repel and unlike poles attract. If
we place two unlike poles near each other, as in Figure 5-5A, the
lines of force flow from the north pole to the south pole. Since these
lines of force tend to shorten, the two magnets are pulled to each
other. If, on the other hand, we place two like poles near each other,
as in Figure 5-5B, the lines of force tend to repel each other and the
two magnets are pushed apart.

The magnetic lines of force are known as the *magnetic flux* and are
considered as flowing in a magnetic circuit, somewhat as current
flows in an electrical circuit. Like the current, the flux flows in
closed loops. This is illustrated in Figure 5-6 which shows the flux
around a magnet. The lines of force flow out of the north pole,
through the air, and back into the south pole of the magnet. Within
the magnet, they flow back to the north pole, thus completing the
loop. (In the previous figures the flow of flux within the magnets
was omitted for the sake of simplicity.)

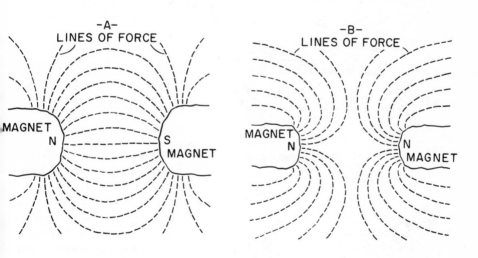

Fig. 5-5. A. Pattern of the resulting magnetic field when two unlike poles
are placed near each other.
B. Pattern of the resulting magnetic field when two like poles
are placed near each other.

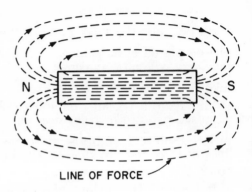

Fig. 5-6.

Magnetic flux around a magnet.

LINE OF FORCE

Continuing our analogy with the electric current, we find that the magnetic flux encounters less opposition flowing through magnetic substances, such as iron, than through nonmagnetic substances, such as air, glass, copper. We call the opposition to flow of magnetic flux, *reluctance.* The reluctances of all nonmagnetic substances are the same. Thus the flux will flow with the same ease (or difficulty) through air, glass, copper, etc.

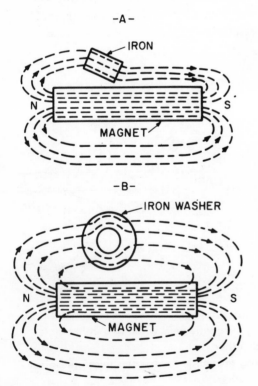

-A-

IRON

N S

MAGNET

-B-

IRON WASHER

N S

MAGNET

Fig. 5-7.

A. Distortion of the magnetic field around a magnet by a piece of iron.

B. Distortion of the magnetic field around a magnet by an iron washer. Note that there are no lines of force in the air space within the washer.

On the other hand, it will flow much more readily through a piece of iron placed in its path. Thus, if a piece of iron is placed within the magnetic field, the lines of force will distort their pattern to take the easier path through the iron, as shown in Figure 5-7A. If, as in Figure 5-7B, an iron washer is placed within the magnetic field, the flux will flow through the iron of the washer and no lines of force will be found in the air space within the washer.

b. Theories of magnetism

It is not enough to smile at the fanciful legends of the ancients. We must arrive at an acceptable explanation of the mysterious powers of the magnet. Let us start by considering a pendulum, which consists of a weight suspended by a string from a fixed point. Normally, the weight hangs straight down, attracted towards the center of the earth by gravity. (See Figure 5-8.)

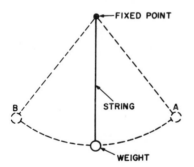

Fig. 5-8. Pendulum.

Force must be applied to raise the weight to position **A**. At this position the weight has acquired the ability to do work since, if released, it would fall back towards its original position. We say the weight has acquired *mechanical energy* and, since this is due to its position, we say that it has *position,* or *potential, energy.*

If the weight is released, it falls back towards its original position. As it does so, it gradually loses the advantage of its position and, accordingly, its potential energy. At the original position, the weight has lost all its potential energy. Nevertheless, it continues to swing upwards towards position **B**. Where does it get the energy for this rise?

The answer is that, as the weight starts to fall from position **A**, its *position,* or *potential,* energy starts to transform into a *motion,* or *kinetic*, energy. The faster the weight moves, the more its potential energy is changed to kinetic energy. When the weight reaches its original position at the bottom of its swing it is traveling at its fastest and all its potential energy has been changed to kinetic energy. It is this latter energy that keeps the weight moving and raises it to position B.

As the weight passes through its original position and rises towards position B, it travels slower and slower, and finally comes to rest at position B. With the slowing up of the weight its kinetic energy gradually changes back to potential energy. At position B the weight is at rest and all the kinetic energy has been transformed to potential energy. Then the entire cycle is repeated.

We have seen that motion changes potential energy to kinetic energy. The greater the motion, the greater is the change. Further, this action is reversible. Reducing the motion changes the kinetic energy to potential energy. At rest, all the kinetic energy is transformed to potential energy.

A somewhat analogous situation exists between the electrostatic and magnetic fields. An electrostatic field, you will recall, exists around a charged body. If this charged body is made to move, some of the energy of this field is transformed into *magnetic energy*. The faster the charged body moves, the more the electrostatic energy is changed to magnetic energy.

A magnetic field always accompanies the motion of a charged body. Another way of saying this is that the motion of the electrostatic field produces a magnetic field. This action is reversible—the motion of a magnetic field produces an electrostatic field. (This matter will be discussed later when we consider *induced voltage.*)

Let us turn, now, to the structure of the atom. It consists, you will recall, of electrons revolving in concentric shells around a central nucleus. Since each moving electron is a charged particle, each electron, therefore, should be surrounded by a magnetic field. And each atom, accordingly, should have a magnetic field that is the resultant of all the magnetic fields around its electrons.

This theory may explain why certain substances exhibit magnetic properties, but since all substances are made up of atoms with moving electrons, why are not all substances magnetic? The answer lies in the fact that the direction of the magnetic field around a moving electron depends upon whether the electron is rotating clockwise or counterclockwise around the nucleus. All atoms contain electrons moving in both directions. The magnetic field around an electron moving in a clockwise direction will cancel out the field around an electron moving in a counterclockwise direction.

If half the electrons of an atom rotate in one direction and half in the other, the magnetic fields will cancel each other and there will be no resultant field around the atom. Hence it is nonmagnetic. If, on the other hand, more electrons rotate in one direction than in the other, the atom will have a resultant field and will exhibit magnetic properties. It is for this reason that iron is magnetic.

The manner in which atoms are arranged in molecules also has a bearing upon the magnetic properties of these molecules. Because of this, certain alloys—such as *alnico,* an alloy of aluminum, nickel, cobalt, and iron—exhibit excellent magnetic properties. (However, we will not go further into this subject since molecular structure is beyond the scope of this book.)

Another question now arises. How is it that a magnetic substance, such as a piece of iron, does not always act as a magnet? For example, you may find that an iron bar will not attract another piece of iron until the bar is converted into a magnet by stroking it with another magnet. What happens to the bar when it is so stroked?

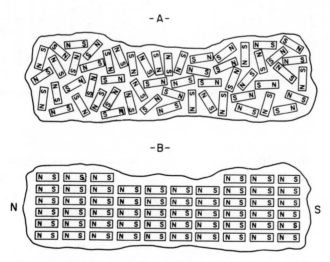

Fig. 5-9. Arrangement of molecules in a piece of magnetic material.
    A. Unmagnetized.
    B. Magnetized.

We now know that the molecules of a magnetic substance are tiny magnets, each with a north and south pole and with a surrounding magnetic field. These molecules may be arranged in a disorderly fashion within the substance (Figure 5-9A). The magnetic fields around the molecules then cancel each other out and, as a result, there is no external magnetic field. We say that, although the substance is magnetic, it is *unmagnetized.*

If the substance is magnetic, it is possible to line up these molecules in an orderly array, with the north pole of one molecule facing the south pole of another (Figure 5-9B). You will notice that all the north poles are facing one way and all the south poles are facing the opposite way. The result, then, is that we have a magnet with an external magnetic field and whose magnetism is concentrated at the two opposite poles. We say that the substance now is *magnetized.*

There is considerable evidence in favor of this theory. If you break a magnet in two, you obtain two magnets, each with a set of poles, as illustrated in Figure 5-10. Furthermore, you can destroy the magnetism of a magnet by any means that will disarrange the orderly array of the molecules, such as by heating or jarring the magnet.

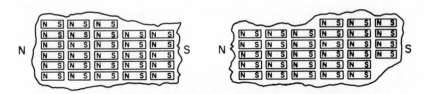

Fig. 5-10. Arrangement of molecules showing why two magnets are formed when a magnet is broken in two.

On the other hand, you can make a magnet of any magnetic substance by placing it within the magnetic field of another magnet. For example, you may stroke the magnetic substance with a magnet. The attraction between the external magnet and the molecules of the magnetic substance causes these molecules to line up in the necessary orderly array (Figure 5-11). This also explains why a magnet will attract a piece of magnetic material that is placed in its field.

A nonmagnetic substance, such as glass or copper, resists all attempts to align its molecules in orderly fashion. Nor do all magnetic substances submit to this lining-up process to the same degree. In some substances, such as soft iron, the molecules are easily moved and will line up readily under the influence of the magnetic field of another magnet. However, once the external magnetic field is removed, the molecules of the soft iron revert to their original, disorderly condition. The soft iron forms a *temporary magnet,* which is magnetized only so long as it is acted on by an external magnetic field.

On the other hand, the molecules of some substances, such as steel, require a much greater magnetic force to produce an orderly arrangement. However, when the external magnetic field is removed, these molecules will retain their positions, and consequently these substances form *permanent magnets.* As we have seen, however, heating or jarring the magnet will disarrange its molecules and thus destroy its magnetic properties.

Magnets may be made in a great variety of shapes. The earliest type, of course, was the natural one dug from the earth. Because the ore could be used as a compass to guide the mariner, it was called *lodestone* (lead stone). Common shapes of manufactured magnets are the *bar magnet,* which has a pole at each end, and the *horseshoe magnet,* which really is a bar magnet that has been bent into a U or horseshoe shape so that both poles are close together. Thus, practically all its magnetism is concentrated into a smaller space.

Fig. 5-11.

How a piece of magnetic material may be magnetized by stroking with a magnet.

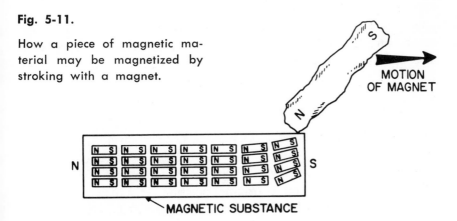

MOTION OF MAGNET

MAGNETIC SUBSTANCE

Fig. 5-12.

Permanent magnets can be constructed in many different shapes.

General Electric Company.

Magnets are also made in a great many other shapes, such as disks, rings, cylinders, and balls. The earth is a ball-shaped magnet. A peculiarity of the earth is that its magnetic poles are not fixed, but vary somewhat from year to year. Furthermore, the earth's lines of force do not describe regular curves from pole to pole, and, consequently, a compass does not point directly to the earth's magnetic poles at all places. In most locations, a slight deviation is noted. This deviation is believed to be due to masses of magnetic material within the earth, which attract the compass and deflect it from a true bearing on the magnetic pole. Mariners must take such deflections into consideration when plotting their courses.

An important use for the permanent magnet is the compass. In addition, the magnet is used in many toys and novelties. Industry uses the permanent magnet for a great many devices such as the magnetic tool holder, certain types of electrical measuring instruments, and the radio loudspeaker. Recently-developed alloys, such as *cobalt-steel* and *alnico*, make possible permanent magnets many times more powerful than those made from steel alone.

2. ELECTROMAGNETISM

In 1819, Hans Christian Oersted, a Danish physicist, brought a small compass near a wire that was carrying an electric current. He noticed that the compass was deflected. When he turned the current off, the compass assumed its original position. This discovery started a chain of events that has helped shape our industrial civilization.

Let us examine the significance of Oersted's discovery. The deflection of the compass while current was flowing through the wire indicated that it was being acted upon by an external magnetic field. Where did this magnetic field come from?

Not from the copper wire, which we know is nonmagnetic. Obviously, it could come only from the electric current flowing through the wire. The compass was deflected only when the current flowed through the conductor and continued to be deflected only so long as the current continued to flow. When the flow of current ceased, so did the deflection.

We believe that a magnetic field always accompanies the motion of a charged particle. It is in this way that we explain the magnetic fields around the electrons revolving about the nucleus of the atom. There is no reason why a magnetic field should not surround an electron moving in a conductor. Since the flow of current consists of the movement of electrons, we should expect a magnetic field around a conductor through which a current is flowing. This Oersted found to be true.

As might be expected, the greater the current flow—that is, the greater the number of electrons flowing per second—the greater is the magnetic field. Experimentation has shown that the pattern of the magnetic field surrounding the conductor is in the shape of a series of concentric cylinders with the conductor at the center. (See Figure 5-13.)

Further experimentation produced a simple method for deter-

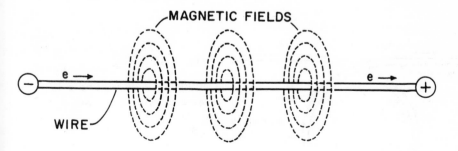

Fig. 5-13. Magnetic field formed around a conductor carrying a current. (For simplicity, the field is shown as a series of concentric circles instead of cylinders.)

mining the direction of this magnetic field. If the conductor is grasped in the left hand with the extended thumb pointing in the direction of the current flow, the fingers then circle the conductor in the direction of the magnetic lines of force. This is illustrated in Figure 5-14.

Fig. 5-14.

Left-hand rule for finding the direction of the magnetic field around a conductor carrying a current.

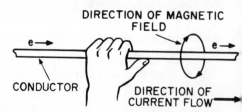

Suppose we bend the current-carrying conductor into a loop. The magnetic field then would appear as illustrated in Figure 5-15. Note that the lines of force all pass through the enclosed portion of the loop. If we add more loops, each loop adds its magnetic field, thus producing a greater over-all magnetic effect. The resulting magnetic field would appear as shown in Figure 5-16.

Note that the coil becomes a temporary magnet (that is—it is a magnet only while current flows through it) with a set of north and south poles. The greater the number of turns, the stronger the magnetic field will be. Also, the greater the current flowing through it, the greater the field will be. Accordingly, we say that the strength of

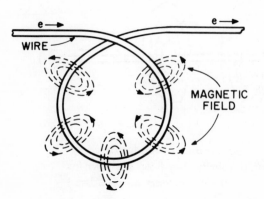

Fig. 5-15.

Magnetic field around a loop of wire carrying a current.

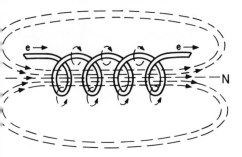

Fig. 5-16.

Magnetic field around a coil of wire through which a current is flowing.

the magnetic field depends upon the *ampere-turns* of the coil. (The ampere-turns are designated by the symbol NI, where N stands for the number of turns and I for the current flowing through these turns.)

The polarity of the magnet formed by the coil may be determined by grasping it in the left hand so that the fingers follow around the coil in the direction in which the electrons are flowing. The extended thumb then will point towards the north pole. (See Figure 5-17.)

Fig. 5-17.

Left-hand rule for finding the polarity of a coil through which a current is flowing.

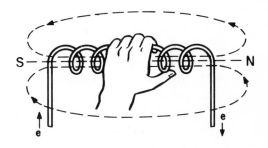

We may increase the strength of the magnetic field by winding the coil on a core of magnetic material. Then the magnetism of the core is added to that of the coil. Since we generally desire the coil to act as a temporary magnet, this core usually is made of some material, such as soft iron, which becomes a magnet only when under the influence of the magnetic field of the coil. The coil with its core is called an *electromagnet*. Without its core the coil usually is called a *solenoid,* or *helix.*

The main factors that determine the magnetic strength of an electromagnet are the number of turns of the coil, the current flowing through it, and the material and size of its core. Other determining factors are the shape and size of the windings and the mechanical arrangement of the core. There are a great many practical applications of the electromagnet. Some of these will be discussed later in this book.

3. MAGNETIC UNITS

We may best understand the magnetic circuit, perhaps, by comparing it to the electrical circuit. In the latter, current is made to flow through a closed loop, or circuit, because of an electrical pressure (electromotive force, or voltage). In flowing through this circuit, the current must overcome opposition or resistance.

The magnetic circuit, too, is a closed one. Corresponding to current is the *magnetic flux* which is designated by the Greek letter ϕ (phi). There are several systems of units in use. In the *English* system the unit of flux is the *line of force*. For most scientific work the *metric*, or *cgs* (centimeter, gram, second) system is employed. In this system the unit of flux is the *maxwell*.

Of greater importance to the engineer who designs magnetic circuits is the *flux density* (designated by B), which is a measure of the flux units per unit area taken at right angles to the direction of flux. In the English system its unit is the *number of lines of force per square inch*. In the metric, or cgs, system the unit of flux density is the *gauss*, which means *maxwells per square centimeter*.

Corresponding to the electromotive force of the electrical system, the *magnetomotive force* (designated by F) is the force that tends to produce the magnetic field. This force may result from a magnetized body (magnet) or it may be produced by a current flowing through a coil of wire. In the latter case, you know that this force is dependent upon the ampere-turns.

The unit of magnetomotive force in the English system is the *ampere-turn*. In the cgs system its unit is the *gilbert* and it may be derived from the following formula:

$$F = K \times NI$$

where F is the magnetomotive force (in gilberts), N is the number of turns of the coil, and I is the current (in amperes) flowing through it. The letter K stands for a constant which is equal to 0.4π. (The Greek letter π, pronounced *pi*, stands for 3.14.)

Corresponding to resistance in an electrical circuit is the *reluctance* (designated by $\mathcal{R}$) of the magnetic circuit. You will recall that in an electrical circuit the resistance depends upon the length, cross-sectional area, and material of the path. The same holds true for the reluctance in a magnetic circuit. The longer the path, the greater is the reluctance; and the greater the cross-sectional area, the less is the reluctance.

We may set up a sort of Ohm's law for magnetic circuits.

In electrical circuits

$$I = \frac{E}{R}.$$

In the magnetic circuit

$$\phi = \frac{F}{\mathcal{R}}$$

or, if we are using cgs units,

$$\phi = \frac{K \times NI}{\mathcal{R}}.$$

The reluctance of a magnetic circuit is seldom considered. For practical purposes it is more useful to employ the *permeability*, designated by the Greek letter μ (pronounced *mew*). If reluctance is a measure of the opposition to the flux in a magnetic circuit, permeability is the ease with which the flux will flow. Thus, permeability is the reciprocal of reluctance, or

$$\mu = \frac{I}{\mathcal{R}} \quad \text{and} \quad \phi = \mu \times F.$$

Actually, the permeability of any material is a measure of the ease with which the molecules of which it is composed may be lined up under the action of a magnetic field. Since the molecules of all non-magnetic materials cannot be lined up, their permeabilities are practically the same. The permeability of all such materials is taken to be unity, that is, 1. When considering a magnetic substance, its permeability is a measure of the number of times easier it is to line up its molecules as those of some nonmagnetic substance, such as air. The permeability of certain magnetic substances may run over 25,000.

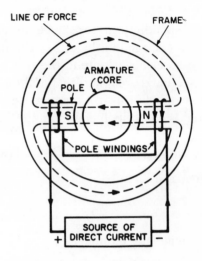

Fig. 5-18.

Magnetic circuit of a
generator.

We have said that the magnetic circuit is a closed one. Let us consider the illustration in Figure 5-18 to show what we mean. Here you see the magnetic circuit of a generator (which will be discussed later in this book). An iron frame contains a set of poles made of the same material. Coils of wire are wound on these poles and, as current flows through these coils, a magnetic field is set up. Its polarity may be determined by means of the left-hand rule previously stated. An iron armature core is suspended between the two poles.

Note that there are two magnetic paths. One starts from the north pole, passes across the right-hand air gap between the right-hand pole and the armature core, through the armature core, across the left-hand air gap, through the left-hand pole, through the upper half of the frame, through the right-hand pole, and back to the north pole. The other path is similar to the first, except that it passes through the lower half of the frame instead of the upper half. Both paths are closed loops.

The magnetic flux is determined by the magnetomotive force and the reluctance of each path. The magnetomotive force depends upon the number of turns on both poles and the current flowing through them (ampere-turns). The reluctance depends upon the permeability of each of the paths, its length and its cross-sectional area.

QUESTIONS

Wherever possible, diagrams should be used to clarify the answers to these questions. These diagrams need not be elaborate, but they should be drawn neatly with the significant portions clearly labeled.

1. List four effects produced by the electric current and give one example of each.
2. List three magnetic substances; three nonmagnetic substances.
3. Draw a diagram showing the magnetic lines of force around a bar magnet.
4. State the law of magnetic attraction and repulsion.
5. Explain why two north poles will repel each other; why a north pole will attract a south pole.
6. A watch contains steel gear wheels. Should these gear wheels become magnetized, the time-keeping quality of the watch will be impaired. How would you protect such a watch from an external magnetic field? Explain.
7. In terms of the electron theory, explain why some substances are magnetic and others nonmagnetic.
8. Explain the difference between a magnetized and an unmagnetized piece of iron.
9. Explain how a magnet can attract an unmagnetized piece of iron. Why will it not attract a piece of wood?
10. What is the difference between a temporary and a permanent magnet?
11. Give two methods for destroying the magnetic property of a permanent magnet. Explain.
12. What is electromagnetism? Explain.
13. Explain the left-hand rule for determining the direction of the magnetic field around a current-carrying conductor.
14. Explain the left-hand rule for determining the magnetic poles of an electromagnet.
15. What are the factors that determine the strength of an electromagnet?
16. Explain what is meant by the *magnetic flux*.
17. Explain what is meant by the *magnetic flux density*.
18. Explain what is meant by *magnetomotive force*.
19. Explain what is meant by *magnetic reluctance*.
20. Explain what is meant by *permeability*.

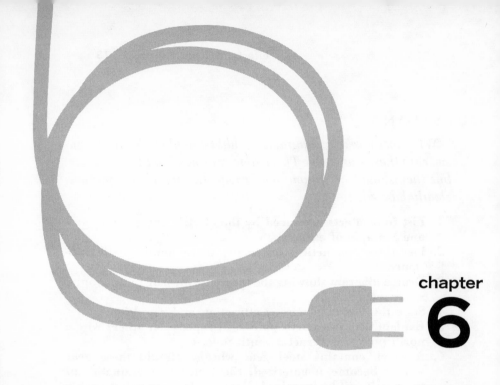

chapter

6

D-C Measuring Instruments

It is extremely important to have instruments by means of which we may measure directly the quantity of certain factors, such as current, voltage, and resistance, that may be present in various portions of the electrical circuit. These instruments are called *meters* and they operate by measuring the various effects produced by the electric current.

Generally, the meter consists of a *movement* which translates current flowing through it into a displacement of a *pointer*, which indicates this displacement on a *scale*. The whole is enclosed in a *case* for protection. Since the displacement is proportional to the current causing it, the excursion of the pointer over the scale indicates this amount of current. Depending upon the circuit in which the meter is connected, the scale may be calibrated in amperes, volts, watts, ohms, and so forth.

A.   *Measurement based upon the chemical effect of electric current*

We have seen that when a current is passed through a solution, such as of table salt, the sodium atoms will be deposited on the negative electrode and the chlorine atoms will accumulate at the positive electrode (Chapter 4, Subdivision B). The stronger the current, the more sodium and chlorine will be accumulated at their respective electrodes. Here, then, is a method for determining the strength of the current by measuring the amount of sodium or chlorine deposited on one of the electrodes in a certain period of time.

In practice, it is difficult to weigh the amount of chlorine so deposited because chlorine is a gas and escapes readily. The sodium atoms, too, are difficult to weigh because they are very active chemically and react with the water of the solution the moment they are formed at the negative electrode. But if we use a silver salt, the silver atoms will be deposited on the negative electrode in the form of a coating or *plate*. Thus, we can weigh this negative electrode before the current flows, permit the current to flow, and then weigh the electrode with its coating of silver after the current has flowed for a definite length of time. The gain in weight represents the amount of silver that has been deposited out of the solution by the current in that length of time.

By careful control and measurement, and by using a silver solution of a certain definite composition, it has been found that one ampere of current will cause 0.001118 gram of silver to be deposited in one second. Of course, you can readily see that this method for measuring current is not very practical and is employed only as a laboratory experiment.

B.   *Measurement based upon the thermal effect of electric current*

When an electric current flows through a conductor, heat is created. Most metallic conductors expand upon heating. Thus, the more current that flows through such a conductor, the more it is

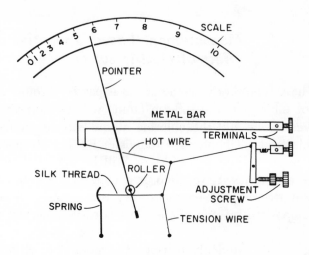

Fig. 6-1. Hot-wire movement.

heated, and the more it expands. We can, therefore, use the amount of expansion of such a conductor to indicate the amount of current flowing through it.

Figure 6-1 illustrates such a measuring instrument which, appropriately enough, is called a *hot-wire movement.* Current passes through a thin wire, usually composed of an alloy of platinum and silver. As the current flows through it, the wire is heated and expands. The heating effect and the resulting expansion is proportional to the current.

Attached to this wire is the *tension wire* and, in turn, a silk thread is attached to the tension wire. This thread passes over a small *roller* and tension is maintained on the whole movement by means of the *spring.* As the hot wire expands, this spring pulls the thread to the left. The motion of the thread causes the roller to rotate. This, in turn, causes the *pointer* to move over the *scale.* Since the amount of expansion (and the consequent movement of the pointer) is proportional to the current flowing through the wire, the amount of current is thus indicated.

When the current ceases flowing, the wire cools and contracts, and the thread is pulled to the right, returning the pointer to zero on the scale. The *adjustment screw* is used to compensate for variations in the tension on the wire.

Note that the scale is not divided into uniform divisions. The heating effect of the current, you will recall (Chapter 5, Subdivision A) is the result of the product of the square of the current and the resistance (I^2R). Thus, the heating effect is not *directly* proportional to the current but, rather, it is proportional to the *square* of the current. If the current is increased two times, the heating effect is increased four times (two squared). If the current is increased three times, the heating effect is increased nine times (three squared). And so on. Accordingly, since the scale indicates current (in amperes) and the pointer moves according to the heating effect, the divisions of the scale cannot be uniform, but resemble those illustrated in Figure 6-1. Such a scale is called a *square-law scale*.

C.   Measurement based upon the magnetic effect of electric current

Most electrical measuring instruments make use of the magnetic effect of the electric current. As you will recall, a conductor carrying an electric current is surrounded by a magnetic field. If this conductor is wound in the form of a coil, the magnetic field is concentrated. The strength of this field will depend upon the number of turns in the coil, and the amount of current flowing through it.

Armed with these facts, we now can construct a current-measuring instrument. Look at Figure 6-2. A soft-iron *vane* fastened to a

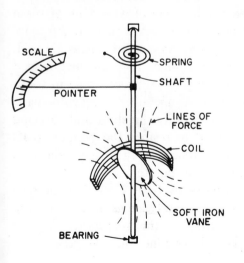

Fig. 6-2.

Inclined-coil movement.

delicately-pivoted shaft is placed inside a coil of wire. (For the sake of simplicity, a cut-away view of the coil is shown.) As current flows through the coil, magnetic lines of force that are parallel to its axis are set up. The iron vane tends to line itself up with these lines of force and, therefore, the vane tends to line itself up with the axis of the coil. In doing so, it rotates the shaft to which it is fastened.

The rotation of the shaft is opposed by the tension of the flat spiral spring that is attached to it. Hence there appear two opposing forces—(1) the rotation of the shaft due to the lining-up effect of the iron vane, and (2) the opposition of the spring. The shaft then will come to rest at a point where these two opposing forces are equal.

The stronger the current flowing through the coil, the greater will be the strength of the magnetic field and, hence, the greater will be the lining-up effect on the iron vane and the greater will be the tendency of the shaft to rotate. Thus the shaft will be able to rotate more before the increasing tension of the spring brings it to a halt. You can see, then, that we may measure the strength of the current flowing through the coil in terms of the amount of rotation of the shaft. This rotation is indicated by a pointer that is fastened to the shaft and that moves over a suitably-calibrated scale.

Note that the coil is mounted in an inclined position. Hence this type of instrument is known as an *inclined-coil movement*.

Another type of instrument depending upon the magnetic effect is the *repulsion-vane movement* illustrated in Figure 6-3. Two soft-iron pieces, or *vanes,* are placed inside a coil of wire. One of these vanes is fixed and the other is free to move. Attached to the movable vane is a shaft carrying a pointer. As current passes through the coil, the vanes become magnetized. Since they are magnetized in the same way (north pole to north pole and south pole to south pole), the two vanes repel each other. As a result, the movable vane is deflected around the center shaft, turning the shaft and carrying the pointer with it. The springs tend to restore the pointer to its original position. The greater the current flowing through the coil, the greater will be the deflection of the pointer.

Note that the scale is of the square-law type. Doubling the current will make the magnetism of each vane twice as great. Thus the repulsive force between them will be four times as large. Tripling the current will make the repulsive force nine times as great.

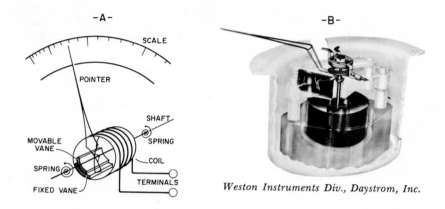

Fig. 6-3. A. Repulsion-vane movement.

B. "Phantom" view of commercial repulsion-vane movement.

Still another instrument is the *solenoid-type movement* illustrated in Figure 6-4. Current passes through a coil of wire (*solenoid*) wound on a hollow tube of some nonmagnetic material. As current flows through the coil, it becomes a magnet and its lines of force tend to pull the soft-iron plunger into the coil. The stronger the current, the greater is the magnetic field and the greater is the pull on the plunger.

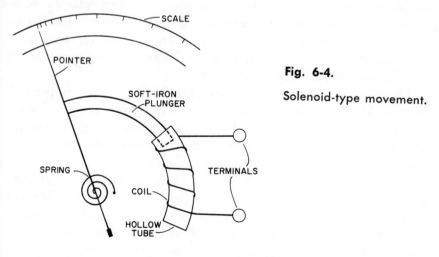

Fig. 6-4.

Solenoid-type movement.

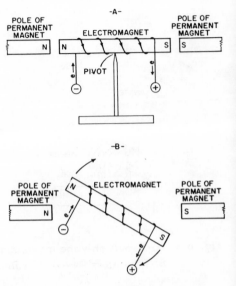

Fig. 6-5. Diagram illustrating the d'Arsonval principle.

A. The electromagnet is pivoted to rotate between two fixed poles of a magnet.

B. Looking down on the top of the electromagnet.

The motion of the plunger pulls the pointer attached to it over the face of the scale. However, the motion of the plunger is opposed by the tension of the flat spiral spring. The pointer comes to rest at the point where the pulling effect of the coil and the opposing force of the spring are equal. Hence the amount of deflection of the pointer over the scale is an indication of the strength of the current flowing through the coil.

Note that here, too, the scale is nonuniform, though not quite of the square-law type. As the soft-iron plunger moves into the solenoid, it strengthens the magnetic field because a greater portion of the coil now has an iron core. Consequently, the force of attraction, and the resulting deflection of the pointer, increases more rapidly than the increase in current.

The types of movements we have described are fairly simple and rugged. However, they are not too accurate, they are inefficient, and not very sensitive. Accordingly, most electrical measuring instruments in use today are based upon a design invented by a French physicist, Arsene d'Arsonval.

In essence, this instrument consists of an electromagnet pivoted between the two opposite poles of a permanent horseshoe magnet (see Figure 6-5). As current flows through the turns of the electromagnet, the latter becomes a magnet. If the current flows as indicated in Figure 6-5A, the left-hand side of the electromagnet becomes a north pole, and the other side a south pole. Since like poles are facing each other, they repel. However, the permanent magnet is fixed and cannot move. Accordingly, the electromagnet rotates around its pivot, as indicated in Figure 6-5B.

The amount of repulsion between the like poles depends upon the relative strengths of the magnetic field around the permanent magnet and that around the electromagnet. Since the magnetic field around the permanent magnet is a fixed value, the stronger the magnetic field around the electromagnet, the greater will be the repulsion and rotating effect. But the strength of the magnetic field around the electromagnet will depend upon the current flowing through it. Thus, the amount of repulsion and the rotating effect will depend upon the strength of the electric current flowing through the coil of the electromagnet.

Here, then, is a convenient way to measure the current flowing through the coil of the electromagnet. All we need do is fix a pointer to this electromagnet and measure the amount of rotation on a suitable scale. Edward Weston, an American scientist, developed a practical instrument using this d'Arsonval principle. (See Figure 6-6.)

The electromagnet, called the *armature*, consists of a coil of very fine wire wound on a soft-iron ball as a core. The complete armature is delicately pivoted upon jewel bearings and is mounted between the poles of a permanent horseshoe magnet. Attached to

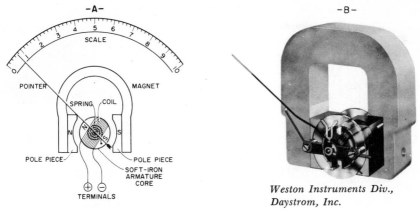

Weston Instruments Div.,
Daystrom, Inc.

Fig. 6-6. A. Moving-coil movement.
      B. "Phantom" view of commercial permanent-magnet moving-coil movement.

these poles are two soft-iron *pole pieces* which concentrate the magnetic field.

As current flows through the armature coil, a magnetic field is set up around it in such a way that it opposes the field of the permanent magnet. As a result, the armature is rotated in a clockwise direction, carrying the pointer which is attached to it. The *spring* opposes the rotation and brings the pointer back to the no-current position when the current ceases. The greater the current, the greater will be the deflection of the pointer. This deflection is indicated on the scale over which the pointer passes.

Note that rotation will take place only when the poles of the permanent magnet face like poles on the armature. Thus the current must flow through the coil of the armature in such a way that this condition prevails. If the current flows in the opposite direction, unlike poles will face and attract each other, and there will be no rotation. Accordingly, the terminals of the instrument are suitably marked *plus* (+) or *minus* (−). If the minus terminal is connected to the high-potential (negative) side of the circuit under test and the plus terminal to the low-potential (positive) side, current will flow through the instrument in the proper direction.

This instrument is called, appropriately, a *moving-coil movement.* Such instruments can be constructed to be highly accurate and ex-

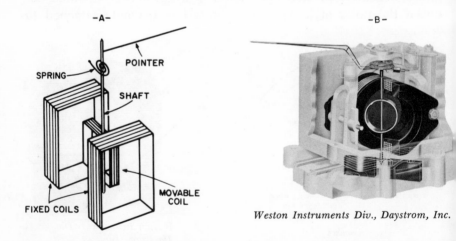

Weston Instruments Div., Daystrom, Inc.

Fig. 6-7. A. Dynamometer movement.

      B. "Phantom" view of commercial dynamometer movement.

tremely sensitive. Its efficiency, too, is high as it requires very little power for its operation. Another advantage is its uniform scale since the deflection of the pointer is directly proportional to the amount of current flowing through the coil of the armature.

A variation of the moving-coil movement is the *dynamometer movement* whose principle is illustrated in Figure 6-7. As in the previous type, a moving coil rotates within a magnetic field and the amount of rotation depends upon the strength of the current flowing through that coil. However, instead of using a permanent magnet to set up this magnetic field, two fixed coils placed on either side of the moving coil are employed. The three coils are connected in series and their magnetic fields are created by the current that flows through all.

The dynamometer-type instrument generally employs a square-law scale. This is because as the current increases, the magnetic fields of *both* the fixed and movable coils increase. Hence the deflection of the pointer, which results from the interaction between the magnetic fields of the fixed and movable coils, increases faster than the current. (But note that in the case of the *wattmeter*, which will be discussed later, the dynamometer movement employs a uniform scale.)

However, since the dynamometer movement does not employ a permanent magnet, it is not subject to changes in its calibration due to aging of the magnet or anything else that may affect its magnetism (such as heating, or jarring). In addition, it has a number of other advantages, as we shall learn a little later.

D.   Types of meters

There are a great many types of electrical meters. Most of them employ movements that are mere variations of the ones we have discussed in the preceding subdivisions of this chapter. Since it is impossible to take up all types of electrical instruments in this book, we shall cover only those that are most common.

1. THE GALVANOMETER

The *galvanometer* is an instrument used to indicate the presence, strength, and direction of very small currents in a circuit. Because we wish to show the presence of very small currents, only the moving-coil type of all those we have discussed is sensitive enough. Because we wish to show the direction of current flow, we cannot use the dynamometer type. Regardless of the direction in which it passes through this instrument, current flow causes a repulsion between the fixed and movable coils, and the pointer is deflected across the scale.

Of all the instruments we have considered, only the Weston-type movement with a fixed permanent magnet is suitable for use as a galvanometer. It has the required sensitivity and, you will recall, its pointer will be deflected only when current flows through its moving coil from its minus terminal to its plus terminal. Thus we can tell, by the manner in which the pointer is deflected, the direction of the current.

Actually, should the instrument be connected so that current flows through it from the plus terminal to the minus one, the pointer will be deflected backwards (to the left), as an examination of Figure 6-6 will show. This may bend the pointer and otherwise damage the instrument. Accordingly, this practice should be avoided.

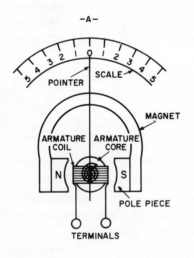

Weston Instruments Div.,
Daystrom, Inc.

Fig. 6-8. A. Zero-center galvanometer.
B. Commercial zero-center galvanometer.

However, it is possible to modify the instrument so that this danger is avoided. The coil and pointer are so mounted that, with no current flowing through the instrument, the pointer comes to rest (zero) at the center of the scale (see Figure 6-8). Then a deflection of the pointer to the right indicates a current flow from the right-hand terminal to the left-hand one. A deflection of the pointer to the left indicates a flow in the opposite direction. Such an instrument is known as a *zero-center* galvanometer.

The numbers on the scale generally are arbitrary ones and merely indicate the *relative* strength of the current. Thus, if the pointer is deflected two divisions, the current is twice as great as one that deflects the pointer one division. Some galvanometers are further calibrated so that the deflection of the pointer may be translated into an indication of the *absolute* strength of current. For example, a deflection from zero to the end of the scale of a certain galvanometer may indicate a current strength of 0.0005 ampere (0.5 milliampere or 500 microamperes). Generally, however, galvanometers are used where only relative values of current are desired.

The moving coil must be light and, hence, is wound with very fine wire. Accordingly, care must be taken that only very small currents flow through it lest the wires burn up. The coil generally is wound with wire that can safely carry a maximum current of about 0.03 ampere (30 milliamperes).

The symbol for the galvanometer, when used in an electrical diagram, is —(G)—.

2. THE AMMETER

The *ammeter* is used to measure the flow of current through a conductor somewhat as a *flowmeter* is used to measure the flow of water through a pipe. In both cases the circuit is broken and the meter is inserted in the break so that all the water (for the water circuit) or all the current (for the electrical circuit) flows through the meter. (See Figure 6-9.) In both cases the meter is inserted in *series* with the circuit under test.

If the current is small enough so that it does not burn up the coil, a meter similar to the moving-coil galvanometer previously described may be used. The scale is calibrated to read milliamperes or microamperes, depending on the magnitude of the current. Gen-

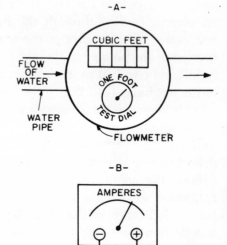

Fig. 6-9.

A. How the flowmeter is connected in the water circuit.
B. How the ammeter is connected in the electrical circuit.

erally, zero-center scales are not employed. Instead, a scale with the zero position at the extreme left is used. Values increase the further the pointer is deflected to the right. Such an ammeter can be used up to about a 30-milliampere full-scale deflection.

As in the case of the flowmeter, which must be connected so that the water flows through it only in one direction, so the moving-coil ammeter must be connected so that the current flows through it only in one direction. Thus the minus (−) terminal must be connected to the high-potential (negative) side of the circuit and the plus (+) terminal must be connected to the low-potential (positive) side.

Where the current to be measured is greater than that which the moving coil can safely pass, a device called a *shunt* is used. This shunt consists of a metal wire or ribbon, usually of some alloy such as *manganin,* which is placed in parallel with the moving coil. Thus the current in the circuit divides, the greater portion flowing through the coil or the shunt, depending upon which has the lower resistance. If the shunt has the same resistance as the coil, half the current will flow through the shunt and half through the coil. If the shunt has half the resistance of the coil, two thirds of the current will flow through the shunt and one third through the coil. The scale of the meter, of course, must be calibrated accordingly.

By choosing the proper resistance ratio between the coil and the shunt, a meter can be used to measure any quantity of current. Assume, for example, that we have a meter whose maximum range is 0.001 ampere and that the resistance of the moving coil is 50 ohms. Suppose we wish to use this meter to measure currents up to 0.1 ampere. We must arrange for a shunt that will be able to carry 0.099 ampere and permit 0.001 ampere to flow through the coil. Hence the resistance of the shunt must be 1/99 that of the coil. The resistance of this shunt then will be 50/99, or 0.5 ohm (approximately). The scale of the meter must be recalibrated to indicate 0.1 ampere for full-scale deflection.

Note that when we use a shunt, the movement actually is serving as a voltmeter, measuring the voltage drop across the shunt. In the example we are considering, the movement has a resistance of 50 ohms and a current of 0.001 ampere flowing through its coil will produce a full-scale deflection. Since $E = I \times R$, a voltage of 0.050 volt applied across the movement will produce a full-scale deflection.

Accordingly, the resistance of any shunt used with this movement must be such as to produce a voltage drop of 0.050 volt when the full-load current flows through the ammeter (movement and shunt). Hence, shunts used with this movement are marked to indicate the full-load current for the ammeter (in amperes) and the voltage required to produce a full-scale deflection of the movement (0.050 volt in this case, which is most commonly used). In this way we are sure that the shunt and movement are properly matched.

Where ammeters are used to measure currents in the order of milliamperes, they are usually called *milliammeters*. Where the full-scale deflection is less than one milliampere, the meter usually is called a *microammeter*. Moving-coil ammeters may be obtained in ranges of from about 10 microamperes (0.00001 ampere) to thousands of amperes. Where shunts are used, they generally are enclosed in the meter case for ammeters up to about 30 amperes. Beyond that, the shunts usually are external to permit adequate heat dissipation. Alloys such as manganin are used for shunts because their resistances vary little with the temperature changes caused by the passage of current.

A single movement may be used with several shunts to make a

multirange ammeter. These shunts may be connected in parallel with the moving coil by means of switches or external connections. In Figure 6-10A is shown a multirange instrument using a tapped resistor (R_s) for that purpose. This is called a *universal,* or *Ayrton,* shunt. Different ranges may be obtained by means of the switch (whose symbol is ⊸⧄) which connects the coil across various portions of the resistor. As shown in the diagram, the ammeter is at its lowest range.

Another type of multirange ammeter using individual shunts is shown in Figure 6-10B. Both switches are connected together (*ganged*) and act in synchronism to switch the various shunts (R_1, R_2, and R_3) across the coil. Of course, the various shunts used in multirange instruments must have the proper resistance ratios to that of the coil for the range employed.

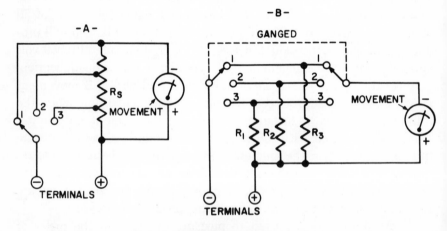

Fig. 6-10. Multirange ammeters.
A. Universal shunt.
B. Individual shunts.

The symbol for the ammeter, when used in an electrical diagram, is —Ⓐ— . If the instrument be a milliammeter, its symbol is —ⓂⒶ— . If it be a microammeter, its symbol is —(μA)— .

The dynamometer movement, also, may be used for the ammeter. However, since the pointer will be deflected the same way regardless of the direction of current flow through the movement, we need not worry about how the terminals are connected to the circuit, provided, of course, that the meter is in series. Where the current is great enough to operate the movement and where great accuracy is not required, any of the other movements previously described may be employed. As in the dynamometer type, their terminals may be connected either way. All the meters may employ shunts to extend their ranges.

3. THE VOLTMETER

The *voltmeter* is used to measure the difference of potential (electrical pressure or voltage drop) between two points in a circuit somewhat as the *pressure gage* is used to measure the water pressure in a pipe. In both cases the measuring instrument is connected in *parallel* with the circuit under test. (See Figure 6-11.)

In Figure 6-11B a moving-coil meter is connected in parallel with the resistor R. The voltage drop across R causes a certain amount of current to flow through the meter. Hence the meter measures this voltage drop in terms of the current set flowing through it.

Since the moving-coil movement will operate only if the current flows through it in the proper direction, care must be taken to connect its minus terminal to the negative side of the circuit and the plus terminal to the positive side. If any of the other types of move-

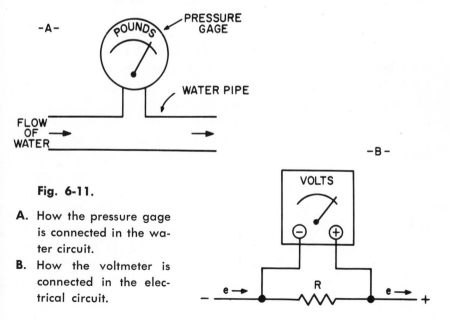

Fig. 6-11.

A. How the pressure gage is connected in the water circuit.

B. How the voltmeter is connected in the electrical circuit.

ments are employed, their terminals may be connected either way.

The resistance of the meter must be large for two reasons. First, since the current flowing through the parallel circuit divides inversely according to the ratio between the resistances of the meter and R, the meter resistance must be large so that very little current will flow through the instrument. Otherwise it will take too much current from the circuit and thus give a false reading of the voltage drop across R. Second, the meter resistance must be large to prevent too much current from flowing through its movement and burning up its movable coil. Since the resistance of the moving coil is low, large resistors, called *multipliers,* are connected in series with it. Thus, the voltmeter consists of the movement and the series multiplier (generally enclosed in the same case).

Assume, for example, that we wish to convert the 1-milliampere meter whose coil has a resistance of 50 ohms to a voltmeter whose full-scale deflection would indicate 100 volts. This means that with 100 volts across the voltmeter, one milliampere (0.001 ampere) of current must flow through it. From Ohm's law we get $R = E/I$, or $R = 100/0.001$. Thus the total resistance of the voltmeter is 100/0.001, or 100,000 ohms. Since the resistance of the coil is 50 ohms, the resistance of the series multiplier must be 99,950 ohms. (Generally, the resistance of the coil is neglected and a series multiplier of 100,000 ohms is employed.)

The multipliers usually are constructed of high-resistance wire, such as manganin, wound on wooden spools. Where the resistance is so high as to make the windings prohibitively large and costly, composition resistors are employed. Some of the less expensive types of voltmeters use composition resistors throughout.

Multirange voltmeters use a number of multipliers which may be placed in series with the moving coil by means of switches or external connections. In Figure 6-12A is shown the circuit of a multirange instrument using a tapped resistor (R_m) for that purpose. Different ranges may be obtained by means of the switch, which connects various portions of the resistor in series with the moving coil. As shown in the diagram, the voltmeter is at its lowest range.

Another type of multirange voltmeter using individual multipliers (R_1, R_2, and R_3) is shown in Figure 6-12B. Of course, the various multipliers used in multirange instruments must have the proper resistance for the range employed.

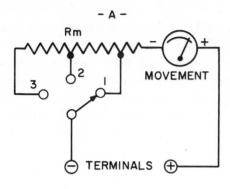

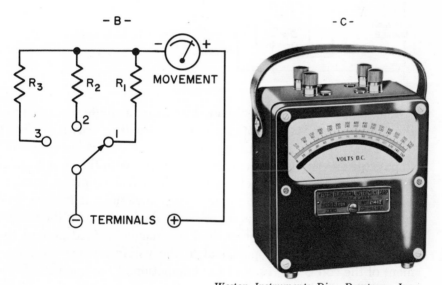

Fig. 6-12. Multirange voltmeters.

A. Using a tapped multiplier resistor.

B. Using separate multiplier resistors.

C. Commercial multirange d-c voltmeter using external posts for connections to series multipliers.

Weston Instruments Div., Daystrom, Inc.

The symbol for the voltmeter, when used in an electrical diagram, is ─Ⓥ─ . If the instrument be a millivoltmeter its symbol is ─ⓂⓋ─ .

Any of the other movements may also be employed as a voltmeter, though, except for the dynamometer type, they seldom are used in this manner. Where the resistance of the movement is too low, suitable multipliers may be employed.

4. THE WATTMETER

The electric power consumed in a circuit is equal to the product of the current and voltage (watts = amperes × volts). A voltmeter and ammeter may be connected to indicate these values and the watts calculated by multiplying the two readings. For example, if we wish to determine the power consumed by a resistor (R) in a circuit, the meters may be connected as indicated in Figure 6-13.

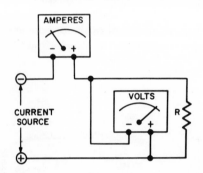

Fig. 6-13.

Circuit used to determine the power consumed by resistor R.

The same result may be obtained by using a single instrument of the dynamometer type connected in the circuit as shown in Figure 6-14. The two fixed coils are wound with wire that is heavy enough to pass the current and are connected in series with the circuit under test. Thus, the magnetic fields around them will be proportional to the current flowing in the circuit. The movable coil is connected in series with a multiplier, and both are connected across the circuit. Thus, they act as a voltmeter, and the magnetic field around the movable coil will be proportional to the voltage. Since the movement of the coil is the result of the interaction of the magnetic fields around the fixed and movable coils, the movement of the pointer across the scale will indicate the watts being consumed by the circuit.

The scale, you will notice, is of the uniform type since it indicates, directly, the product of the current and voltage. Current flows through the fixed and movable coils in the same direction, regardless of how the meter's terminals are connected to the circuit. The symbol for the wattmeter, when used in an electrical diagram, is ─(W)─

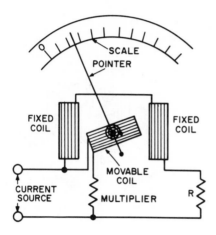

Fig. 6-14. How the wattmeter is connected into the circuit.

5. THE WATTHOUR METER

The *watthour* is the unit for electrical energy (see Chapter 3, Subdivision B, 5). The *watthour meter,* which is used to measure electrical energy, combines the basic principles of the dynamometer movement and the electric motor. (The electric motor will be described in greater detail later in this book. Essentially, a magnetic field around a fixed coil, or coils, called the *field coil,* or *stator,* interacts with the magnetic field around a movable coil wound on an iron core, called the *rotor,* causing the latter to rotate. Current generally is brought to the rotor by means of a set of *brushes.*)

The watthour meter, of a type commonly used to measure the amount of electrical energy consumed by the various circuits in a house, is illustrated in Figure 6-15. The field coils of the motor are wound with heavy wire and are connected in series with the power line. Thus the magnetic field around these coils is proportional to the amount of current drawn from the power line by the house circuits. The rotor coil is wound with fine wire and is connected across the power lines through a series multiplier resistor (R_m). Thus its magnetic field is proportional to the voltage of the line.

The speed of the motor is dependent upon the magnetic fields of

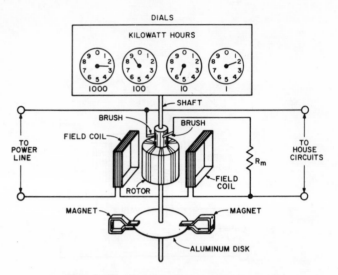

Fig. 6-15. The watthour meter.

the field coils and rotor. Since these magnetic fields are proportional to the line current and voltage, respectively, the speed of the motor depends upon the power (in watts or kilowatts) consumed by the house circuits.

The rotor of the motor is connected through a set of gears to a series of dials that indicate the number of its revolutions. The faster the motor revolves and the longer it continues to do so, the greater will be the dial indications. Accordingly, the dials indicate the power being consumed by the house circuits and the length of time such power is being consumed. But power × time = energy (in watthours or kilowatthours). Accordingly, these dials indicate the kilowatthours of electrical energy consumed by the house circuits. The right-hand dial indicates kilowatthours in units of 1; the next one in units of 10; the next in units of 100; and the left-hand dial in units of 1000.

Note the aluminum disk attached to the lower portion of the rotor shaft. This disk rotates between the poles of two permanent magnets. As this disk rotates and cuts across the magnetic fields of the magnets, a current, called an *eddy current,* is set flowing in it (as you will learn later in this book). This current sets up a magnetic field around the disk that interacts with the magnetic fields of the permanent magnets. As a result of this interaction, the disk, and the rotor which is attached to the same shaft, are braked down. This prevents the rotor from rotating too fast and from continuing to rotate after the current is turned off.

6. THE OHMMETER

The measurement of resistance is based upon current flowing through the circuit under test and on the voltage drop across the circuit produced by that current. If the current and voltage drop are known, the resistance can be calculated from Ohm's law ($R = E/I$). The basic circuit for this resistance measurement is shown in Figure 6-16.

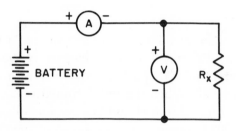

Fig. 6-16. Basic circuit for the resistance test.

Assume that a voltage source, such as a *battery,* of 100 volts is connected in series with an ammeter (A) and an unknown resistor (R_x) whose resistance we wish to measure. (Later in this book we shall discuss electric cells and batteries. The symbol for the cell is ⊣⊢ , and for a battery of cells the symbol is ⊣|||||⊢ .) The voltmeter (V) will indicate the voltage drop across R_x. Since we will neglect here the slight voltage drop across the ammeter and connecting wires and the slight amount of current flowing through the voltmeter, the reading on the voltmeter will be 100 volts, the voltage of the battery. If the ammeter reads, say, 2 amperes, then, since $R = E/I$, $R_x = 100/2 = 50$ ohms.

You can readily see that if the voltage remains constant, we may remove the voltmeter and can calibrate the ammeter to read resistance directly. The greater the resistance, the less the current flowing in the circuit and the less will be the reading on the ammeter. We call the recalibrated ammeter with its voltage supply an *ohmmeter.*

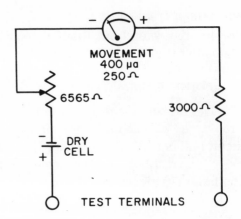

Fig. 6-17.
Typical ohmeter circuit.

Triplett Electrical Instrument Co.

The circuit of a commercial ohmmeter is shown in Figure 6-17. A 400-microampere, 250-ohm microammeter is connected in series with a fixed resistor of 3,000 ohms, a variable resistor of 6,565 ohms, and a 1.5-volt dry cell. When the test terminals are short-circuited, current will flow through the circuit. To obtain full-scale deflection of the meter (0.0004 ampere) the resistance of the circuit must be 3,750 ohms ($R = 1.5/0.0004$). The variable resistor is adjusted to obtain this full-scale deflection.

If any resistance now is introduced into this circuit, less current will flow and the deflection no longer will be full-scale. The greater this new resistance, the less will be the reading on the meter. Thus, the meter can be calibrated directly in terms of the amount of resistance introduced. If no resistance is introduced (test terminals short-circuited), the reading will be full-scale. If a resistance equal to the resistance of the circuit (3,750 ohms) is introduced, 200 microamperes will flow and the reading will be half-scale. If twice the resistance of the circuit (7,500 ohms) is introduced, the deflection will be one third of full-scale. With three times the resistance (11,-250 ohms), the deflection will be quarter-scale. Thus, resistances up to about 250,000 ohms may be measured.

Note that the scale runs backward; zero resistance produces full-scale deflection and the higher the unknown resistance, the smaller the deflection. Note, too, that the scale is not uniform, but crowds together toward the left-hand side of the scale. When discussing ohmmeter ranges we generally speak of the resistance that will produce half-scale deflection—in this case, 3,750 ohms. Since the divisions crowd up at the left-hand side of the scale, we generally can obtain readings with a fair degree of accuracy up to about ten times the half-scale value.

The variable resistor is used to compensate for variations in the dry cell produced by aging. Before each test, the test terminals should be short-circuited by some metallic conductor and the variable resistor adjusted to produce a full-scale deflection. When this can no longer be obtained, the dry cell should be replaced.

To obtain different ohmmeter ranges, the values of the calibrating resistors, the voltage of the battery, or both, may be changed. The circuit of a commercial multirange ohmmeter is shown in Figure 6-18A. The unknown resistor is connected across the terminal marked COMMON and one of the others, depending upon the range desired. At the $R \times 1$ range, the center-scale reading is 25 ohms. At $R \times 10$, the center-scale reading is 250 ohms and all scale readings should be multiplied by 10. At $R \times 100$, the center-scale reading is 2,500 ohms and all scale readings are multiplied by 100. All these

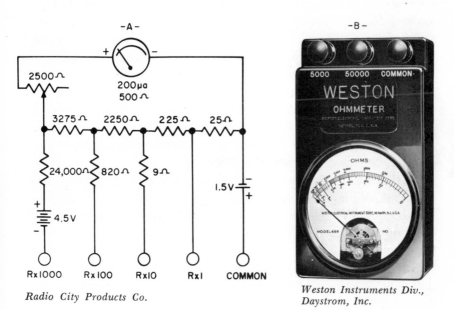

Radio City Products Co.

Weston Instruments Div.,
Daystrom, Inc.

Fig. 6-18. A. Typical multirange ohmmeter circuit.
B. Commercial ohmmeter.

three ranges use the 1.5 volt dry cell. At the $R \times 1000$ range, the 4.5-volt battery is connected in series. The center-scale reading then is 25,000 ohms and all scale readings should be multiplied by 1,000. In all cases, the zero adjustment is made for full-scale deflection with the test terminals shorted before attempting to measure the un-known resistance.

7. MISCELLANEOUS NOTES

The meter is a delicate instrument and should be handled with care. If it is of the magnetic type it should not be placed within a strong magnetic field. The position of the meter, too, is important, since the effect of gravity on the movement may throw off the calibration. If the meter is placed in an improper position, excessive friction in the bearings may cause inaccurate readings. A meter should be operated in the position for which it is designed—namely, vertical, horizontal, or inclined.

The pointer is a little distance from the scale. Thus, if it is viewed from the side, an error of several divisions may occur. This phenomenon is called *parallax*. To avoid this error, the meter should be viewed from a position directly in front of the pointer. Some meters have a mirror incorporated in the scale so that the error may be discerned more readily. If the meter is viewed properly, the pointer and its image coincide. If the meter is viewed from the side, the image in the mirror appears to one side of the pointer.

Most meters are equipped with a screw adjustment to set the pointer at zero before it is connected in the circuit. This is called the *zero-set* adjustment and care must be taken that the pointer is properly adjusted before using the meter.

The ammeter must be connected in series with the circuit under test. If it be connected in parallel, its low resistance would act as a short-circuit and the large current set flowing through it would burn up, or otherwise damage the instrument. The voltmeter, on the other hand, must be connected in parallel with the circuit under test. If it be connected in series, its high resistance tends to restrict the flow of current through the circuit and the meter may be damaged.

If the meter be of the permanent-magnet moving-coil type, its terminals must be connected properly to the circuit under test. Thus the minus terminal must be connected to the negative side of the circuit and the plus terminal to the positive side. If the terminal connections are reversed, damage may result to the movement.

Care must be taken, too, that the current flowing through the meter is not great enough to burn out the movement. Thus the proper range should be employed. When testing a circuit whose current or voltage is unknown, start with the highest range and work down to the proper one. In this respect, it should be noted that the proper range is one where a significant deflection is evident. It would be extremely difficult, for example, to obtain an accurate reading of a current in the neighborhood of one milliampere on a 1,000-milliampere scale. Generally, it is best to use a range where the reading appears at about mid-scale. Where the scale is nonuniform, try to use a range where the reading is obtained on the most spread-out portion of the scale.

The full-scale range of an ammeter is a measure of its *sensitivity*. Thus an 0-500 microampere meter is more sensitive than an 0-1 milliampere one. If 500 microamperes flow through the former, it produces a full-scale deflection. If the same current flows through the latter, it will produce only a half-scale deflection.

The sensitivity of a voltmeter, on the other hand, is determined by dividing the resistance of the meter (including the multiplier) by the reading of a full-scale deflection. Thus, if an 0-100 volt voltmeter has a resistance of 100,000 ohms, its sensitivity is 100,000/100, or *1000 ohms per volt*. The greater the number of ohms per volt, the greater is the sensitivity of the voltmeter. Since the voltmeter is connected in parallel with the circuit it measures, the higher the sensitivity of the meter (the greater the number of ohms per volt) the less power the meter draws from that circuit.

QUESTIONS

Wherever possible, diagrams should be used to clarify the answers to these questions. These diagrams need not be elaborate, but should be drawn neatly with the significant portions clearly labeled.

1. **By means of a simple diagram, explain the hot-wire meter movement.**
2. **By means of a simple diagram, explain the solenoid-type meter movement.**

3. By means of a simple diagram, explain the D'Arsonval moving-coil meter movement.
4. Explain how a D'Arsonval-type galvanometer may be converted into an ammeter; into a voltmeter.
5. Assume you have a milliammeter whose resistance is 100 ohms and whose full-scale deflection is 1 milliampere. What must be the resistance of the shunt needed to convert the meter to read a full-scale deflection of 1 ampere?
6. Assume you have a milliammeter whose full-scale deflection is 1 milliampere and whose resistance is 100 ohms. What must be the resistance of a series multiplier to convert this meter to a voltmeter whose full-scale deflection reads 500 volts?
7. Explain how you would find the resistance of a resistor using an ammeter and voltmeter.
8. What is meant by the sensitivity of an ammeter; of a voltmeter?

Alternating- Current Electricity

Induced EMF and the A-C Cycle

A. *Induced current*

Oersted discovered that an electric current flowing through a conductor can create a magnetic field. Can a magnetic field create an electric current in a conductor? In 1831, Michael Faraday, the famous English scientist, discovered that this could be done. Strangely enough, at about the same time, Joseph Henry, an American scientist and teacher, working independently, discovered the same thing.

. Let us try an experiment to illustrate this point. Connect the terminals of a zero-center galvanometer to a coil of about 50 turns of wire wound in the shape of a cylinder about two inches in diameter. Now plunge the north end of a permanent magnet into the center of the coil (Figure 7-1A). You will observe that the pointer is deflected to the right, showing that an electric current was set flowing for a moment in the coil and galvanometer.

When the magnet comes to rest inside the coil (Figure 7-1B), the pointer swings back to zero, showing that the current has ceased flowing. Now remove the magnet from the coil (Figure 7-1C). As you do so, the pointer swings to the left, showing that once more an electric current is set flowing, but this time in the opposite direction. The same effect may be obtained if the magnet is held stationary and the coil moved..

How can we explain this? You know that the permanent magnet is surrounded by a magnetic field. As the magnet is moved into or out of the coil, this magnetic field cuts across the wire of the coil. *When a conductor cuts through a magnetic field, an electromotive force is set up between the ends of the conductor.* If an external circuit is connected to the ends of the conductor, this electromotive

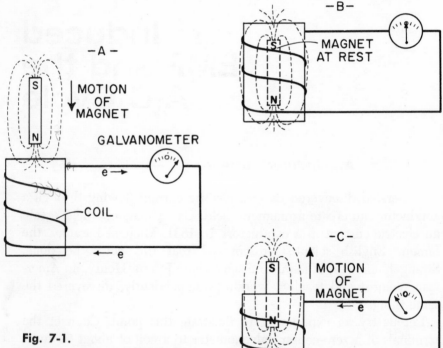

Fig. 7-1.

Demonstration of how a current is induced in a conductor as it cuts across a magnetic field.

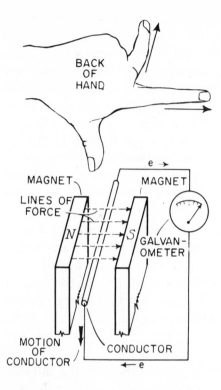

BACK
OF
HAND

e →

MAGNET

MAGNET

LINES OF
FORCE

N

S

GALVAN-
OMETER

Fig. 7-2.

Left-hand rule for determining the direction of induced current flowing in a conductor.

MOTION
OF
CONDUCTOR

CONDUCTOR

← e

force will cause current to flow through the conductor and the external circuit. If there is no external circuit, no current will flow even though the electromotive force is present, just as water under pressure will not flow when the faucet is closed.

It makes no difference whether the conductor is stationary and the magnetic field is moving across it, or the magnetic field is stationary and the conductor is moving through it. But if both the conductor and magnetic field are stationary (as in Figure 7-1B), no electromotive force will be set up and no current will flow.

We call an electromotive force set up in a conductor in this way an *induced electromotive force*. And the current set flowing as a result is an *induced current*.

Experimentation has evolved a rule to determine in which way an induced current will flow. Examine Figure 7-2, where a conductor is moving across a magnetic field set up between two poles of a horseshoe magnet.

Assume that the conductor is moving down between the poles of the magnet. Extend the thumb, the forefinger, and the middle finger of the left hand so that they are at right angles to one another. Let the thumb point in the direction in which the conductor is moving (down). Now let the forefinger point in the direction of the magnetic lines of force (you will recall that we assume they go from the north to the south pole). The middle finger then will indicate the direction in which electrons will be set flowing by the induced electromotive force (away from the observer).

There is another important principle in connection with induced currents. Turn back to Figure 7-1. As the north pole of the magnet enters the coil, a current is induced in this coil. You already know that when a current flows through the conductor, it sets up a magnetic field around this conductor. Thus, the coil becomes an electromagnet. The induced current in this coil is set flowing in such a direction that the end of the coil facing the north pole of the magnet becomes a north pole, too. Since like poles repel, this arrangement of magnets tends to prevent the insertion of the north pole of the magnet into the coil. Work must be done to overcome the force of repulsion.

When you try to remove the magnet from the coil, the induced current is reversed. The top of the coil becomes a south pole and, by attraction to the north pole of the magnet, tends to prevent you from removing it. Thus, once again, work must be done—this time to overcome the force of attraction. You see, you must perform work to create the induced electric current. Of course, the same holds true if the magnet is stationary and the coil is moved.

These results may be summarized in a law formulated by Heinrich Lenz, a German scientist who investigated this phenomenon. According to Lenz's law:

> *An induced current set up by the relative motion of a conductor and a magnetic field always flows in such a direction that it forms a magnetic field that opposes the motion.*

Let us return again to the coil and magnet arrangement illustrated in Figure 7-1. The stronger the field around the permanent magnet, the greater will be the induced current in the coil as it cuts through this magnetic field. Also, the more turns in the coil, the greater the number of conductors cutting the magnetic field. Since each conductor adds its induced electromotive force to the total, the greater the number of turns in the coil, the greater will be the total induced electromotive force and the induced current.

Notice too, inserting the magnet slowly into the coil causes a slight deflection of the galvanometer pointer. Rapid insertion causes greater deflection. Thus, the faster the conductors cut across the magnetic field, the greater will be the induced current.

From all this we may conclude:

1. The stronger the magnetic field, the greater the induced current.

2. The greater the number of conductors cutting the magnetic field, the greater the induced current.

3. The greater the speed of relative motion between the magnetic field and conductors, the greater the induced current.

It has been found that if a conductor cuts across 100,000,000 lines of force in a second, an electromotive force of one volt will be induced between its ends.

B. *The simple generator*

Here, then, is the beginning of our electrical age. We could convert the mechanical energy of a steam engine or water turbine to electric current for light, heat, and power to operate the marvelous electrical machines that soon were invented.

From a mechanical point of view, it is not practical to move our magnet in or out of a stationary coil of wire, or to move the coil over a stationary magnet. The same thing can be accomplished more simply by rotating a loop of wire between the poles of a magnet, thereby inducing a current in the wire as the magnetic field is cut. Let us examine such an arrangement, as illustrated in Figure 7-3.

A simple loop of wire (called an *armature coil*) is mounted so that it may be rotated mechanically on a shaft between the north and south poles of a magnet. The two ends of the loop are connected to two brass or copper rings, **A** and **B** respectively, called *collector rings*, which are insulated from each other and from the shaft on which they are fastened. These collector rings rotate with the loop. Two stationary *brushes* (A_1 and B_1) make a wiping contact with these rotating collector rings and lead the current that has been induced in the loop to the external circuit. These brushes usu-

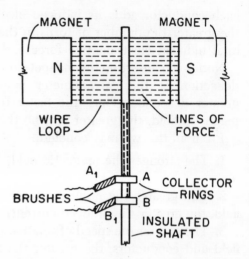

Fig. 7-3.

Simple generator consisting of a loop of wire revolving between the poles of a magnet.

ally are made of copper or carbon. This arrangement of loop, magnetic field, collector rings, and brushes constitutes a simple *generator*.

Let us assume that the loop starts from the position shown in Figure 7-4A, and rotates at a uniform speed in a counterclockwise direction. In its initial position, no lines of force are being cut because conductors 1-2 and 3-4 (the arms of the loop) are moving parallel to the lines of force, not across them.

As the loop revolves, however, the conductors begin to cut across the lines of force at an increasing rate and, therefore, the induced electromotive force becomes larger and larger. At the position shown in Figure 7-4B, the loop has the maximum electromotive force induced in it because conductors 1-2 and 3-4 cut across the maximum number of lines of force per second, since the conductors are moving at right angles to the magnetic field.

As the loop rotates to the position of Figure 7-4C, the electromotive force is still in the same direction, but is diminishing in value, until it is zero again. The loop now has made one-half turn, during which the induced electromotive force increased to a maximum and then gradually fell off to zero. Since conductors 1-2 and 3-4 are now in reversed positions, the induced electromotive force changes direction in both conductors. The electromotive force, however, again increases in strength and becomes maximum when the loop is again cutting the lines of force at right angles (Figure 7-4D).

Finally, the last quarter of rotation brings the loop back to its original position (Figure 7-4A), at which point the electromotive force is zero again. As the rotation is continued, the cycle is repeated.

This, then, is how the generator operates. Of course, practical generators are not constructed as simply as the one illustrated here. We shall discuss them further in a subsequent chapter.

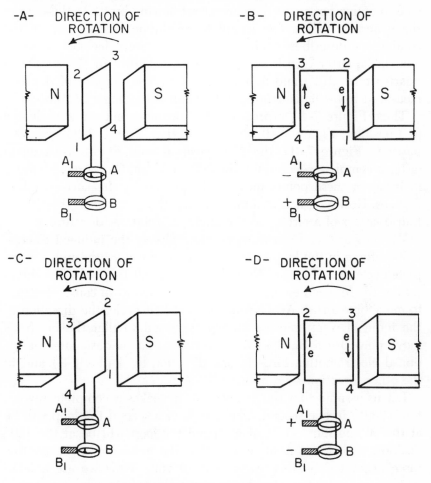

Fig. 7-4. Cycle of the generator.
  A. Start.
  B. Quarter turn (90°).
  C. Half turn (180°).
  D. Three-quarter turn (270°).

C. The alternating-current cycle

The term *cycle* really means "circle"—a circle or series of events which recur in the same order. A complete turn of the loop of the generator is a cycle. So, also, is the series of changes in the induced electromotive force and the current set flowing by it. As the loop of the generator makes one complete revolution, every point in the conductors describes a circle. Since the circle has 360 degrees (360°), a quarter turn is equal to 90°; a half turn to 180°; a three-quarter turn, 270°; and a full turn, 360°. The number of degrees, measured from the starting point, is called the *angle of rotation*.

Thus, Figure 7-4A represents the starting point, or zero-degree (0°) position; Figure 7-4B, the 90° position; Figure 7-4C, the 180° position; Figure 7-4D, the 270° position; and Figure 7-4A again (after a complete revolution), the 360° position. Of course, positions in between these points may be designated by the corresponding degrees. However, it is customary to use the *quadrants* (that is, the four quarters of a circle) as the angles of rotation for reference.

We now are ready to examine more closely the induced electromotive force in the loop of the generator as it goes through a complete cycle or revolution. Note that during half the cycle, the direction of the induced electromotive force is such as to cause electrons to move onto Brush A_1. During the next half-cycle, the direction of the induced electromotive force is reversed so that the electrons move onto Brush B_1. To avoid confusion, let us designate the induced electromotive force in one direction by a plus $(+)$ and in the other direction by a minus $(-)$.

Let us assume that the armature loop makes a complete revolution $(360°)$ in one second. Then, at $\frac{1}{4}$ of a second the loop will be at the 90° position, at $\frac{1}{2}$ of a second the loop will be at the 180° position, and so on. Assume, too, that the maximum electromotive force generated by this machine is 10 volts. Now we are able to make a table showing the electromotive force being generated during each angle of rotation.

Time in seconds	0	$\frac{1}{4}$	$\frac{3}{4}$	$\frac{1}{2}$	1
Angle of rotation	0°	90°	180°	270°	360°
Induced electromotive force (volts)	0	+10	0	−10	0

You will note that in one complete revolution of the loop there are two positions (Figures 7-4A and C) at which there is no induced voltage and, therefore, no current flowing to the brushes (or to the external circuit that is connected to them). There are also two positions (Figures 7-4B and D) at which the induced voltage is at its maximum value, although in opposite directions. At intermediate positions, the voltage has intermediate values.

Note that as the loop rotates, there are two factors that are continuously changing—the position of the loop and the value of the induced electromotive force, or voltage. The *graph* is a useful device to show instantaneous relationships between two such changing factors.

A graph is a drawing or a picture. Many kinds of graphs are used in science, mathematics, and economics. The most common kind of graph shows, by means of a line called a *curve*, the course of events when two different conditions are changing.

For example, assume a circuit in which we have a constant electromotive force of ten volts. Let us employ a graph to show the relationship between the electromotive force and the time during which it is acting. First we draw a horizontal line and call it the *line of zero voltage* (Figure 7-5). This line is divided into equal intervals of time (in this case, seconds). At the zero point, a line is erected at right angles to this line of zero voltage. The new line is

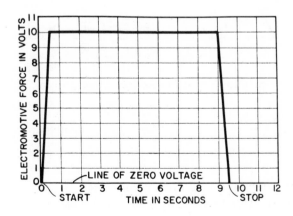

Fig. 7-5. Graph of a steady, direct electromotive force.

divided into equal intervals indicating the electromotive force in volts.

Let us start with the circuit open. The electromotive force in the circuit is zero. Now complete the circuit. The electromotive force in the circuit rises almost instantly to its maximum value (10 volts, in this case). Since this voltage is constant, the graph shows a level, horizontal line at the 10-volt mark. When the circuit is broken 9 seconds later, the electromotive force drops to zero again. (In the graph pictured here the rise and fall of voltage is shown to take place in a half-second. Actually, in most circuits, such rise and fall will occur in a much smaller interval of time.)

Suppose the electromotive force is not constant, but varies continually. The current flow resulting from this varying voltage will vary accordingly. In Figure 7-6 we may see a graph depicting such a current flow. Let us see if we can interpret it.

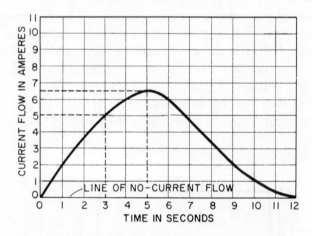

Fig. 7-6. Graph of a fluctuating, direct current.

Before the circuit is completed, no current will flow. When the circuit is completed, the current will start rising gradually, reaching 5 amperes after 3 seconds. After 5 seconds, the current will have reached 6.5 amperes, its maximum value. Then it will start declining, reaching zero after 12 seconds when the circuit is broken. From this graph we may tell the current strength at any instant of flow.

Note that in the graphs of Figures 7-5 and 7-6 the curves at no time went below the line of zero voltage or no-current flow. This indicates that the direction of electromotive force, or the current resulting from it, was only in one direction. You will recall that when the current flows only in one direction we call it a *direct current* (Chapter 3, Subdivision B, 2). In Figure 7-5 we have shown the graph of a *steady* direct current. In Figure 7-6, we have the graph of a *fluctuating* direct current.

1. THE SINE CURVE

Now let us return to our table (p. 108) which shows the relationship between the induced electromotive force in the loop of the generator and the degrees of rotation of the loop (or, what amounts to the same thing, the time in seconds during which the loop rotated). Let us try to show this relationship by means of a graph.

First draw the horizontal line of zero voltage (Figure 7-7) and divide it into four equal sections of a quarter-second each. Since we assume that the loop makes one revolution (360°) in one second, each quarter-second will correspond to 90°. Accordingly, these sections may be marked in degrees as well.

Next, draw the vertical line showing the induced electromotive

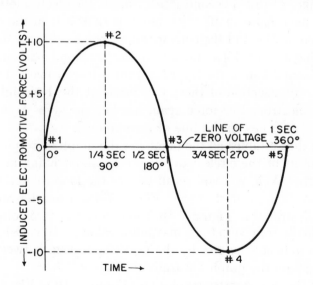

Fig. 7-7. Graph showing the sinusoidal waveform of the generator's alternating-voltage output.

force in volts. You will recall that this voltage is in one direction for half the cycle and then reverses and is in the other direction during the next half-cycle. You will recall, too, that we decided to indicate the voltage in one direction by a plus (+) sign and that in the other direction by a minus (−) sign. All the plus values of voltage will appear above the line of zero voltage, and all the minus values below it. Accordingly, all the numbers indicating induced voltage that appear above the line of zero voltage bear plus signs, and all those below bear minus signs.

We now are ready to transpose the values of our table to the graph. At 0° rotation, the table shows the time to be zero and the induced electromotive force to be zero as well. This point is located on the graph where the horizontal line meets the vertical (#1). At the 90° or ¼-second mark, the induced electromotive force has risen to a value of +10 volts. We find this point on the graph by drawing a vertical line up from the ¼-second (90°) mark and a horizontal line to the right from the +10-volts mark. Where these two lines intersect is the required point (#2).

At the ½-second (180°) mark, the electromotive force has fallen to zero again and the point (#3) on the graph lies on the line of zero voltage. At the ¾-second (270°) mark, the electromotive force has risen once more to 10 volts, but this time it is in the opposite (−) direction. We find the corresponding point (.#4) on the graph by dropping a vertical line down from the ¾-second mark and drawing a horizontal line to the right from the −10-volt mark. The point lies on the intersection of these two lines. At the 1-second (360°) mark, the electromotive force again has become zero. Accordingly, this point (#5) lies on the line of zero voltage.

Having thus established the points on the graph corresponding to the quadrants of the circle, how do we go about filling in the rest of the curve? Well, you will recall that as the loop rotated from its original position, as illustrated in Figure 7-4A, a quarter-revolution (90°), as illustrated in Figure 7-4B, the induced electromotive force rose gradually from zero to its maximum value (+10 volts). Accordingly, we indicate this rise by the curve appearing between points #1 and #2 on the graph illustrated in Figure 7-7.

During the next quarter-revolution (Figure 7-4B to Figure 7-4C), the electromotive force dropped gradually from its maximum value to zero. This is indicated by the curve connecting points #2 and

#3 on the graph. During the next quarter-revolution (Figure 7-4C to Figure 7-4D), the electromotive force reversed its direction and again rose to its maximum value (−10 volts), as indicated by the curve connecting points #3 and #4. During the next quarter-revolution (Figure 7-4D back to Figure 7-4A), the electromotive force dropped gradually to zero again (as indicated by the curve connecting points #4 and #5).

Thus we obtain a graph that illustrates the electromotive force generated by the armature coil as it makes one complete revolution (and the flow of current in the external circuit connected to the brushes resulting from this electromotive force). Now you must not get the impression that the current is flowing in this scenic-railway type of path. Actually, the current is flowing back and forth through the external circuit. What this curve does show, however, is the strength of the induced electromotive force (and the resulting current flow) and its direction (+ or −) at any instant during one revolution.

So at the ¼-second mark, the electromotive force is 10 volts and is acting in the direction indicated by plus (+). At the ¾-second mark, the electromotive force again is 10 volts, but this time it is acting in the opposite direction, as indicated by minus (−). In the interval between the ¼-second mark and the ¾-second mark, the electromotive force changes from +10 volts to −10 volts, dropping to zero at the ½-second mark, at which instant the electromotive force changes its direction.

We call an electromotive force whose strength and direction varies as indicated by the curve of Figure 7-7, an *alternating electromotive force*. The current that is set flowing by such an electromotive force will show a similar curve and is called an *alternating current* (abbreviated *ac*).

Note well the curve of Figure 7-7. This curve is typical for alternating currents and is known as the *sine curve*. This curve is said to be the *waveform* of the alternating current produced by the generator. Usually, we desire alternating current to be of this *sinusoidal* (that is, in the form of a sine curve) waveform.

Each *cycle* of alternating current represents one complete revolution of the armature coil of the generator. The number of cycles per second, which is known as the *frequency*, depends upon the number of revolutions per second. In Figure 7-7, the alternating current has a frequency of one cycle per second. Alternating current supplied to house mains in this country generally has a frequency of 60 cycles per second. In radio, we encounter frequencies that run into millions and billions per second. Of course, no generator can be rotated at such a tremendous number of revolutions per second, but we have other means of producing high-frequency currents. These methods will be discussed later in the section on Electronics.

To facilitate discussing such high frequencies, we use the term *kilocycle* (abbreviated *kc*) which means 1,000 cycles per second; and *megacycle* (abbreviated *mc*) which means 1,000,000 cycles per second. The symbol for the cycle is the sine curve ($\sim$). Thus 60-cycle alternating current may appear as 60 $\sim$ ac. It is from this symbol of a sine curve that we obtain the symbol for the alternating-current generator which is ⏤◯⏤ .

2. MAXIMUM VALUES

Alternating electromotive force and current are changing constantly in magnitude—that is, the *instantaneous* values are changing. From the sine curve, you can see that there are two *maximum,* or *instantaneous peak,* values for each cycle: a positive maximum and a negative maximum. We call the magnitude of these peak values— that is, the values represented by the distance of these peaks from the zero line in the graph shown in Figure 7-7—the *amplitude.* Thus, in our illustration, the amplitude of the generated voltage is 10 volts.

3. AVERAGE VALUES

If you observe the sine curve of alternating electromotive force or current, you will see that the true average value for a full cycle is zero, because there is just as much of the curve above the zero line (+) as there is below it (−). But when we use the *average values* in connection with alternating electromotive force or current, we do not refer to the average of the full cycle, but to the average of a half-cycle (or *alternation,* as it is also called).

It can be proved mathematically that the average value of a half-cycle of a sine curve is equal to 0.636 times the maximum or instantaneous peak value. Thus,

Average current = 0.636 × maximum current

and

$$\text{Average emf} = 0.636 \times \text{maximum emf.}$$

4. EFFECTIVE, OR ROOT-MEAN-SQUARE, VALUES

In practice, we generally use neither the instantaneous nor average values of the electromotive force or current. To make alternating current compare as nearly as possible to direct current, it is necessary to use an *effective value*. In other words, we must find the value for the sine curve of alternating electromotive force or current that would have the same effect in producting *power* as a corresponding direct-current value. You will recall that the direct-current formulas for power are

$$P = I^2R \qquad \text{and} \qquad P = \frac{E^2}{R}$$

From this relationship, you can see that the power is proportional to the square of the current (I^2) or to the square of the electromotive force (E^2). Thus, we must get the average (or *mean*) of the instantaneous values squared (instantaneous value $\times$ instantaneous value), and then calculate the square root of this average.

Because of the method used to determine the effective value, it is known as the *root-mean-square* (abbreviated to *rms*) value. By means of mathematics, it can be proved that the effective value is equal to 0.707 times the maximum, or peak, value and that the peak value is equal to 1.41 times the effective value.

QUESTIONS

Whenever possible, diagrams should be used to clarify the answers to these questions. These diagrams need not be elaborate, but they should be drawn neatly with the significant portions clearly labeled.

1. Explain what is meant by an *induced electromotive force;* an *induced current.*
2. Explain the left-hand rule for determining the direction of induced current flowing in a conductor.
3. State and explain Lenz's law.
4. What are the three factors that determine the strength of an induced current?

5. Draw a diagram of a simple generator and explain its action.

6. Explain the reversal in direction of current flow as the armature coil of the generator rotates through its cycle.

7. What is meant by a *graph?*

8. What is meant by the *waveform* of an electric current?

9. Draw a graph showing the waveform of the alternating voltage produced as the armature coil rotates through one cycle. (Assume the maximum induced voltage is 20 volts.)

10. What is meant by a *cycle* of alternating current? What is meant by the *frequency* of alternating current?

11. What is meant by the *instantaneous values* of alternating current; by the *maximum values?* What is meant by the *amplitude?*

12. What is meant by the *average value* of alternating current? What is its relationship to the maximum value of the current?

13. What is meant by the *effective,* or *root-mean-square, value* of alternating current? What is its relationship to the maximum value of the current?

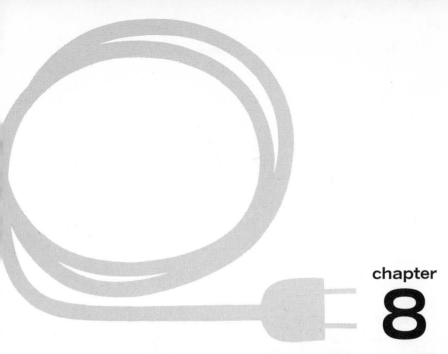

Characteristics of Alternating Current

A. Phase relationships

Flow of current through a circuit is caused by the electrical pressure, or electromotive force. If this electromotive force is direct, the current, too, is direct. If the electromotive force is alternating, the resulting current is alternating as well.

If an alternating electromotive force, or voltage, of sinusoidal waveform is applied to a circuit, the natural tendency will be to cause to flow a current with a similar sinusoidal waveform. Current and voltage will reach zero together, rise and fall together, and attain peak values together. We say that the voltage and current are in step, or *in phase*. This relationship is illustrated in the graph shown in Figure 8-1.

(Note that the relative sizes of the curves have no significance here. They are plotted for different units—the EMF curve in volts and the CURRENT curve in amperes. They are shown of different sizes primarily for the sake of clarity in presentation. What is important is the fact that they are in phase.)

In practical circuits, however, for reasons we will discuss later, the electromotive force and current may not be in step with each

117

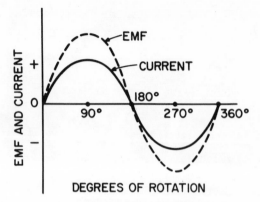

Fig. 8-1.

Graph showing voltage and current in phase.

other. The current may either lag behind or lead the electromotive force. We then say that the electromotive force and the current are *out of phase* with each other.

In Figure 8-2 we see such a condition. Note that the EMF curve reaches its peak 90 degrees (90°) before the CURRENT curve and that it crosses the zero line 90° ahead of the current. We say the electromotive force is *leading* the current by 90°, or that the current is *lagging* 90° behind the electromotive force.

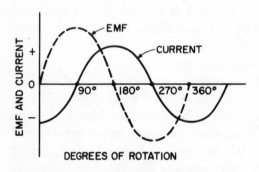

Fig. 8-2.

Graph showing current lagging 90° behind voltage.

In Figure 8-3 the current is leading the electromotive force by 30°. Another way of describing this difference in phase between electromotive force and current is to say that the *phase angle* is 30°. The electrical symbol for phase angle is the Greek letter θ (*theta*).

So far, we have been considering phase relationships between

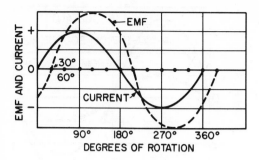

Fig. 8-3.

Graph showing current leading voltage by 30°.

voltage and current coming from the same source. We may have phase differences between two or more currents (or voltages) coming from different sources.

In direct-current circuits (where there are no phase differences), if current is supplied from two or more sources, the resulting current (or voltage) is obtained merely by algebraic addition. Look at Figure 8-4.

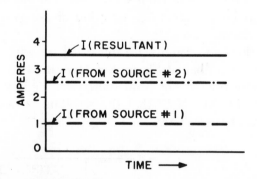

Fig. 8-4. Graph showing resultant of two direct currents.

Here, we have assumed that source #1 supplies a steady direct current of 1 ampere to the circuit. Source #2 supplies a similar current of 2.5 amperes. As a result, a steady direct current of 3.5 amperes flows through the circuit. (In Figure 8-4 we have assumed that the direction of current flow is the same from each source. Hence the two currents are added. If the directions of current flow are different for each source, we subtract the smaller current from the larger, and the direction of flow of the resultant is that of the larger.)

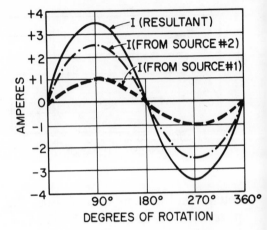

Fig. 8-5.

Graph showing the resultant of adding two alternating currents in phase.

A similar effect is produced with alternating currents only when the currents from sources #1 and #2 are in step, or in phase, with each other. (See Figure 8-5.) The current from source #1 rises and falls in step with the current from source #2. The resultant current (which is found by the algebraic addition of the two) also is in phase.

However, if the two currents are out of phase with each other, the result is different. Look at Figure 8-6. Here the two currents are out of phase, with the current from source #1 leading the current from source #2 by 90°. Note that the resultant current is out of phase with both of the others.

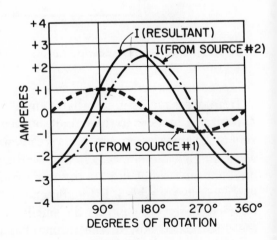

Fig. 8-6.

Graph showing the resultant of adding two alternating currents 90° out of phase.

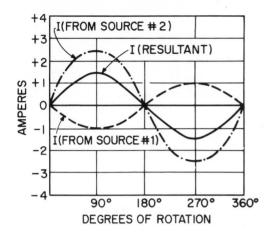

Fig. 8-7.

Graph showing the result-
ant of adding two alternating currents 180° out of
phase.

In Figure 8-7 you see the result when the currents are 180° out of phase with each other. The resultant current is obtained by subtracting one from the other (since one is always positive when the other is negative, and vice versa) and it is in phase with the larger current. But note that if the two currents were of equal value, the resultant would be zero since the positive and negative loops would cancel out. Of course, similar results are obtained when we add voltages from different sources.

B.   Vectors

The magnitude and direction of factors such as force, pressure, etc., may be shown graphically by means of an arrow called a *vector*. The direction of the force is shown by the arrowhead. The magnitude of the force is indicated by the length of the arrow, choosing any convenient scale. Thus, a vector one inch long may be taken to represent, say, a force of 10 pounds. Then, using the same scale, a vector two inches long would represent 20 pounds.

When we wish to add the electromotive forces (or currents) from two direct-current sources, such as batteries, the process is a simple problem of addition or subtraction, as illustrated vectorially in Figure 8-8. In Figure 8-8A we have assumed that the two batteries have been connected so that their electromotive forces reinforce each other (that is, the direction of electromotive force is the

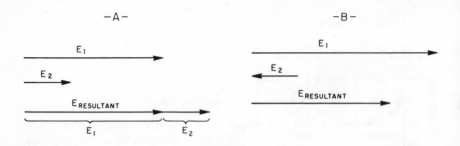

Fig. 8-8. A. Vectorial diagram showing two direct electromotive forces reinforcing each other.
B. Vectorial diagram showing two direct electromotive forces opposing each other.

same for each). The electromotive force of the first battery is represented by the vector E_1, using some suitable scale. The electromotive force of the second battery is represented by the vector E_2, using the same scale. The resultant vector ($E_{Resultant}$), then, is the sum of the two (drawn to the same scale).

In Figure 8-8B we have assumed that the two electromotive forces oppose each other, as indicated by the opposing directions of E_1 and E_2. The resultant, then, is the difference between the two.

But when we wish to add together two alternating electromotive forces (or currents), we have a different problem. The electromotive forces (or currents) may not be in phase. For example, suppose we wish to add together two alternating electromotive forces with one (E_1) leading the other (E_2) by 30°.

The vectorial diagram for this problem is illustrated in Figure 8-9. Using any convenient scale, draw a horizontal line (OB) to represent the vector for E_2. From point O and at an angular distance of 30° (vectorial diagrams are read in a counterclockwise direction) draw vector OA to represent E_1, using the same scale. Thus you will note that we have represented E_1 as leading E_2 by 30°.

From point A draw a line parallel to OB and from point B draw a line parallel to OA. These lines intersect in point C. Line OC represents the vector for the resulting electromotive force (measured on the same scale as the other two electromotive forces). $E_{Resultant}$ leads E_2 by the angular distance between OC and OB, but lags behind E_1 by the angular distance between OC and OA. We follow

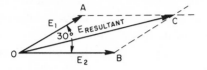

Fig. 8-9.

Vectorial diagram showing the addition of two alternating voltages 30° apart in phase.

the same procedure in adding together two alternating currents.

We can also show the phase relationship between the electromotive force and current from the same source by means of a vectorial diagram. Assume we wish to show the voltage leading the current by 30°. Draw a horizontal vector for the current, using any convenient scale. From the tail end of the current vector, and at the proper angular distance (30°), draw the voltage vector, as shown in Figure 8-10A. Since we are dealing here with two different factors, we need not use the same scale for the voltage vector.

Note that the diagram shows the voltage leading the current by 30°. Should we wish to show the voltage lagging, say, 90° behind the current, the vector diagram would appear as in Figure 8-10B.

Fig. 8-10.

A. Vectorial diagram showing the voltage leading the current by 30°.

B. Vectorial diagram showing the voltage lagging behind the current by 90°.

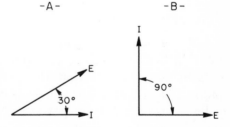

C. Power in a-c circuits

In any circuit, the electrical power consumed at any instant equals the product of the voltage and current at that instant. The equation may be written as

$$p = e \times i$$

where p is the instantaneous power (in watts), e is the instantaneous voltage (in volts), and i is the instantaneous current (in amperes).

(It is common practice to use the small-letter equivalent of the capital letter to indicate an *instantaneous* value. Thus, whereas *I* stands for current, *i* stands for instantaneous current.)

The instantaneous power equation applies regardless whether the current is direct or alternating. If the current be a steady direct current, the power, too, will be steady. But if the current be alternating, the power will vary from instant to instant with the changing current.

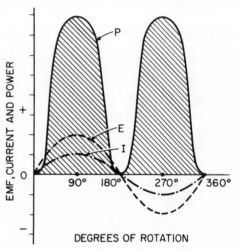

Fig. 8-11.

Graph showing the relationship between voltage, current, and power when voltage and current are in phase. Shading is used to emphasize the power curve.

Let us examine the graph in Figure 8-11, which shows the relationship between voltage, current, and power in an alternating-current circuit. Note that the power curve is the result of the product of instantaneous values of voltage and current. Where both voltage and current are positive, the power, too, is positive since the product of two positive values is another positive value. Where both voltage and current are negative, the power, again, is positive since the product of two negative values is a positive value. Thus, except when it drops momentarily to zero, the power is always positive. That means that the source (which may be a generator) is constantly delivering electrical energy to the circuit.

Note, however, this situation exists if the current and voltage are in phase. Let us see what happens to the power in an out-of-phase circuit.

A graph depicting the relationship between current and voltage in an out-of-phase circuit was shown in Figure 8-2. By multiplying the instantaneous values of current and voltage we may obtain the power curve, as shown in Figure 8-12.

For the first 90° of the cycle, the voltage is positive and the current is negative. The product of a positive value and a negative value is a negative value. Accordingly, the resulting power is negative. That means that electrical energy is flowing from the circuit back to the source.

During the next 90° of the cycle, both current and voltage are positive. Accordingly, the power, which is the product of the two, also is positive, and energy is flowing from the source into the circuit.

For the next 90° of the cycle, the current is positive and the voltage is negative. The power is negative and energy again flows from the circuit back to the source. During the last 90° of the cycle, both current and voltage are negative. The power, thus, is positive and energy flows once more from the source into the circuit.

Examination of the graph shows that the positive power is equal and opposite to the negative power. As a result, they cancel out and the net result is zero. That is, the circuit consumes, or dissipates, no power. The electrical energy merely flows from the source into the circuit and back again. Note, however, that this condition holds only when the phase angle is 90°.

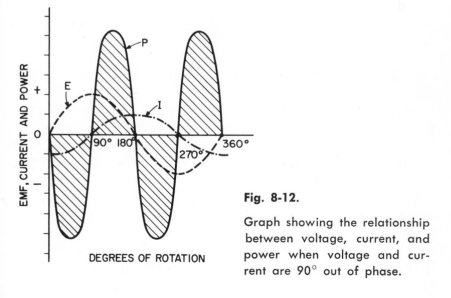

Fig. 8-12.

Graph showing the relationship between voltage, current, and power when voltage and current are 90° out of phase.

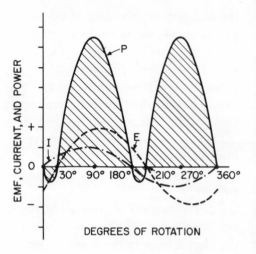

Fig. 8-13.

Graph showing the relationship between voltage, current, and power when voltage and current are 30° out of phase.

Now, what if the phase angle is some other value such as, for example, 30°, as shown by the graph of Figure 8-3? Examine Figure 8-13.

Note that the power is negative only during the intervals between 0° and 30° and between 180° and 210°. During the rest of the cycle the power is positive. Thus, the average power is not zero, as in the case of a circuit where the phase angle is 90°, but some positive value. However, it is less than the average power dissipated by a comparable circuit where the current and voltage are in phase.

D. *Power factor*

The instantaneous power consumed in any circuit, you will recall, is the product of the instantaneous voltage (e) and the instantaneous current (i). In alternating-current circuits, however, we generally deal with effective, or rms, values. As such, the $P = E \times I$ equation for power holds only when the current and voltage are in phase. (See Figure 8-11.) Under such conditions, electrical energy flows only from the source to the circuit.

However, when the current and voltage are out of phase there are intervals when electrical energy is flowing back to the source from the circuit. (See Figures 8-12 and 8-13). Accordingly, the *true power* consumed by the circuit is less than the *apparent* power calculated by multiplying the effective voltage (E) by the effective current (I).

The ratio of the true power to the apparent power is called the *power factor*. Thus,

$$\text{Power factor} = \frac{\text{true power}}{\text{apparent power}}.$$

This ratio may be expressed either as a fraction or as a percentage. We may say that the power factor is, for example, one half, or 50 per cent.

The power factor is a function of the phase angle. Where the current and voltage are in phase (phase angle = zero), the apparent power is equal to the true power. The power factor in this case is *unity* (that is, one), or 100 per cent. Where the current and voltage are out of phase, the power factor is some lesser value, depending upon the phase angle.

The power factor should be stated as *leading* or *lagging*. This refers to the current with respect to the voltage. If, when discussing the characteristics of an electrical circuit, we say the power factor is 65 per cent lagging, we mean that the current is lagging behind the voltage in the circuit.

The apparent power can be calculated by using a voltmeter to measure the rms voltage and an ammeter to measure the rms current. Multiplying the two values thus obtained gives us the apparent power. The true power, on the other hand, can be obtained directly by measuring it with a wattmeter. To differentiate between the two, we generally measure the apparent power in units of *volt-amperes*. The true power we measure in units of *watts*.

What is the significance of the power factor? Well, consider an electric motor being run from an a-c line. Generally, we wish the motor to consume its full rated electrical power, because only in this way can we get the full rated mechanical power from the motor. If, during a portion of the cycle, electrical energy is being fed back to the line (power factor is less than 100 per cent, or unity), the motor is not consuming its proper share of power and, hence, is not operating at full efficiency. Accordingly, we wish the power factor of the circuit to be as near 100 per cent as possible.

E. Ohm's law for alternating-current circuits

You will recall that when we were studying Ohm's law for direct-current circuits (Chapter 3, Subdivision C) we found the relationship between current (I), electromotive force (E), and resistance (R) expressed in the equation

$$I = \frac{E}{R}$$

where I is measured in amperes, E in volts, and R in ohms. In d-c circuits, the resistance expresses the total opposition to current flow.

In alternating-current circuits, however, except where the voltage and current are in phase, there are other factors besides resistance that oppose the flow of current. (We shall learn about these factors a little later.) Accordingly, our Ohm's law does not apply to a-c circuits unless we substitute for the resistance some value that will take into consideration the increased opposition to current flow.

This new value of total opposition to current flow is called *impedance* and is represented in electrical equations by the capital letter Z. Since impedance, like resistance, measures the opposition to current flow, it has the same unit of measurement, the *ohm*.

Where the current and voltage are in phase, the impedance of the circuit is equal to the resistance. But where a phase difference exists, the impedance becomes larger than the resistance.

If, now, we substitute impedance (Z) for resistance (R), our Ohm's-law equations apply equally well to alternating-current circuits. Thus

$$I = \frac{E}{Z}, \; E = I \times Z, \text{ and } Z = \frac{E}{I}$$

where I is the current (in amperes), E is the electromotive force (in volts), and Z is the impedance (in ohms).

QUESTIONS

Wherever possible, diagrams should be used to clarify the answers to these questions. These diagrams need not be elaborate, but they should be drawn neatly with the significant portions clearly labeled.

1. What is meant when we say that an alternating current and voltage are *in phase?* Draw a graph illustrating this condition.
2. What is meant when we say that an alternating current and voltage are *out of phase?* Draw a graph showing the current *leading* the voltage by 90 degrees.
3. What is meant by *phase angle?*
4. Draw a graph showing the resultant of the addition of two steady direct currents, one 5 amperes and the other 6 amperes.
5. Draw a graph showing the resultant of the addition of two alternating currents, one whose maximum value is 2 amperes and the other with a maximum value of 3 amperes, that are in phase with each other.
6. Draw the graph showing the resultant of the same two currents as in Question 5, if the phase angle between them is 90 degrees.
7. *a)* What is a *vector? b)* What two conditions does it describe?
8. Draw the vector diagram showing the resultant of the addition of two steady direct voltages, one +3 volts and the other −5 volts.
9. Draw the vector diagram showing the resultant of the addition of an alternating current whose maximum value is 3 amperes leading by 45° another alternating current whose maximum value is 5 amperes.
10. In any a-c circuit, what must be the phase angle between the voltage and current for the power to be *a)* at its maximum; *b)* at its minimum?
11. Draw a graph showing the power in an a-c circuit where a maximum voltage of 5 volts leads by 60 degrees a maximum current of 2 amperes.
12. What is meant by the *power factor* of a circuit?
13. What is the power factor of a circuit where the voltage and current are in phase?

14. In a certain circuit it was known that the current was lagging behind the voltage. When measured by means of a voltmeter and ammeter, the effective voltage was found to be 100 volts and the effective current to be 5 amperes. When measured with a wattmeter, the power was found to be 400 watts. What is the power factor of the circuit?

15. What is meant by *impedance?* State Ohm's law for a-c circuits.

Factors Affecting Alternating Current

A. *Resistance*

Resistance, we have learned, opposes the flow of current through a circuit. This is true, regardless whether the current be direct or alternating. If the circuit contains nothing but resistance, Ohm's law for direct current $(I = E/R)$ applies equally well for alternating current, and the impedance (Z) is equal to the resistance (R). However, when dealing with alternating-current circuits we encounter instantaneous, peak, average, and rms values. Accordingly, care must be taken to employ similar values for both current and voltage in each case.

Furthermore, resistance does not affect the phase relationship between current and voltage in an a-c circuit. That is, the current and voltage remain in phase. Since the voltage and current are in phase, the power factor of the circuit is unity, or 100 per cent, and the apparent power is equal to the true power.

B. Inductance and inductive reactance

1. INDUCTANCE

In discussing induced currents (Chapter 7, Subdivision A), we have seen that if a coil is cut by a magnetic field, an induced voltage is developed in the coil. It makes no difference how the magnetic field is produced. It may be produced by a permanent magnet, as illustrated in Figure 7-1. Or else, it may be produced by current set flowing through the turns of the coil by some voltage source. As the current starts flowing through it, a magnetic field is built up around the coil. As this field is built up, it cuts across the turns of the coil, inducing therein an electromotive force. When the current reaches a steady value, the magnetic field, too, becomes steady, and the induced electromotive force drops to zero. When the current drops, the magnetic field collapses, cutting across the coil again, and the induced electromotive force comes into being once more.

We have also learned, from Lenz's law, that the induced electromotive force and the induced current it sets flowing are always in such a direction as to oppose any change in the existing magnetic field. Thus, if the original (source) current is increasing and is causing the magnetic field around the coil to expand, the induced electromotive force sets the induced current flowing in such a direction as to build up a magnetic field in opposition to the one set up by the source current. If the source current is decreasing and causing the magnetic field to collapse, the induced electromotive force sets the induced current flowing in such a direction as to build up a magnetic field that aids the original magnetic field and thus tends to prevent its collapse. (See Figure 9-1.) Because it acts in opposition to any change in the source current and the source voltage that causes this current to flow, the induced electromotive force is called a *counter voltage*, or *counter electromotive force* (abbreviated *cemf*).

The property of a circuit to oppose any change in the current flowing through it is called *inductance*. This property is due to the voltages induced in the circuit itself by the changing magnetic field. Components of the circuit that produce inductance, such as the coil we have been discussing, are called *inductors*. As we have learned,

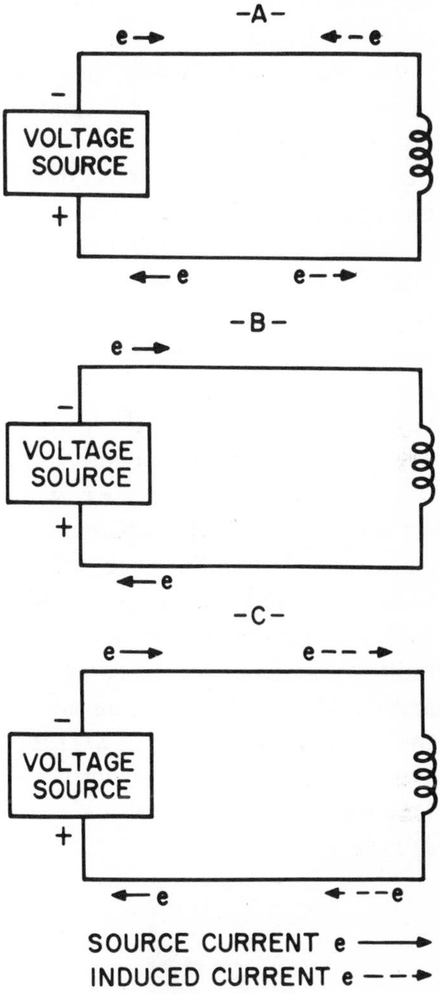

Fig. 9-1. Flow of current in a circuit containing an inductor.

A. Source current is increasing. Induced current opposes source current.
B. Source current is steady. There is no induced current.
C. Source current is decreasing. Induced current aids source current.

SOURCE CURRENT e ⟶
INDUCED CURRENT e – – ➤

the induced voltage depends upon the strength of the magnetic field set up around the coil, the number of its turns, and the speed with which the changing magnetic field cuts across these turns. Hence the inductance of the inductor depends upon these factors.

Anything that affects the magnetic field also affects the inductance of the inductor. For example, increasing the number of turns of the inductor increases its inductance. Similarly, substituting an iron core for an air core also increases its inductance. The symbol

for an inductor having an air core is ⎯◯◯◯⎯ . If it has an iron core
its symbol becomes ⎯◯◯◯⎯ (See Figure 9-2.)

The speed with which the magnetic field around an inductor is
changing also affects its inductance. Thus, if a steady direct current flows through a circuit, there is no inductance except for those
instants when the circuit is completed and broken. However, when
dealing with alternating currents, the current strength is constantly
changing and inductance becomes a factor in such a circuit.

The faster the current changes (that is, the greater its *frequency*),
the larger the inductance will be. Since even a straight wire has a
surrounding magnetic field when current is flowing through it, the
wire has some inductance. However, unless the frequency of the
current is very great or the wire extremely long, the inductance of a
straight wire is small enough to be neglected.

The symbol for inductance, when used in electrical formulas, is *L*.
Its unit is the *henry* (abbreviated h) which is the inductance of a
circuit or component that will produce an induced electromotive
force of one volt with a change of one ampere per second in the current flowing through it. (Since current variations seldom are at a
uniform rate, a circuit or component has an inductance of one henry
if it develops an *average* induced electromotive force of one volt as
the current changes at an *average* rate of one ampere per second.)
Where the henry is too large a unit, we may use the *millihenry*
(*mh*) which is 1/1000 of a henry, or the *microhenry* (*μh*) which is
1/1,000,000 of a henry.

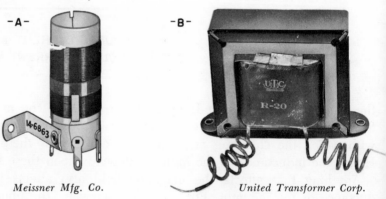

-A-

-B-

Meissner Mfg. Co.

United Transformer Corp.

Fig. 9-2. A. Air-core inductor.
B. Iron-core inductor.

Inductors, like resistors, may be connected in series, in parallel, or in series-parallel circuits. The total inductance of several inductors connected in series (provided the magnetic field of one inductor cannot act upon the turns of another) is equal to the sum of the inductances of the individual inductors. Thus:

$$L_{total} = L_1 + L_2 + L_3 +, \text{ and so forth.}$$

If two or more inductors are connected in parallel (again, providing there is no interaction, or *coupling*, of their magnetic fields) we can find the total inductance from the following formula:

$$\frac{1}{L_{total}} = \frac{1}{L_1} + \frac{1}{L_2} + \frac{1}{L_3} +, \text{ and so forth.}$$

Note the similarity to the formulas for resistors connected in series and parallel.

As in the case of resistors, the total inductance of inductors connected in a series-parallel circuit (if there is no coupling of magnetic fields) may be obtained by first finding the joint inductance of the inductors in parallel and then adding this inductance to the inductances in series with it as though it were a straight series-inductor circuit.

2. EFFECT OF INDUCTANCE ON THE PHASE RELATIONSHIPS BETWEEN VOLTAGE AND CURRENT

In an a-c circuit containing only resistance, the voltage and current constantly remain in phase. This relationship is shown graphically in Figure 9-3A. (The relative amplitudes of the voltage and current curves have no significance here.) Now let us consider an a-c circuit that contains nothing but inductance. (Such a circuit is only theoretically possible since all circuits contain some resistance.)

As you know, the induced electromotive force always opposes the change in the source current. When this current is rising, the induced electromotive force tends to keep the value of current less than the source voltage alone would do. Accordingly, the rise in the source current takes place later than does the rise in source voltage. When the current is decreasing, the induced electromotive force tends to oppose the decrease. Hence, the fall of source current, too, takes place later than does the fall in source voltage. Thus the

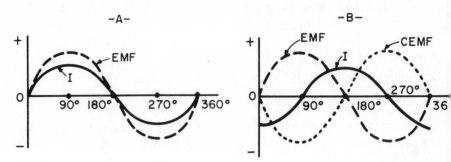

Fig. 9-3. A. Phase relationship between current and voltage in a circuit containing only resistance.
B. Phase relationship in a circuit containing only inductance.

source current lags behind the source voltage throughout the entire cycle.

The induced electromotive force (*cemf*) is greatest when the current is changing at its fastest rate. If you examine Figure 9-3B, you will see that this occurs as the current passes through zero at the 90° position. Since the source voltage in a circuit containing only inductance is equal and opposite to the induced electromotive force, the source voltage is at its positive peak at the same 90° position.

The induced electromotive force drops to zero as the current reaches its lowest rate of change. This occurs at the 180° position where the current reaches its positive peak. Since the source voltage is equal and opposite to the induced electromotive force, it, too, is zero at that point. Thus, you can see that, in an a-c circuit containing only inductance, the current lags behind the source voltage by 90° or, what is the same thing, the source voltage leads the current by 90°. In practical circuits, because of the presence of resistance, the current lag is some value less than 90° behind the voltage.

We have already learned that the use of vectors furnishes us with a convenient means for picturing the relationships between currents and voltages. Thus, if an alternating-current circuit has, theoretically, nothing but inductance in it, the vector diagram appears as in Figure 9-4B.

In this diagram, the length of the voltage vector (*E*) is independent of the length of the current vector (*I*) and the length of

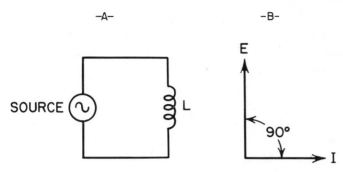

Fig. 9-4. A. A-c circuit containing only inductance.
   B. Vector diagram showing the phase relationship between current (*I*) and voltage (*E*) in this circuit.

each vector depends upon its own scale. Further, because of the inductance, the voltage leads the current (we always read vector diagrams in a counterclockwise direction). The phase angle is 90°.

If a wattmeter, which measures *true* power consumed by a circuit, is connected in a circuit containing only inductance, the meter will register zero. You can verify this by looking at Figure 8-12, which shows the true power in a circuit wherein the current lags behind the voltage by 90°. Note that the positive and negative loops are equal and, hence, cancel out. In such a circuit the electrical energy is merely transformed into magnetic energy in the inductor and back to electrical energy again. Thus no power is consumed. Since

$$\text{Power factor} = \frac{\text{true power}}{\text{apparent power}}$$

and the true power is zero, the power factor, too, must be zero.

3. INDUCTIVE REACTANCE

In Chapter 8, Subdivision *E*, we learned that the impedance of an a-c circuit is the total opposition that circuit offers to the flow of current. Where only pure resistance is present in the circuit, the impedance is equal to the resistance. But we have seen that the presence of an inductor in the circuit causes a counter electromotive force to be built up which further opposes the flow of current. Under such conditions, the impedance of the circuit is greater than the resistance.

The factor which, in an a-c circuit, causes the impedance (Z) to be larger than the resistance (R) is called the *reactance* (X). Since this reactance is due to the presence of inductance, we call it the *inductive reactance*. To show that it is inductive reactance, we add the subscript L to the symbol for reactance (X) and we now get X_L as the symbol for inductive reactance.

[This method of adding a subscript to identify an electrical value is commonly used. Thus, the current (I) flowing through the inductor is shown as I_L. The voltage (E) across the inductor becomes E_L. This type of notation is not restricted to inductors. Thus, for example, the voltage drop across a resistor may be designated as E_R and the current flowing through it as I_R.]

Since impedance represents an opposition to the flow of current and has the ohm as its unit, the inductive reactance, which increases the impedance, also has the ohm for its unit.

The inductive reactance depends upon the magnitude of the induced voltage. This voltage, in turn, depends upon two factors: the inductance of the circuit (L) and the rate or frequency (f) at which the current (and, therefore, the magnetic field) is changing.

The formula for inductive reactance is

$$X_L = 2\pi f L$$

where X_L is the inductive reactance in ohms, f is the frequency in cycles per second, and L is the inductance in henrys. The factor 2π is necessary to make the result come out in ohms. Since π is equal, approximately, to 3.14, 2π therefore equals 6.28.

Example. What is the inductive reactance of a coil of 2 henrys as a 60-cycle alternating current flows through it?

$$X_L = 2\pi f L = 6.28 \times 60 \text{ cycles per second} \times 2 \text{ henrys}$$
$$= 753.6 \text{ ohms.} \quad Ans.$$

If we assume a theoretical circuit that has only inductance, we may substitute the inductive reactance (X_L) for the impedance (Z) in the formulas that state Ohm's law for a-c circuits. These formulas are expressed as follows:

$$I = \frac{E}{Z}, \qquad E = I \times Z, \qquad Z = \frac{E}{I}.$$

Substituting inductive reactance for impedance, we get for a theoretical circuit with inductance only,

$$I = \frac{E}{X_L}, \qquad E = I \times X_L, \qquad X_L = \frac{E}{I}.$$

4. MUTUAL INDUCTANCE

We have seen that when a changing current flows through a circuit that possesses the property of inductance, an induced voltage is generated in that circuit which opposes the changes in current. The ability of the circuit to act in this manner is called *self inductance*. We have seen, too, that when two or more inductors are connected in series in such a way that their magnetic fields do not interact, the total inductance is the sum of the inductances of all the inductors. That is to say, the total inductance is the sum of the self inductances of all the inductors.

If, however, two inductors are placed close to each other, their magnetic fields will interact and the magnetic field of one may induce a voltage in the other as it cuts across the turns of wire. We say, then, that the inductors are *coupled*. Each inductor has its own self inductance, but, in addition, there is a further inductance due to the induced voltage produced by coupling between the inductors. We call this further inductance, *mutual inductance*. We say the two coils are coupled together by mutual inductance. The terms *magnetic*, or *inductive, coupling* are sometimes used.

Mutual inductance, whose electrical symbol is M, is measured in the same unit as self inductance, the *henry*. When a change of 1 ampere per second in one inductor induces 1 volt in the other, the two inductors have a mutual inductance of 1 henry.

Mutual inductance, whose electrical symbol is M, is measured in the same unit as self inductance, the *henry*. When a change of one ampere per second in one inductor induces one volt in the other, the two inductors have a mutual inductance of one henry.

Inductors can be series-connected in two ways. Figure 9-5A shows the inductors connected so that the two magnetic fields aid each other. The effect of mutual inductance is to increase the total inductance, and our formula becomes

$$L_{total} = L_1 + L_2 + 2M.$$

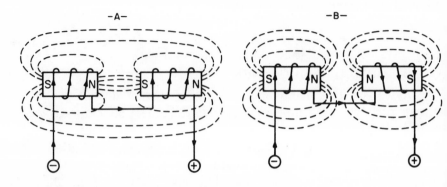

Fig. 9-5. Two inductors connected in series.
A. Magnetic fields aid each other.
B. Magnetic fields oppose each other.

The two inductors may also be connected in series in such a way that the magnetic fields oppose each other. Figure 9-5B shows this circuit. The effect of the mutual inductance is to decrease the total inductance, and our formula becomes

$$L_{\text{total}} = L_1 + L_2 - 2M.$$

A similar relationship holds true for two inductors connected in parallel. If the two magnetic fields aid each other, the formula for the total inductance becomes

$$\frac{1}{L_{\text{total}}} = \frac{1}{L_1 + M} + \frac{1}{L_2 + M}.$$

Where the magnetic fields oppose each other, the formula becomes

$$\frac{1}{L_{\text{total}}} = \frac{1}{L_1 - M} + \frac{1}{L_2 - M}.$$

Inductors are said to be *closely coupled* when a large portion of the magnetic lines of force set up by one of the inductors cut across the turns of the other. When only a small portion of the lines of one cut the turns of the other, they are said to be *loosely coupled*. If all the magnetic lines of one cut across all the turns of the other, we say we have *maximum coupling*.

In practice, such a condition never exists since some of the lines of one never succeed in cutting the turns of the other. Accordingly, an expression to give the degree of coupling is used. Maximum coupling is considered *100 per cent coupling*, or, as it is often called, *unity coupling*. If only half the lines of force cut all the turns, or if all the lines cut half the number of turns, the degree of coupling is said to be 50 per cent. Only when the two coils are wound on the same iron core that tends to concentrate the lines of force does the coupling approach 100 per cent.

The coupled inductors need not both be parts of the same circuit. One may be part of one circuit and the other part of another. In this way electrical energy may be transferred from one circuit to another as the current flowing through one inductor induces a voltage in the other. A device that operates in this manner is the *transformer*, which will be discussed further later in this book.

C. *Capacitance and capacitive reactance*

1. CAPACITANCE

The outermost electrons of the atoms of a conductor, we have learned (Chapter 1, Subdivision B, 2), are loosely held and easily removed. Insulators, or *dielectrics*, on the other hand, have their electrons more firmly fixed. If a dielectric is placed between two conductors (see Figure 9-6A) a *capacitor* is formed. (Formerly, a capacitor was called a *condenser*. However, since the latter term is misleading, the term *capacitor* is preferred.)

Normally, the electrons of the atoms of the dielectric revolve around their nuclei in more or less circular orbits, as indicated in Figure 9-6A. If, however, the capacitor is connected to a voltage source, as in Figure 9-6B, electrons will flow onto plate B and away from plate A. Thus plate B will receive a negative charge and plate A a positive charge. This is called *charging the capacitor*.

In spite of these charges, electrons cannot flow through the dielectric. However, its electrons will be attracted towards the positive plate A and their orbits will be distorted, as indicated in Figure 9-6B. If the voltage source now is removed (Figure 9-6C), the charges will remain on the plates. Accordingly, the electrons of the dielectric will retain their distorted positions. The capacitor remains in its charged condition.

If, now, a resistor (R) is placed across the capacitor, it will start to *discharge* through this resistor (Figure 9-6D). Electrons will move from plate B around the circuit towards plate A until they are distributed equally over the entire circuit. As the charges are re-

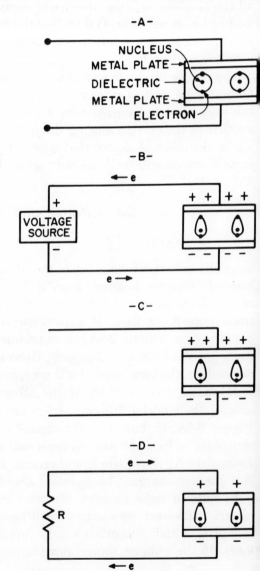

Fig. 9-6.

A. Uncharged capacitor.
B. Charging the capacitor.
C. Voltage source removed, capacitor retains its charge.
D. Discharging the capacitor.

moved from the plates of the capacitor, the electrons of the dielectric will gradually resume their normal unstrained positions.

Note what happened. As the capacitor was charged, electrical energy from the voltage source was stored in the electrostatic field across the dielectric. As the capacitor discharged, the energy of this electrostatic field furnished the current that flowed through the circuit. The property of a capacitor (or a circuit) to store electrical energy is called *capacitance*, the symbol for which is *C*.

(Note that we have mentioned the capacitance of a circuit as well as that of a capacitor. Any two conductors separated by a dielectric form a capacitor. Thus two of the connecting wires separated by air may constitute a capacitor. Even two adjacent turns of a wire coil, separated by their insulation, exhibit the property of capacitance. Such capacitance is called *stray*, or *distributed*, capacitance in contrast to the *concentrated* capacitance of a capacitor.)

The unit of capacitance is the *farad* whose electrical symbol is f. The farad can be defined as being the capacitance present when one coulomb of electrical energy is stored in the electrostatic field of the capacitor or circuit as one volt is applied.

So far, we have been discussing capacitance in direct-current terms. When considering a-c circuits we must take a somewhat different point of view. In Figure 9-6B, as the capacitor was charged, electrons flowed from the voltage source towards plate B, placing a negative charge on that plate, and from plate A towards the voltage source, placing a positive charge on that plate. Because of these charges, a counter electromotive force was set up that was opposed to the voltage from the source. Electrons, then, would continue to flow until the counter electromotive force of the capacitor equalled the voltage of the source.

If, for any reason, the voltage of the source should now rise, more electrons would flow from the source to the capacitor. If the source voltage should fall below that of the counter electromotive force, electrons would flow back from the capacitor to the source. Thus, if the source voltage were changing, electrons would flow back or forth, depending upon which voltage were higher. (Remember that in a-c circuits the voltage is changing constantly.)

If the capacitor had a capacitance of one farad, a change of one volt in the source would cause the charge on the plates to increase or decrease by one coulomb. That is, it would cause one coulomb to flow through the circuit. Should the voltage change by one volt per second, it would cause one coulomb per second to flow through the circuit. Since one coulomb per second is equal to one ampere, the change of one volt per second would cause one ampere to flow through the circuit. We now can say that a capacitor (or circuit) has a capacitance of one farad if one ampere of current flows through the circuit when the applied voltage changes at the rate of one volt per second.

The farad is too large a unit for ordinary purposes. Accordingly, we have the *microfarad* (whose symbol is μf) which is 1/1,000,000 of a farad. Where even the microfarad is too large a unit, we may use the *micromicrofarad* ($\mu\mu$f) which is 1/1,000,000 of a microfarad.

If a capacitor is placed in series with a source of steady direct current, current flows for an instant until the capacitor is sufficiently charged to develop a counter electromotive force equal to the voltage of the source. Then no current would flow in the circuit.

If the d-c source is replaced by an a-c one, a different situation arises. As the voltage rises from zero to its maximum positive value, current flows from the source to the capacitor, building up a counter electromotive force across its plates. As the source voltage starts decreasing, this counter electromotive force sends current flowing back from the capacitor to the source.

The source voltage next reverses its direction and rises to its maximum negative value. Now the current set flowing by the counter electromotive force and the current from the source are flowing in the same direction. As a result, the currents flow through the circuit to the capacitor, building up a new counter electromotive force across its plates (though opposite in direction to the original counter electromotive force). As the source voltage decreases from its negative peak value, the counter electromotive force sends current from the capacitor back to the source. Then the entire cycle is repeated.

Note that during the entire cycle current is flowing through the circuit (excepting the dielectric of the capacitor). If a lamp, or any other device, were placed in series in this circuit it would indicate a continuous current flow through it. It is for this reason that we say that current can flow through an a-c series circuit containing a capacitor.

2. CAPACITORS

A capacitor is a device that is purposely constructed and inserted in the circuit to introduce the desired capacitance. Any two conductors separated by a dielectric will have the property of capacitance. Thus, to make a capacitor, all that is necessary is to have two or more metallic plates separated by air or some other insulating material. The dielectrics in general use are air, mica, waxed paper, glass, ceramics, oil, and, in certain types, gas films.

Assume we have a capacitor made of two metal plates separated by a dielectric sheet. The ability of this capacitor to store electrical energy—that is, its capacitance—depends upon the electrostatic field between the plates and the degree of distortion of the orbits of the electrons of the dielectric. Thus, increasing the area of the plates increases the capacitance. Also, if the plates are brought closer together, thus intensifying the electrostatic field, the capacitance increases.

The degree of distortion of the orbits of the electrons of the dielectric depends upon the nature of the substance and is known as the *dielectric constant.* The dielectric constant of a substance is a measurement of its effectiveness when used as the dielectric of a capacitor. Air is taken to have a dielectric constant of unity, or 1. If, in a certain capacitor using air as a dielectric, as the air is replaced by mica and all other things remain equal, the capacitance becomes six times as great, the mica is said to have a dielectric constant of 6. Paper has a dielectric constant of from 2 to 3; paraffin about 2; titanium oxide from 90 to 170. The electrical symbol for dielectric constant is K.

The formula for calculating the capacitance of a capacitor may be stated as follows:

$$C = \frac{0.0885 \times K \times A}{T}$$

where C is the capacitance in micromicrofarads ($\mu \mu$ f), K is the dielectric constant of the dielectric, A is the area (in square centimeters) of one side of one of the plates that is in actual contact with the dielectric, and T is the thickness of the dielectric (in centimeters).

Example. Calculate the capacitance of a capacitor having two tin-foil plates each 2.5 centimeters wide and 250 centimeters long. The waxed paper that separates these plates has a thickness of 0.025 centimeter and has a dielectric constant of 2.

Substituting these values in the formula we get

$$C = \frac{0.0885 \times 2 \times 625}{0.025} = 4{,}425 \ \mu\mu\,\text{f.}$$

Thus, the capacitance of this capacitor is 4,425 micromicrofarads, or 0.004,425 microfarad. *Ans.*

If the voltage across the plates of the capacitor becomes too large, the dielectric may be ruptured and the capacitor ruined. The ability of the dielectric to withstand such rupture is called its *dielectric strength* and is measured in the maximum number of volts a one-centimeter thickness of the dielectric can withstand. Air has a dielectric strength of about 30,000 volts and mica a dielectric strength of about 500,000 volts.

Capacitors may be fixed or variable. In its simplest form the fixed capacitor consists of two metal plates separated by a dielectric of mica or some ceramic material and enclosed in a plastic case for protection. Wire leads through the case make contact with the plates. Sometimes the metallic plates are deposited electrolytically directly upon the opposite sides of the dielectric sheet.

To increase the plate area, and, hence, the capacitance, a number of plates may be sandwiched between a number of sheets of di-

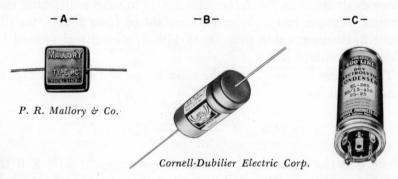

−A− −B− −C−

P. R. Mallory & Co.

Cornell-Dubilier Electric Corp.

Sprague Products Co.

Fig. 9-7. A. Mica capacitor.
B. Paper capacitor.
C. Electrolytic capacitor.

electric. Alternate plates are connected together, thus forming two sets with a larger effective area. The capacitances of the capacitors we have described generally are quite small.

A fixed capacitor of greater capacitance can be made by placing a strip of waxed paper between two strips of tin foil about an inch wide and several feet long. The large area of the tin-foil plates will permit this capacitor to have a large capacitance. To save space, the whole is rolled up and encased in cardboard. This is called a *paper capacitor*.

Another type of fixed capacitor, commonly used where larger capacitances are required, is the *electrolytic capacitor*. In such a capacitor, a sheet of aluminum is kept immersed in a borax solution (called the *electrolyte*). An extremely thin coating of aluminum oxide and oxygen gas forms on the surface of the aluminum. If we consider the aluminum as one plate of the capacitor and the borax solution as the other, the coating of aluminum oxide and oxygen gas, which will not conduct electricity, becomes the dielectric. The aluminum need not be a straight sheet, but may be folded over many times or loosely rolled to save space. Because the "plates" are separated by an extremely thin dielectric, the capacitance of such a capacitor is very high.

A variation of this type of electrolytic capacitor (called a *wet* type because of the solution) is the *dry* type. Although this capacitor is not strictly dry, it is so called because, instead of the liquid electrolyte, a gauze saturated with borax solution is used. This "dry" electrolytic capacitor has a definite advantage in that the solution cannot spill.

Care must be taken to always connect the aluminum plate of the electrolytic capacitor to the positive (+) side of the line; otherwise, the dielectric will be punctured and the capacitance destroyed. Fortunately, the "wet" type of capacitor is self-healing and a new coating of oxide and gas will form once the proper connections are made. In the "dry" type, however, puncturing the dielectric may permanently damage the capacitor.

If the electrolytic capacitor is connected in an a-c circuit, the dielectric will be punctured constantly since the voltage continuously reverses its direction. There is a variation of the electrolytic capacitor, however, that may be used safely in a-c circuits. This is the *a-c capacitor* formed by mounting two self-healing electrolytic

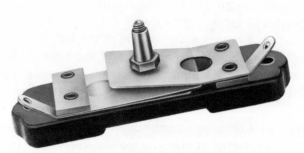

Fig. 9-8. Trimmer capacitor.

capacitors back to back—that is, with the solution joining one to the other. Connections are made to the two outside plates. Now, whatever the direction of the voltage, one capacitor will always be connected properly (and the other punctured).

The capacitance of a capacitor may be varied by changing the effective areas of the plates or the distance between them. One type of variable capacitor is the *trimmer* or *padder* capacitor illustrated in Figure 9-8. Two metal plates are arranged like the pages of a book. The springiness of the metal keeps the "book" open. Between the "pages" is a sheet of mica or other dielectric material. The metal plates may be brought closer together or further apart by the adjustment of a screw. Thus the capacitance may be varied.

Another type of variable capacitor that frequently is employed to "tune in" radio stations in the radio receiver is illustrated in Figure 9-9. Here, two sets of meshing metal plates use air as their dielectric. The effective areas of the opposing sets of plates (and, hence, the capacitance of the capacitor) are varied by sliding one set of plates (called the *rotor*) between the other set (called the *stator*).

When used in electrical diagrams, the symbol for the fixed capacitor is ⊥ . The curved element of this symbol represents the plate that is connected to the negative portion of the circuit. Sometimes, where electrolytic capacitors are involved, the polarity is further identified by plus and minus signs. The symbol for the variable capacitor is ⊥ . The curved element generally indicates the movable portion of the capacitor.

Capacitors may be connected in series, in parallel, or in series-parallel circuits. Where capacitors are connected in series, they act as though we were adding to the thickness of the dielectric. Accordingly, the total capacitance decreases. Thus, for capacitors connected in series, the following formula applies:

$$\frac{1}{C_{\text{total}}} = \frac{1}{C_1} + \frac{1}{C_2} + \frac{1}{C_3} +, \text{ and so forth.}$$

If we connect capacitors in parallel, they act as though we were adding to the areas of their plates. Accordingly, the total capacitance increases. Thus, for capacitors connected in parallel, the following formula applies:

$$C_{\text{total}} = C_1 + C_2 + C_3 +, \text{ and so forth.}$$

Note that this is the reverse action of resistors and inductors connected in series and parallel. Where capacitors are connected in series-parallel circuits, we first find the joint capacitance for the series-connected capacitors and add it in series to the joint capacitance of the parallel-connected capacitors.

When rating a capacitor, we must take into consideration its capacitance and the dielectric strength of its dielectric. The *breakdown voltage* is the maximum voltage that the dielectric of a particular capacitor can stand without being punctured or "breaking down." The *working voltage* of the capacitor is the maximum safe d-c voltage that the manufacturer recommends be placed across its plates. Thus, for example, a capacitor may be rated as "0.1 µf, 600 volts, d-c-working voltage." [Remember that, unless otherwise

Fig. 9-9. Variable air capacitor.

stated, a-c voltages generally are stated in rms values. Thus an a-c
voltage of 600 volts (rms) has peak values of 846 volts. If this voltage is applied to a capacitor rated at 600 volts, d-c working voltage,
the capacitor may be destroyed.]

3. EFFECT OF CAPACITANCE ON PHASE RELATIONSHIPS BETWEEN VOLTAGE AND CURRENT

We have seen that the effect of inductance on an a-c circuit
is to make the current lag 90° behind the voltage. Now let us see the
effect of capacitance on such a circuit. Assume we have a circuit containing nothing but capacitance (again, this is only theoretical). We
know that current will flow from the source to the capacitor only
while the source of voltage is rising, and that the greatest current
will be flowing when the voltage is rising most rapidly. If we examine Figure 9-10 we will see that the source voltage is rising most
rapidly at the 0° position (and again at the 180° position, though in
a negative direction). Thus the current flow at the 0° position is at its
maximum positive value.

Fig. 9-10.

Phase relationship between
current and voltage in a
circuit containing only capacitance.

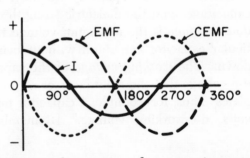

From the 0° to the 90° position the source voltage continues to
rise at an ever-decreasing rate. At 90° this rise has come to a halt.
Hence, the current gradually falls from its maximum positive value
to zero at the 90° point. Meanwhile the capacitor has become fully
charged and the counter electromotive force (cemf) has reached its
maximum value.

Now the source voltage begins to fall. Since the counter electromotive force finds itself greater than the source voltage, current
starts flowing from the capacitor to the source, as indicated by the
negative-current loop of Figure 9-10. At the 180° point the source
voltage falls to zero again and the current reaches its maximum nega-

tive value. The capacitor, however, has become discharged and the counter electromotive force falls to zero.

The source voltage now changes its direction and continues to rise, at an ever-decreasing rate, and the current starts to decrease from its maximum negative value towards zero. Meanwhile, the capacitor becomes charged again (this time, in the opposite direction to the original charge) and the counter electromotive force rises once more.

At the 270° mark the rise of the source voltage ceases and the current reaches zero. As the source voltage starts to fall, the counter electromotive force starts the current flowing in the opposite (positive) direction until this current reaches its positive peak at the 360° mark. Then the entire cycle commences again.

If you examine Figure 9-10, you will see, then, that the effect of capacitance is to make the current *lead* the source voltage by 90° or, what is the same thing, to make the source voltage lag behind the current by 90°. In practical circuits, because of the presence of resistance, the current lead is some value less than 90° ahead of the voltage.

The vector diagram for an a-c circuit that, theoretically, contains only capacitance is illustrated in Figure 9-11B. As in the case of the vector diagram shown in Figure 9-4B, the length of the voltage vector (E) is independent of the length of the current vector (I) and the length of each vector depends upon the scale selected for each. As in the case for inductance, the phase angle is 90°. But this time the current leads the voltage.

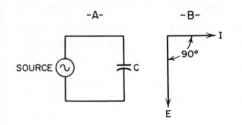

-A-   -B-   **Fig. 9-11.**

A. A-c circuit containing only capacitance.

B. Vector diagram showing the phase relationship between current and voltage in this circuit.

In a circuit where the phase angle between the voltage and current is 90°, the true power is zero. It makes no difference whether one leads or lags behind the other. Since, in a circuit containing only capacitance the phase angle is 90°, such a circuit has a power factor of zero and consumes no power. The electrical energy is merely converted to the energy of the electrostatic field across the capacitor and back to electrical energy again.

4. CAPACITIVE REACTANCE

Just as inductance, because of its counter electromotive force, increases the opposition to current flow in a circuit by a factor known as inductive reactance (X_L), so capacitance, for the same reason, increases the opposition by a factor known as *capacitive reactance* (X_C). As is true for inductive reactance, the unit for capacitive reactance is the *ohm*.

As a capacitor is charged, it builds up a counter electromotive force across its plates. The larger the plates of the capacitor, the more thinly the charge (that is, the number of electrons) is spread, that is, the smaller the counter electromotive force becomes. But the smaller the counter electromotive force, the smaller is the capacitive reactance. Hence, the larger the plates of the capacitor (or, what is the same thing, the larger its capacitance), the smaller is its capacitive reactance.

If a capacitor is placed in series in a d-c circuit, current flows shortly until the capacitor is fully charged and then the counter electromotive force becomes equal and opposite to the applied electromotive force. Current ceases to flow in the circuit. We might say that a capacitor in a d-c circuit has infinite inductive reactance.

But if we place the capacitor in a rapidly-alternating circuit, it has no time to charge up fully before the source voltage starts falling and the capacitor starts discharging. Thus, the more quickly the current is alternating—that is, the higher its frequency—the less the counter electromotive force and, hence, the less the capacitive reactance of the capacitor will be.

From the above, we may say that the capacitive reactance is inversely proportional to the capacitance of the capacitor and the frequency of the current. This relationship may be stated in the following formula:

$$X_C = \frac{1}{2\pi fC}$$

where X_C is the capacitive reactance in ohms, f is the frequency of the current in cycles per second, and C is the capacitance in farads. The constant 2π (6.28) is necessary to make the result come out in ohms.

Example. What is the capacitive reactance of a 10-microfarad capacitor in a 60-cycle alternating-current circuit?

$$X_c = \frac{1}{2\pi fC} = \frac{1}{6.28 \times 60 \times 0.00001} = 265.3 \text{ ohms.} \quad Ans.$$

As is true of a purely inductive circuit, in a purely capacitive circuit we may substitute the capacitive reactance (X_c) for the impedance (Z) in the formulas that state Ohm's law for a-c circuits. Thus, instead of

$$I = \frac{E}{Z}, \quad E = I \times Z, \quad \text{and} \quad Z = \frac{E}{I},$$

we may state

$$I = \frac{E}{X_c}, \quad E = I \times X_c, \quad \text{and} \quad X_c = \frac{E}{I}.$$

D. Circuits containing resistance, inductance, and capacitance

So far in our discussion, we have considered theoretical circuits that contained only inductance or capacitance. Practical a-c circuits, however, contain resistance, inductance, and capacitance. In addition to the resistance of resistors deliberately introduced into the circuit, there are the resistances of the connecting wires, the wire of the inductors, and so forth. Furthermore, there always are the stray inductance and capacitance of the wires and the various components. However, except at very high frequencies such as those encountered in certain types of radio equipment, the stray inductance and capacitance usually are of small importance and, therefore, generally neglected.

1. CIRCUITS CONTAINING RESISTANCE AND INDUCTANCE

As we have learned, pure resistance has no effect on the phase relationship between current and voltage. Thus, if our circuit has nothing but resistance in it, the vector diagram shows us that the

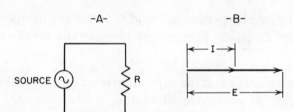

Fig. 9-12. A. A-c circuit containing only resistance.
B. Vector diagram showing the phase relationship
between current and voltage in this circuit.

voltage and current are in phase (Figure 9-12B). As in Figures
9-4B and 9-11B, the length of the voltage vector (E) is independent
of the length of the current vector (I) and the length of each vector
depends upon the scale selected for each. Here there is no phase
angle between the two, that is, they are in phase.

Another use of the vector diagram is to enable us to add voltages
and currents. If we have two resistors in series, it is a simple arith-
metical problem to add the voltage drop across each of the resistors
in order to calculate the total voltage supplied by the source. See
Figure 9-13B. (Although here the current and voltage vectors may
employ different scales, the vectors of all the voltages must use the
same scale.) Note that we merely have added the vector for the
voltage drop across resistor R_2 (E_{R2}) to that for the voltage drop
across R_1 (E_{R1}) to obtain the vector for the total voltage (E_{Total}).

If, however, we have an inductor and a resistor in series, we cannot simply add the voltage drop across each to give us the total
voltage. We must take into consideration the fact that inductance
affects the phase relationships. This situation appears in the vector
diagram of Figure 9-14B. Note that I and E_R are in phase, but that
I and E_L are 90° out of phase. To obtain the total voltage supplied
by the source, we must make use of the parallelogram method described in Chapter 8, Subdivision B.

Note, too, that the voltage of the source (E_{Total}) is out of phase
with the current (I). But the phase difference between the two no
longer is 90°. It is some lesser value depending upon the relative
values of E_L and E_R. By varying these relative values, the phase difference between the current and the voltage of the source may be

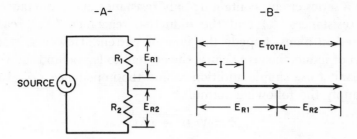

Fig. 9-13. A. A-c circuit containing two resistors connected in series.
 B. Vector diagram showing the phase relationship between the current and the voltages in this circuit.

varied. Further, note that whereas E_L leads the source voltage, E_R lags behind it.

If you examine Figure 8-13, you will note that, if the phase angle between the voltage and current is some value less than 90° (it makes no difference which leads the other), the true power consumed by the circuit is some positive value, though less than if there were only resistance present. None of this power is consumed by the inductor (assuming a theoretically perfect inductor, that is, one that has no resistance). It all is consumed by the resistor. The power factor, too, is not zero (as it would be if there were only inductance present), but some value less than 1 (as it would be if resistance alone were present).

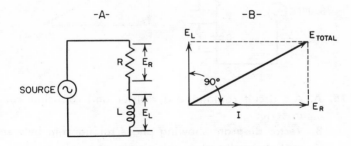

Fig. 9-14. A. A-c circuit containing a resistor and inductor connected in series.
 B. Vector diagram showing phase relationship between current and voltages in this circuit.

In a series circuit containing only resistance and inductance, both the resistance (R) and the inductive reactance (X_L), each expressed in ohms, impede the flow of current. However, since the effect of inductance is to cause the current to lag behind the voltage, we cannot use simple addition to find the impedance (Z). Instead, we apply the following formula:

$$Z = \sqrt{R^2 + (X_L)^2} \cdot$$

Example. What is the total impedance of a series circuit containing a resistor of 3 ohms and an inductor whose inductive reactance is 4 ohms?

$$Z = \sqrt{R^2 + (X_L)^2} = \sqrt{9 + 16} = 5 \text{ ohms.} \quad Ans.$$

2. CIRCUITS CONTAINING RESISTANCE AND CAPACITANCE

As you have learned, in an a-c circuit containing only capacitance the current leads the voltage by 90°. (See Figure 9-11B.) If,

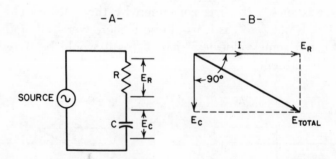

Fig. 9-15. A. A-c circuit containing a resistor and capacitor connected in series.

B. Vector diagram showing phase relationship between current and voltages in this circuit.

however, we have a capacitor and resistor in series, the vector diagram appears as in Figure 9-15B. Note that I and E_R are in phase, but that I and E_C are 90° out of phase. Once again, we employ the parallelogram method to obtain the total source voltage (E_{Total}).

Note, too, that E_{Total} is out of phase with I and that, again, this phase difference is less than 90°, depending upon the relative values of E_C and E_R. Further note that, whereas E_R leads the source voltage, E_C lags behind it.

The effect of resistance in such a circuit is to reduce the voltage lag from 90° to some smaller value, depending upon the amount of resistance. Hence, the true power consumed by the circuit is not zero (as it would be if only capacitance were present), but some positive value, though less than if there were only resistance.

All this power is consumed by the resistor, none being consumed by the capacitor (assuming a theoretically perfect capacitor). The power factor, too, is not zero (as it would be if there were only capacitance present), but some value less than one.

As is true for the inductance-resistance circuit, the total impedance offered to alternating current by a series circuit containing resistance and capacitance may be found by means of the following formula:

$$Z = \sqrt{R^2 + (X_C)^2} \; .$$

There is an aspect of the resistance-capacitance (R-C) circuit that is of particular interest. If a capacitor is connected to a d-c source, such as a battery, the moment the circuit is completed, a heavy charging current will flow. This current will fall off quickly as the capacitor becomes charged and a counter electromotive force is built up. When the capacitor is fully charged, this counter electromotive force will equal the electromotive force of the battery and no more current will flow.

If a resistor is placed in series with the battery and the capacitor (Figure 9-16A), the time it would take the capacitor to reach full charge would depend upon the values of the capacitor and the resistor. Actually, the capacitor never succeeds in becoming fully charged. Accordingly, we calculate the time it takes the capacitor to reach 63 per cent of its full-charge value and call that the R-C *time constant* of the circuit.

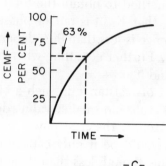

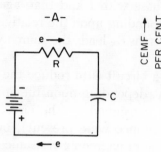

Fig. 9-16.

A. R-C circuit.
B. Graph showing counter electromotive force as capacitor is charged.
C. Graph showing counter electromotive force as capacitor is discharged.

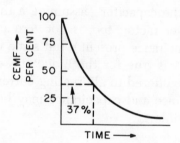

The time constant of a circuit may be calculated from the following formula:

$$t \text{ (in seconds)} = C \text{ (in farads)} \times R \text{ (in ohms)}.$$

Example. What would be the R-C time constant of a series circuit containing a 0.001-microfarad capacitor and a resistor of 50,000 ohms?

$t \text{ (seconds)} = 0.000,000,001 \text{ farad} \times 50,000 \text{ ohms}.$
$t \qquad\quad = 0.000,05 \text{ second, or 50 microseconds.}$ *Ans.*

Actually, we are more concerned usually with the counter electromotive force built up across the capacitor than the current flowing into it. How this counter electromotive force is built up is shown graphically in Figure 9-16B. The time constant, as before, is taken at the point where the counter electromotive force reaches a value of 63 per cent of its full-charge value.

When a fully-charged capacitor discharges through a resistor, the counter electromotive force drops rapidly at first and then more slowly. (See Figure 9-16C.) Thus the time constant would be the time required to discharge the capacitor to 37 per cent of its full-charge value. The procedure for calculating this time constant is the same as before.

3. CIRCUITS CONTAINING INDUCTANCE AND CAPACITANCE

If an a-c circuit contains only a capacitor and inductor in series, the only opposition to current flow will be the inductive reactance (X_L) and capacitive reactance (X_C). (We assume here that the inductor and capacitor are of the theoretically perfect types—that is, they contain no resistance.)

Note, however, that, whereas the inductive reactance tends to cause the current to lag 90° behind the voltage, the capacitive reactance tends to cause the current to lead by a similar amount. Hence the two reactances tend to cancel each other out. Thus, the total reactance (X) is equal to the difference between the inductive and capacitive reactances. This may be expressed in the following formula:

$$X = X_L - X_C.$$

Subtraction is performed algebraically. If the answer is a positive value, the resulting reactance (X) has the characteristics of an inductive reactance. That is, the current tends to lag behind the voltage. If the answer is a negative value, the resulting reactance has the characteristics of a capacitive reactance.

Example. What is the reactance of a 60-cycle, a-c circuit containing an inductor of 2.5 henrys and a capacitor of 10 microfarads connected in series?

$$X_L = 2\pi f L = 6.28 \times 60 \times 2.5 = 942 \text{ ohms.}$$

$$X_C = \frac{1}{2\pi f C} = \frac{1}{6.28 \times 60 \times 0.00001} = 265.3 \text{ ohms.}$$

$$X = X_L - X_C = 942 - 265.3 = 676.7 \text{ ohms}$$
(inductive reactance). *Ans.*

We may illustrate the above vectorially as shown in Figure 9-17.

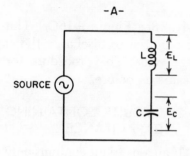

Fig. 9-17.

A. A-c circuit containing inductance and capacitance.
B. Vectorial diagram when E_L
is greater than E_C.
C. Vectorial diagram when E_C
is greater than E_L.

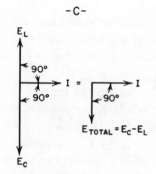

Since the voltage across the inductor (E_L) leads the current by 90°
and the voltage across the capacitor (E_C) lags 90° behind the current, the two voltages are 180° out of phase and their vectors are
shown on the same straight line. Since these vectors are in opposite
directions, we may subtract one from the other to get the vector for
the resulting voltage (E_{Total}).

Assume (as illustrated in Figure 9-17B) X_L is larger than X_C and
hence the voltage drop (E_L) across the inductor is larger than the
voltage drop (E_C) across the capacitor. The result, then, is as if we
had nothing in the circuit but an inductor whose voltage-drop vector
is the difference between vector E_L and vector E_C. If, as in Figure
9-17C, E_C is larger than E_L, the result is as if we had nothing in the
circuit but a capacitor whose voltage-drop vector is the difference
between vectors E_C and E_L.

Since inductive reactance and capacitive reactance tend to cancel out, if a circuit contains inductive reactance, we may reduce the
total reactance by adding some capacitive reactance. This may be
done by placing a capacitor in series in the circuit. If the circuit contains capacitive reactance, we may reduce the total reactance by

adding some inductive reactance (by placing an inductor in series). In this way we may improve the power factor of the circuit and increase the true power consumed by it.

Practical circuits always contain some resistance. To find the total impedance (Z) of a circuit containing resistance as well as inductance and capacitance, we use the following formula:

$$Z = \sqrt{R^2 + (X_L - X_C)^2}.$$

Example. What is the total impedance of an a-c circuit containing a resistor, inductor, and capacitor in series if the resistance is 30 ohms, the inductive reactance is 210 ohms, and the capacitive reactance is 250 ohms?

$$Z = \sqrt{R^2 + (X_L - X_C)^2} = \sqrt{(30)^2 + (210 - 250)^2}$$
$$= 50 \text{ ohms.} \quad Ans.$$

4. RESONANCE

a. Series resonance

If we connect an inductor and capacitor in series in an a-c circuit, we may determine the inductive reactance from the following formula:

$$X_L = 2\pi f L$$

where X_C is the capacitive reactance in ohms, f is the frequency in cycles per second, and L is the inductance in henrys. Increasing the frequency increases the inductive reactance and decreasing the frequency decreases it.

The capacitive reactance is determined from the following formula:

$$X_C = \frac{1}{2\pi f C}$$

where X_C is the capacitive reactance in ohms, f is the frequency in cycles per second, and C is the capacitance in farads. Increasing the frequency decreases the capacitive reactance and decreasing the frequency increases it.

The total reactance (X) may be determined by the formula $X = X_L - X_C$. Substituting the above values of X_L and X_C we get:

$$X = 2\pi f L - \frac{1}{2\pi f C}.$$

Examining the above formula, we find that at a certain frequency X_L becomes equal to X_C and the total reactance becomes zero. This condition is called *resonance* and the frequency at which resonance occurs is called the *resonant frequency* (whose symbol is f_r). Because the inductor and capacitor are in series, we call such a circuit a *series resonant circuit*. Note that at resonance, because the voltage-leading effect of X_L balances out the voltage-lagging effect of X_C, the current and voltage are in phase.

We have seen that

$$2\pi f_r L = \frac{1}{2\pi f_r C}.$$

Multiplying both sides of the equation by f_r we get:

$$2\pi f_r^2 L = \frac{1}{2\pi C}.$$

Dividing both sides by $2\pi L$ we get:

$$f_r^2 = \frac{1}{(2\pi)^2 LC}.$$

Taking the square root of both sides we get:

$$f_r = \frac{1}{2\pi \sqrt{LC}}.$$

where f_r is the resonant frequency in cycles per second, L is the inductance in henrys, and C is the capacitance in farads.

Example. Find the resonant frequency of an a-c circuit containing a 1-henry inductor and a 16-microfarad capacitor connected in series.

$$f_r = \frac{1}{2\pi \sqrt{LC}} = \frac{1}{6.28 \sqrt{1 \times 0.000016}} = \frac{1}{6.28 \times 0.004}$$
$$= 39.8 \text{ cycles per second. } Ans.$$

The impedance of the circuit, if we neglect resistance, is equal to the total reactance which, in turn, is equal to the difference between X_L and X_C. At resonance X_L and X_C are equal. Thus the total reactance and impedance become zero. Since by Ohm's law $I - E/Z$, if Z becomes zero, the current becomes infinitely large. In practical circuits, however, the current reaches some finite value, limited by the resistance in the circuit. If the resistance is very low, the current may become quite large.

Under such conditions the voltage drop across each component may become quite large, too. In fact, the voltage drops may become greater than the voltage of the source. Thus the capacitor, for example, which is able to stand up under the voltage of the source, may break down at resonance.

b. Parallel resonance

Now let us see what happens when an inductor and a capacitor are connected in parallel in an a-c circuit, as illustrated in Figure 9-18. We will neglect any resistance in the circuit for the time being.

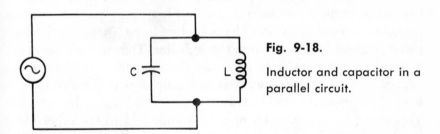

Fig. 9-18.

Inductor and capacitor in a parallel circuit.

Current flowing from the generator divides into two paths: one through the capacitor and the other through the inductor. The greater current will flow through the path of lower reactance.

At low frequencies, the capacitive reactance will be higher, and thus more current will flow through the inductor. At high frequencies, the inductive reactance will be higher, and·now more current will flow through the capacitor. At some certain frequency (the *resonant frequency*) both reactances will be the same, and thus equal currents will flow through both paths.

But the inductive reactance would tend to cause the current through the inductor to lag behind the voltage by 90°, and the capacitive reactance would tend to cause the current through the capacitor to lead the voltage by 90°. Thus, the currents flowing in each path would be 180° out of phase—that is, they would be flowing in opposite directions. The net result would be that they would cancel each other out, and no current would flow from the generator. This is the same as saying that, *at the resonant frequency the parallel combination of inductor and capacitor offers an infinite impedance to the source of current.*

A circuit of this type is called a *parallel-resonant* circuit. Since its action is opposite to that of the series-resonant circuit, which offers zero impedance at the resonant frequency, the parallel-resonant circuit is also known as an *antiresonant circuit.* As is true of the series-resonant circuit, the voltage and the current of the source are in phase.

Keep in mind, however, that there may be large currents flowing around the loop formed by the capacitor and the inductor. It is not that there are no currents present, but rather that the currents are equal and opposite, to explain why the net result is zero.

We may obtain a better picture, perhaps, if we consider what is happening in the closed loop at resonant frequency. As the capacitor becomes charged, a counter electromotive force is generated which causes current to flow through the inductor. This, in turn, produces a counter electromotive force across the inductor that charges the capacitor. Thus electric energy is stored up, first in the electrostatic field of the capacitor and then in the magnetic field of the inductor. This energy continually changes from one field to the other. As a result, current flows back and forth. We call this back-and-forth flow of current *oscillation* and, theoretically, it should continue indefinitely, once started.

The presence of resistance upsets this theoretical picture. As the current flows in the loop, some electric power is dissipated by this resistance, and this loss must be replaced from the outside source. Hence, some current flows from the generator and the parallel-resonant circuit acts as a very high, rather than an infinite, impedance.

5. FILTERS

Electrically, *filters* are used to separate currents of certain frequencies from those of other frequencies. (For our discussion here, we may consider direct current as having a zero frequency.) Assume that you have as an electrical source a battery (whose symbol is $=\mid\pm$) supplying direct current, a generator of low-frequency alternating current ($-\!\!\bigodot\!\!-$L.F.), and a generator of high-frequency alternating current ($-\!\!\bigodot\!\!-$ H.F.). Assume that they are all connected in series and supply current to a load through a resistor (R) in series, as shown in Figure 9-19. The resistor will not have any filtering action, since it impedes equally all currents that pass through it, regardless of frequency.

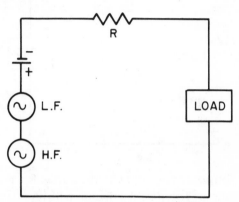

Fig. 9-19.

Circuit showing direct, low-frequency, and high-frequency currents feeding a load through resistor R in series.

Now assume that you replace the resistor with a capacitor (Figure 9-20). The direct current will be completely filtered out, since the capacitor offers infinite impedance to its passage. Since $X_C = 1/(2\pi f C)$, the higher the frequency, the less will be the impedance. Hence, the low-frequency current will be more strongly impeded (or *attenuated*) than the high-frequency current.

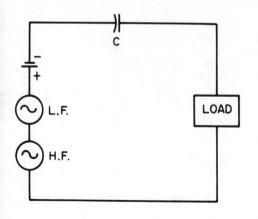

Fig. 9-20.

Circuit showing direct, low-frequency, and high-frequency currents feeding a load through capacitor C in series.

Now assume that the capacitor is replaced by an inductor (Figure 9-21). The direct current will be only slightly impeded, owing to the resistance of the inductor. Since $X_L = 2\pi f L$, the higher the frequency, the greater the impedance will be. Hence, the high-frequency current will be more strongly attenuated than the low-frequency current.

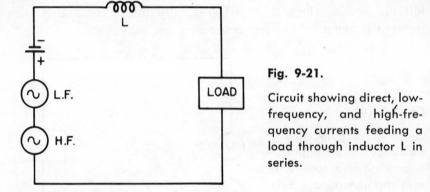

Fig. 9-21.

Circuit showing direct, low-frequency, and high-frequency currents feeding a load through inductor L in series.

Suppose we connect the capacitor across the load (Figure 9-22). None of the direct current will flow through the capacitor, all of it going through the load. Since the capacitor offers a fairly high impedance to low-frequency current, most of this, too, will flow through the load. But since the capacitor offers a low impedance to high-frequency current, most of this current will flow through the capacitor rather than through the load. This type of circuit is called a *low-pass filter*, since it passes the low-frequency currents on to the load,

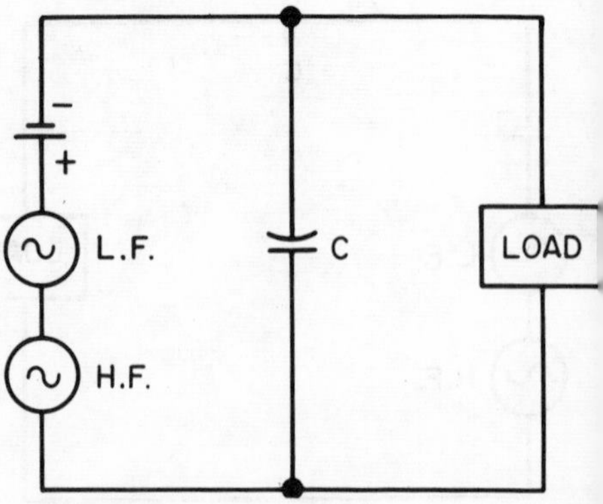

Fig. 9-22.

Circuit showing direct, low-frequency, and high-frequency currents feeding a load with capacitor C in parallel.

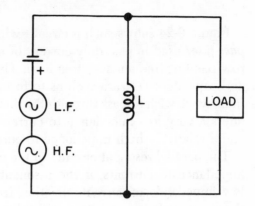

Fig. 9-23.

Circuit showing direct, low-frequency, and high-frequency currents feeding a load with inductor L in parallel.

bypassing the high-frequency currents (that is, high-frequency currents bypass the load).

In Figure 9-23, the capacitor is replaced by an inductor. This inductor offers a low-impedance path to the direct and low-frequency currents. Hence, most of these currents are bypassed and do not reach the load. But the high-frequency current finds the inductor a high-impedance path, and thus most of this current flows through the load. This type of circuit is called a *high-pass filter,* since it passes the high-frequency currents on to the load.

a. Resonant circuits as filters

Where the filtering action is to be limited to a single frequency or, at most, to a narrow band of frequencies, resonant circuits are used. Filters of this type are used extensively in electronic circuits.

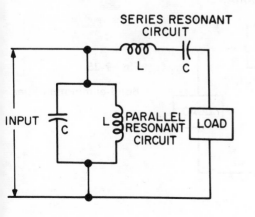

Fig. 9-24.

Band-pass filter.

Figure 9-24 shows such a circuit, which is an example of a *band-pass filter* used to pass only current of a single frequency (or a narrow band of frequencies) to a load. The values of the inductors (*L*) and capacitors (*C*) are such as to form resonant circuits at the frequency we wish to pass through the filter. The series resonant circuit offers a very low impedance to currents of the resonant frequency and a relatively high impedance to currents of other frequencies.

The parallel resonant circuit, on the other hand, offers a very high impedance to currents of the resonant frequency and a relatively low impedance to currents of other frequencies. Thus, currents of the resonant frequency pass easily through the filter while currents of all other frequencies are bypassed through the parallel resonant circuit.

In Figure 9-25 is shown the circuit used to filter out current of a particular frequency (or a narrow band of frequencies). Here, too, *L* and *C* are shown to form resonant circuits at the desired frequency. Currents of this frequency will find the parallel resonant circuit an extremely high-impedance path, whereas the series resonant circuit forms a very low-impedance path.

Currents of other frequencies, however, will find the parallel resonant circuit a fairly low-impedance path, but the series resonant circuit furnishes a relatively high-impedance path. Thus, currents of the resonant frequency will be stopped and bypassed, while currents of all other frequencies will pass through. This type of filter is called a *band-stop,* or *band-elimination, filter.*

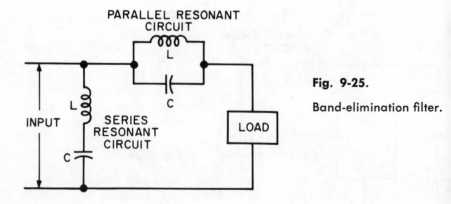

Fig. 9-25.

Band-elimination filter.

QUESTIONS

Wherever possible, diagrams should be used to clarify the answers to these questions. These diagrams need not be elaborate, but they should be drawn neatly with the significant portions clearly labeled.

1. What is the effect of resistance upon the phase relationship between current and voltage in an a-c circuit? What is the power factor of a circuit containing only resistance?
2. What is *inductance?* What is it due to?
3. What is the unit of inductance? What does it mean?
4. Assuming there is no interaction between their magnetic fields, what would be the total inductance of an inductor of 4 henrys and one of 2 henrys if *a*) they are connected in series; *b*) they are connected in parallel?
5. What is the effect of inductance upon the phase relationship between the voltage and current in an a-c circuit?
6. What is the phase angle between the voltage and the current in an a-c circuit that contains only inductance? What is the *true* power consumed in such a circuit?
7. What is *inductive reactance?* In what units is it measured?
8. What is the inductive reactance of a coil of 10 henrys as a 400-cycle alternating current flows through it?
9. In an a-c circuit containing only inductance, what will be the current if the voltage is 100 volts and the inductive reactance is 25 ohms?
10. Explain what is meant by *mutual inductance.*
11. Explain what is meant by *close coupling; loose coupling; unity coupling?*
12. What is *capacitance?* What is it due to?
13. What is the unit of capacitance? What does it mean?
14. What is a *capacitor?* What factors determine its capacitance?
15. A capacitor is made by two sheets of brass, each 60 centimeters long by 50 centimeters wide, placed at either side of a sheet of glass that is 3 millimeters thick. If the dielectric constant of the glass is 7, what is the capacitance of the capacitor thus formed?
16. Two capacitors, one 6 microfarads and the other 3 microfarads, are connected in series. *a*) What will be the resulting capacitance? *b*) What will be the resulting capacitance if they are connected in parallel?
17. What is the effect of capacitance upon the phase relationship between the voltage and the current in an a-c circuit?

18. What is the phase angle between the voltage and current in an a-c circuit that contains only capacitance? What is the *true* power consumed in such a circuit?
19. What is *capacitive reactance?* In what units is it measured?
20. What is the capacitive reactance of a 5-microfarad capacitor placed in a 400-cycle a-c circuit?
21. What is the effect of resistance upon the phase angle between the voltage and current in an a-c circuit containing inductance?
22. In an a-c circuit containing a resistor of 12 ohms in series with an inductor whose inductive reactance is 16 ohms, how much current will flow if the voltage is 100 volts?
23. What is the effect of resistance upon the phase angle between the voltage and current in an a-c circuit containing capacitance?
24. A capacitor and a 4,000-ohm resistor are connected in series in an a-c circuit. If, with a voltage of 100 volts, 20 milliamperes of current flows through this circuit, what is the reactance of the capacitor?
25. What is the total reactance in an a-c circuit containing an inductor whose inductive reactance is 2,500 ohms and a capacitor whose capacitive reactance is 3,000 ohms, connected in series? What will be the nature of this reactance?
26. What is the total impedance of an a-c circuit containing a resistor, inductor, and capacitor in series, if the resistance is 150 ohms, the inductive reactance is 300 ohms, and the capacitive reactance is 500 ohms?
27. What is meant by the *resonant frequency* of an a-c circuit?
28. Find the resonant frequency of an a-c circuit containing a 5-henry inductor and a 5-microfarad capacitor connected in series.
29. At the resonant frequency, what is the theoretical impedance of *a*) a series-resonant circuit *b*) a parallel-resonant circuit?
30. What is the function of an electrical filter? Explain.
31. Draw the circuit of resonant circuits used as a *band-pass filter*. Explain its action.
32. Draw the circuit of resonant circuits used as a *band-stop filter*. Explain its action.

chapter

10

A-C Measuring Instruments

A. *Meter movements that may be used for a-c or d-c measurement*

Most of the d-c movements described in Chapter 6 may be used for a-c measurement as well. In the case of the hot-wire movement (see Figure 6-1), the wire is heated as current flows through it, regardless whether the current be direct or alternating. In the inclined-coil movement (see Figure 6-2), the iron vane tends to line itself up with the magnetic lines of force around the coil, regardless of the direction of these lines of force. Similarly, the vanes of the repulsion-vane movement (see Figure 6-3) tend to repel each other, regardless whether this repulsion is due to two north poles or two south poles.

In the solenoid-type movement (see Figure 6-4), the solenoid is energized and the plunger attracted, regardless of the direction of current flow through the coil. Hence, this type of movement can be used on either direct or alternating current. In the dynamometer

171

movement (see Figure 6-7), the movable and fixed coils are connected in series. Hence, the relative attraction or repulsion between coils remains the same, regardless of the direction of the current that flows through all of them. For this reason, this movement, too, can be used for a-c, as well as d-c, measurement.

When they are connected in an a-c circuit, all of the above movements, except the hot-wire movement, suffer from a common fault. As the current reverses its direction of flow, the movable member of the movement tends to vibrate, causing the pointer to flutter and making it difficult to obtain an exact reading. To overcome this flutter, a process called *damping* is employed.

One method, called *air damping*, is to attach a small, light vane to the same shaft that carries the pointer. This vane is permitted to swing in a closed box that is just large enough to accommodate the vane. As the shaft rotates, the vane swings in the box, compressing the air in front of it. The pressure of the compressed air on the vane tends to slow up its swing and thus reduce the flutter of the pointer.

The other method, called *magnetic* damping, employs a device similar to that used in the watthour meter discussed in Chapter 6 (see Figure 6-15). A small, light vane of aluminum or copper is attached to the shaft and passes between the poles of a permanent magnet. As the movement vibrates, the vane cuts across the field of the magnet. The resulting induced current in the vane (the *eddy current*) sets up its own magnetic field which, interacting with the field of the magnet, slows up the swing of the vane, thus reducing the pointer flutter.

Air damping generally is used for movements such as the inclined-coil, repulsion-vane, and solenoid types since they are most sensitive to the disturbing effect of the magnetic field of a nearby magnet. Care must be taken with all the movements, except the hot-wire type, to keep them away from large metal objects. Otherwise, the varying magnetic fields that surround their coils as alternating current flows through them would induce currents in these metals. These induced currents represent losses that produce false readings by the meters.

All of the above movements, it has been stated, will operate on alternating current. However, if the frequency is too high, before the pointer has a chance to move from its zero position, the current reverses itself and is flowing in the opposite direction. The pointer, under such conditions, merely vibrates around zero. Hence the movements can be used only with alternating currents of relatively low frequencies, such as the 60-cycle current used in most house circuits.

The hot-wire movement is an exception. Since the heating effect of the current does not depend upon its frequency, currents of any frequency can be measured.

As is true for d-c operation, all of these movements may be used as a-c ammeters or voltmeters, provided that they are properly connected into the circuits. Ammeter ranges may be extended by means of shunts, and voltmeter ranges through the use of multipliers. There is still another method for extending the ranges of a-c ammeters and voltmeters. This is through the use of a *transformer* (which will be discussed further later in the book).

The transformer is a device that may be used to step-up (increase) or step-down (decrease) an alternating current or voltage. Suppose we wish to measure a very large alternating current. By means of a step-down transformer (known as a *current transformer*) we step this current down, say, 200 times. Assume that, as the output of the transformer is measured by an a-c ammeter, a reading of 5 amperes is indicated. The original current, then, is 5 × 200, or 1,000 amperes.

Step-down transformers (known as *potential transformers*) may be used similarly to measure large alternating voltages. Current transformers may have different step-down ratios and usually are designed to produce a maximum output of 5 amperes. Accordingly, they generally are used with 0-5 amperes a-c ammeters. Potential transformers, too, may have different step-down ratios and generally are designed to produce a maximum output of about 100 volts.

Except for some specially designed types, all a-c voltmeters and ammeters indicate the *effective,* or *rms,* values of voltage and current. (See Chapter 7, Subdivision C, 2, 3, 4.) Theoretically, the a-c wattmeter measures the product of the *instantaneous* values of voltage and current (Chapter 8, Subdivision C). However, since the meter cannot follow the quick variations of these instantaneous values, it indicates, instead, the *average* value of true power.

B. Adapting the D'Arsonval-type moving-coil movement to a-c measurement

The D'Arsonval-type moving-coil movement (see Figure 6-6) has a number of advantages over the other types. It is efficient, may be very accurate, and may have great sensitivity. Besides, it has the desired uniform scale. It has one main disadvantage. It cannot be used to measure alternating current. With the current flowing through it in one direction, the pointer moves from its left-hand zero position to the right across the scale. However, as the current reverses and flows through the movement in the other direction, the pointer attempts to move left from the zero position. Thus it may be bent or the instrument otherwise damaged.

Accordingly, there have been two methods devised for adapting this movement to a-c measurement. These operate by converting the alternating current to direct current and then using the instrument to measure this direct current.

1. RECTIFIER METHOD

The first method changes the alternating current directly into direct current by means of a process called *rectification*. It has been found that if a copper disk is coated on one side with a thin layer of copper oxide, current will flow quite easily from the copper to the copper oxide, but will encounter an extremely high resistance if it attempts to flow in the opposite direction Thus the copper-copper oxide disk furnishes a one-way passage for electric current. We call this combination a *copper-oxide rectifier*. The symbol for the rectifier is ──▶▮── . The flow of current is taken to be from the heavy vertical bar to the arrow tip.

Now let us see what happens if the rectifier is placed in series in an a-c circuit (see Figure 10-1A). The waveform of the output current from the a-c generator (──Ⓝ──) is shown graphically in Figure 10-1B. For one half of each cycle, current flows through the rectifier and load. During the other half-cycle, current cannot flow through the rectifier and, hence, there is no current flow through the circuit. This is shown graphically in Figure 10-1C.

Note that the graph of Figure 10-1B indicates an alternating cur-

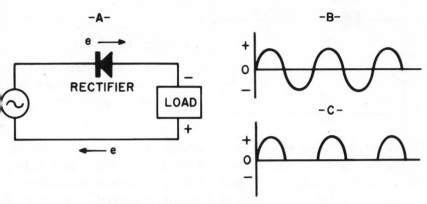

Fig. 10-1. A. Rectifier connected in series in an a-c circuit.
B. Waveform of input to rectifier.
C. Waveform of output from rectifier.

rent, that is, a flow first in one direction and then a flow in the other. The graph of Figure 10-1C, on the other hand, shows a flow in only one direction. Hence it is a direct current. It is true that it is not a *steady* direct current. Rather, the effect of a rectifier is to convert an alternating current to a *pulsating direct current*. Because only half the cycle is utilized (the other half being blocked out), the circuit shown in Figure 10-1A is called a *half-wave rectifier circuit*.

Now let us connect a moving-coil milliammeter in series in this circuit, as shown in Figure 10-2. Because a direct current flows in this circuit, the meter will indicate this current. However, the inertia of the movement is such that it cannot follow the rapid series of pulses (there are 60 pulses per second if the current furnished by the generator has a frequency of 60 cycles per second). Instead, it registers the *average* value of these pulses. Since most a-c meters are calibrated to indicate *effective*, or *rms*, values, we must multiply the average values registered on this meter by 1.11 to obtain the rms values. This is done on the instrument scale, which is marked directly in rms values.

The ratio between average and rms values holds true only if the waveform of the current is sinusoidal. If it be some other shape, the 1.11-relationship does not hold. Accordingly, care must be taken to use the moving-coil meter, which is marked in rms values, only with currents that have the sinusoidal waveform.

If you examine Figure 10-2, you will see that current flows through

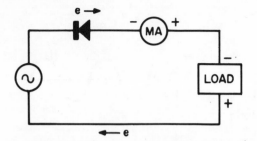

Fig. 10-2.

How a moving-coil milli-ammeter is connected in a half-wave rectifier circuit.

the circuit only during half of each cycle. A more efficient circuit, called the *full-wave*, or *bridge, rectifier circuit*, utilizes both halves of each cycle, as shown in Figure 10-3A. It employs four rectifiers.

During one half-cycle, current flows (as indicated by e ⟶) from the generator, through rectifier #2, through the meter, through rectifier #3, through the load, and back to the generator. Current is prevented from flowing through the other portions of the bridge circuit by the high resistances of the alternative paths.

During the next half-cycle, current flows (as indicated by e - - -►) from the generator, through the load, through rectifier #4, through the meter, through rectifier #1, and back to the generator. Again, current is prevented from following alternative paths through the bridge circuit by the high resistances of these paths.

Note that, although the current flows in both directions through the load, current flow through the meter during the entire cycle is

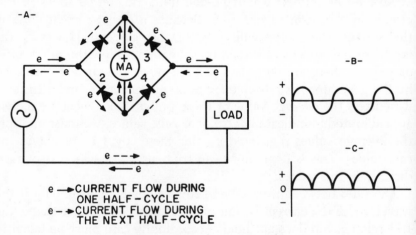

e ─►CURRENT FLOW DURING
ONE HALF-CYCLE
e ─ ►CURRENT FLOW DURING
THE NEXT HALF-CYCLE

Fig. 10-3. A. Bridge-rectifier circuit.
B. Waveform of input to rectifier.
C. Waveform of output from rectifier.

always in the same direction. Hence the current flowing through the meter is a direct current, which it is able to register.

The output of the full-wave rectifier circuit is shown graphically in Figure 10-3C. Note that there are now two pulses produced during each cycle. Accordingly, the average d-c values registered by the meter are higher than for an equivalent half-wave rectifier circuit. As before, the scale is marked in rms values. Also, the calibrations of the scale hold true only if the current is sinusoidal in waveform.

The rectifier-type meter can be used as an ammeter or as a voltmeter, as illustrated in Figure 10-4. Where the meter is used as an ammeter and a shunt is employed, the shunt is placed across the entire rectifier-movement circuit (Figure 10-4A) so that the bulk of the line current flows through the shunt. If the shunt were placed merely across the meter movement, the entire line current would flow through the rectifiers, thus damaging them. Of course, when calculating the value of the shunt, we now must take into consideration the total resistance offered by the rectifiers and meter movement.

Similarly, when calculating the resistance of the voltage multiplier for the voltmeter (see Figure 10-4B), the total resistance of the meter movement and rectifiers, too, must be taken into consideration. As is true of other types of meters, the range of the rectifier-type meter may be varied by using different values for the shunts and multipliers.

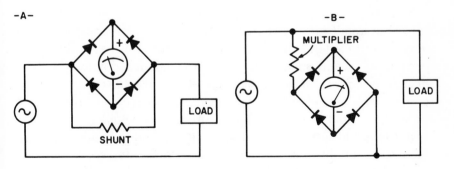

Fig. 10-4. A. Circuit of bridge-rectifier meter used as ammeter.
B. Circuit of bridge-rectifier meter used as voltmeter.

Fig. 10-5.

Multirange a-c ammeter.

Weston Instruments Div., Daystrom, Inc.

Note that when the rectifier is in its current-opposing position, it acts as a capacitor. As a result, it offers a certain amount of capacitive reactance to the current. If the frequency of this current is low, the capacitive reactance is very high and very little current can flow through the rectifier. If, however, the frequency is high, the capacitive reactance is low and considerable current can flow through the rectifier, upsetting its rectifying action. Accordingly, the rectifier-type meter is not suitable for currents of very high frequencies. It generally is not used where the frequency of the current is higher than about 20,000 cycles per second.

The copper - copper-oxide disks used as meter rectifiers usually are about a half inch in diameter. Because the copper-oxide layer is very thin, it cannot stand high voltage without breaking down. Accordingly, several such disks may be sandwiched together (connected in series with the copper side of one disk in contact with the copper-oxide side of another) to form a larger rectifier unit that can withstand a higher voltage. The entire unit is bolted together, care being taken to insulate the disks from the bolt on which they are mounted. Suitable terminals and metallic fins for radiating away some of the heat produced are provided. (See Figure 10-6.) Where a bridge-type rectifier is employed, all four rectifiers may be mounted in one such stack with suitable insulation between units and terminals for each.

Fig. 10-6.

Meter rectifier.

Another type meter rectifier frequently used is made of selenium coated on one side of an iron disk. Its action is the same as that of the copper - copper-oxide type and it is constructed in the same way. (There are other types of rectifiers, some of which will be discussed later.)

Since an ammeter must be placed in series with the circuit whose current is to be measured, this circuit must be opened every time we wish to insert the measuring instrument. Sometimes this is difficult to do. Accordingly, a clever device, called a *clamp-type ammeter,* may be used to measure the current in an a-c circuit without the necessity for opening the circuit.

Essentially, it consists of a transformer that has a *primary winding* coupled to a *secondary winding* by means of an iron *core.* As a result of the magnetic field set up by the alternating current flowing through the primary winding, a current is induced in the secondary winding. The strength of the magnetic field around the primary winding depends upon the number of turns in that winding and the current flowing through it. Thus, if all other factors remain constant, the greater the current flowing through the primary winding, the greater will be the current induced in the secondary winding.

The primary winding is the conductor in the circuit whose current we wish to measure and may be considered to consist of a single turn. This is coupled to the secondary winding (contained within the clamp-type ammeter illustrated in Figure 10-7A) by means of the iron core. To avoid the necessity for opening the circuit, this core is split and hinged. Thus the core may be opened and placed around the conductor. Then it is closed and the primary is effectively coupled to the secondary winding.

–A–

Weston Instruments Div., Daystrom, Inc.

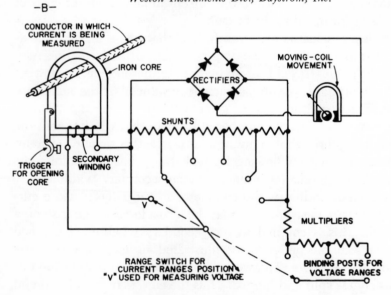

–B–

CONDUCTOR IN WHICH
CURRENT IS BEING
MEASURED

IRON CORE

RECTIFIERS

MOVING–COIL
MOVEMENT

SHUNTS

TRIGGER
FOR OPENING
CORE

SECONDARY
WINDING

V

RANGE SWITCH FOR
CURRENT RANGES POSITION
"V" USED FOR MEASURING VOLTAGE

MULTIPLIERS

BINDING POSTS FOR
VOLTAGE RANGES

Fig. 10-7. A. Clamp-type a-c volt-ammeter.
B. Circuit of clamp-type a-c volt-ammeter.

Hence a current, proportional to the amount of current flowing through the conductor, is induced in the secondary winding. This induced current is then measured by means of a rectifier-type, moving-coil ammeter. The scale of the ammeter is calibrated to read the current flowing in the conductor. As in any other type of ammeter, shunts may be used to vary the range of the instrument.

Frequently, the same moving-coil instrument may be used as a voltmeter as well, by employing suitable multipliers. As in ordinary voltmeters, the instrument then must be connected in shunt with the circuit to be measured. The circuit of a typical clamp-type voltmeter-ammeter is shown in Figure 10-7B. Current is measured by clamping the core around the current-carrying conductor. Voltage is measured by a pair of leads connecting the terminals in the side of the instrument across the circuit. The ammeter range is chosen by means of the switch on the front of the instrument. When voltage is to be measured, the switch is turned to VOLTS. The voltmeter range is determined by selecting the proper set of terminals. The trigger is used to open or close the core.

2. THERMOCOUPLE METHOD

The other method for changing alternating current into direct current is an indirect process that first converts the alternating current into heat and then uses this heat to generate a direct current. It has been found that if two dissimilar metal wires or strips are joined at one end and this junction heated, a small direct voltage will appear between the cool, open ends. Further, this voltage is directly proportional to the difference in temperature between the hot and cold ends. This phenomenon is known as the *thermoelectric effect* and the combination of the metal wires or strips is called a *thermocouple*.

If we connect a resistor (called the *heater*) in series with the a-c line, the current heats the resistor as it flows through it. The amount of heat is proportional to the square of the current (heating effect $= I^2R$). This heat is applied to the junction of a thermocouple. As a result, a direct voltage, directly proportional to the heat, appears across the cool, open ends. We can measure this voltage (or the current set flowing by it) by means of a moving-coil millivoltmeter or milliammeter. The reading on the meter, then, will be an indication of the alternating current flowing in the line. (See Figure 10-8.)

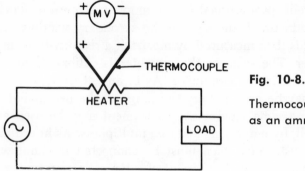

THERMOCOUPLE

Fig. 10-8.

Thermocouple meter used as an ammeter.

Any two dissimilar metals may be used for the thermocouple. However, two different alloys, *constantan* and *manganin,* are frequently employed. The thermocouple and heater generally are formed into one unit. For measuring currents up to about 100 milliamperes, the entire unit usually is sealed into an evacuated glass tube to reduce heat loss to the surrounding air. Wire leads sealed into the glass make contact with the various elements. For higher currents, where the heat loss is not serious, the entire unit may be exposed to the air.

The combination of thermocouple, heater, and millivoltmeter is called a *thermocouple meter.* Such meters can be used to measure current or voltage. Their ranges may be extended through the use of shunts or voltage multipliers. Because the heating effect of the current is not affected by its frequency, thermocouple meters can be used in high-frequency circuits.

Note that the scale of the meter is of the square-law type, since the heating effect is proportional to the square of the current. The scale can be modified to a uniform type by changing the shape of

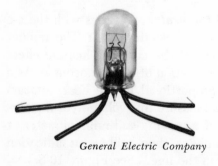

General Electric Company

Fig. 10-9.

Thermocouple enclosed in glass bulb.

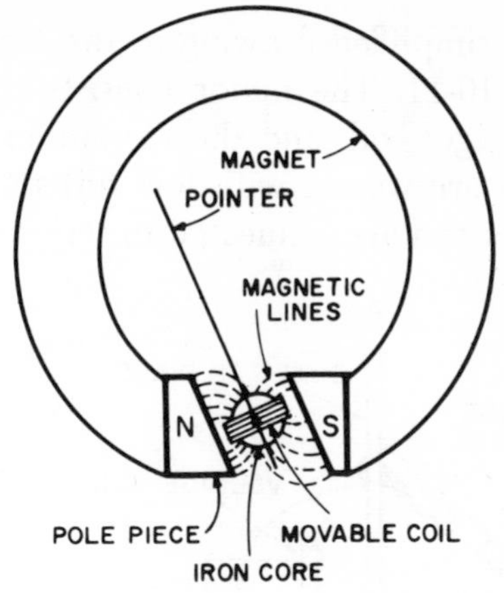

Fig. 10-10.

How the pole pieces of thermo-couple meter are modified to make the scale linear.

the pole pieces to that illustrated in Figure 10-10. Note that when the moving coil is in its low-scale position (pointer to the left), it is cutting across the stronger portion of the magnetic field (as indicated by the concentration of the magnetic lines). When the coil is in its high-scale position (pointer to the right), it is in the weaker portion of the field. This weakening of the magnetic field as the coil moves to its high-scale position reduces the sensitivity of the meter for that portion of the scale and tends to change the square-law relation to a linear one.

An interesting variation of the thermocouple meter is the *pyrometer*, an instrument used to measure temperature. Here, only the thermocouple and millivoltmeter are used. The junction of the thermocouple becomes the probe that is applied to the object whose temperature is to be measured; the meter scale is marked in degrees of temperature.

C. The a-c watthour meter

The a-c watthour meter operates on the same general principle as the d-c type described in Chapter 6, Subdivision D, 5. An a-c motor (which will be discussed later in the book) revolves at a speed that is determined by the amount of power being consumed by the house circuits. The length of time this power is being consumed determines the length of time this motor rotates. The shaft of the motor is attached to a set of dials that record the electrical energy (power × time) in kilowatthours consumed by the circuits.

A simplified drawing of the a-c watthour meter is shown in Figure 10-11. The motor consists of the current coils, the potential (voltage) coil, and the aluminum disk between them. The current coils are wound with few turns of heavy wire on a set of soft-iron cores and are connected in series with the power line. The potential

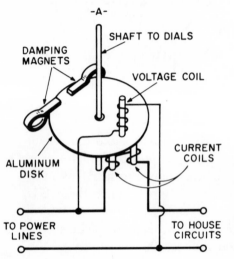

Westinghouse Electric Corp.

Fig. 10-11.

A. Simplified diagram of a-c watthour meter.

B. Commercial a-c watthour meter.

coil is wound with many turns of fine wire on an iron core and is connected across the power line. Note that these coils are fixed. The aluminum disk is the rotor. As current flows through the coils, the aluminum disk rotates between them. The damping magnets perform the same function here as they do in the d-c watthour meter.

D.   *The frequency meter*

In a-c work it sometimes is necessary to keep the frequency of the current constant. Accordingly, a *frequency meter* may be con-

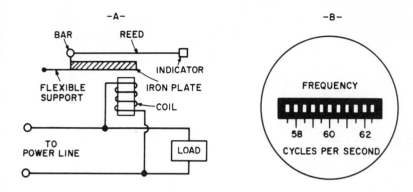

Fig. 10-12. A. Frequency meter.
B. Dial of frequency meter.

nected to the circuit to indicate the frequency at any given time. There are a number of different types of frequency meters, but the simplest, perhaps, is the type illustrated in Figure 10-12.

A coil of many turns of fine wire wound on a soft-iron core is connected across the line. Near it is a soft-iron plate held in place by a flexible support. As current flows through the coil, the iron plate is attracted twice each cycle as the current reaches its positive and negative peaks. Between these peaks the springiness of the support restores the plate to its original position. Thus the plate makes two vibrations for every cycle of the current.

Attached to the plate, and moving with it, is an iron bar. A set of thin reeds are attached to the bar in such a way that they are able to vibrate freely. These reeds have natural frequencies that differ in sequence by two vibrations per second. (If a reed, or any other object, is free to vibrate, it normally will do so at a frequency that is determined by its physical characteristics, such as kind of material, length, thickness, etc. This frequency is known as the *natural frequency* of the object.)

As the iron plate vibrates, the reeds vibrate also. But the reed whose natural frequency matches the rate of vibration of the plate will vibrate most strongly. Thus, by noting which reed vibrates most vigorously, we may determine the rate of vibration of the iron plate and, hence, the frequency of the current.

Light-weight indicators are attached to the free ends of the reeds so that their vibrations may be seen more easily. The vibrating-reed frequency meter does not cover a broad band of frequencies but, rather, a narrow range of frequencies from a few cycles per second below the desired frequency to a few cycles per second above. Thus, if the frequency of the current falls or rises a few cycles per second, the deviation may be noted and steps taken to restore the current to the desired frequency.

QUESTIONS

Wherever possible, diagrams should be used to clarify the answers to these questions. These diagrams need not be elaborate, but they should be drawn neatly with the significant portions clearly labeled.

1. Explain why the D'Arsonval-type moving-coil movement cannot be used directly for a-c measurement. Why can the dynamometer movement be so used?
2. Describe two methods commonly used to convert the D'Arsonval-type moving-coil movement to a-c measurement.
3. Draw and explain a half-wave rectifier circuit using a copper-oxide rectifier.
4. Draw and explain a full-wave bridge-rectifier circuit using copper-oxide rectifiers.
5. Explain the operation of a thermocouple as applied to a meter movement.
6. Explain the operation of an a-c watthour meter.
7. Explain the operation of a vibrating-reed frequency meter.

Generators of Electricity

chapter

11

Mechanical Generators

A. *Alternating-current generators*

1. GENERATOR USING PERMANENT MAGNETS FOR FIELD

Michael Faraday discovered, you will recall, that if a conductor cuts across a magnetic field, an electromotive force is generated between the ends of the conductor. This is the principle of the simple generator illustrated in Figure 7-3. A single loop of wire revolves between the poles of a magnet, cutting the magnetic field between the poles as it rotates. As a result, an electromotive force is induced in the loop.

We also now know (see Chapter 7, Subdivision A) that the induced voltage (and the induced current resulting from it) will be greater if:

1. the magnetic field is made stronger.
2. the number of conductors cutting across the magnetic field is increased.

3. the speed of relative motion between the magnetic field and conductors is increased.

A practical application of the above principles is the *magneto* illustrated in Figure 11-1A. The stronger magnetic field is obtained through the use of several horseshoe magnets so mounted that all similar poles are together, producing the effect of a large north pole and a large south pole. The number of conductors cutting across the magnetic field is increased by the use of a coil of many turns of wire instead of a single loop. Each turn of the coil adds its share of induced voltage to that of the others, resulting in a larger total induced voltage. The speed of relative motion between the magnetic field and conductors is increased by means of a system of gear wheels which multiplies the speed at which the crank is turned.

Figure 11-1B shows the *armature* of the magneto. Many turns of insulated copper wire (the *armature coil*) are wound on the iron armature *core*. This core not only supports the coil, but also furnishes

– A –

Fig. 11-1.

A. Magneto.
B. Armature and other rotating portions.
C. Cross-sectional view.

Western Electric Co., Inc.

–B–

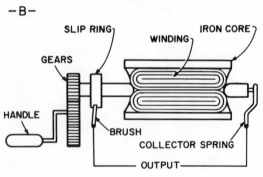

–C–

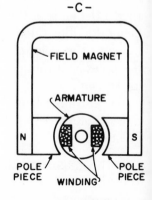

an easy path for the magnetic flux from the north field pole to the south. One end of the coil is connected to a metal *collector,* or *slip, ring* mounted on the armature shaft, but insulated from it. A metallic *brush* makes a wiping contact with this ring. The other end of the coil is attached to the armature shaft which, in turn, makes a wiping contact with the *collector spring.* The induced voltage appears between the brush and the collector spring.

A cross-sectional view of the magneto appears in Figure 11-1C. The armature coil is wound in slots in the armature core. Note the *pole pieces,* which are made of soft iron. Since magnetic lines of force will travel much more readily through soft iron than through air, these pole pieces concentrate the magnetic flux near the armature. Thus the magnetic field being cut by the armature coil is increased and, as a result, the induced voltage is greater.

A generator such as the one illustrated in Figure 11-1A is used in portable telephone systems to ring a bell at the far end of the line; it is called a *bell-ringing magneto.* Somewhat similar magnetos are used by certain types of gasoline engines (for airplanes, motorcycles, motorboats, and the like) to generate the high voltage required for ignition purposes. In some of these the field magnets are stationary and the armature revolves. In others, the armature is stationary and the field magnets revolve. The results are the same— a voltage is induced as a magnetic field is cut by a conductor.

2. GENERATORS USING ELECTROMAGNETS FOR FIELD

For simple, low-current purposes, the magneto described above may be suitable. However, where large amounts of current are required as, for example, for lighting and for operating machinery, electromagnets are used instead of permanent magnets to produce the necessary magnetic field. Not only can we obtain stronger magnetic fields by means of electromagnets, but we can control the field of the electromagnet much more easily, simply by varying the strength of the current flowing through it.

A steady magnetic field is required. Accordingly, a direct current must be sent through the electromagnet. This direct current may be obtained from storage batteries. Usually, however, it is obtained from a direct-current generator (which will be described later in this chapter).

The direct current for the field is called the *exciting current* and the d-c generator that supplies it is called the *exciter*. Frequently, the mechanical energy that rotates the exciter comes from the same source that drives the alternating-current generator. Often, both generators are mounted on the same shaft.

The alternating-current generator is also known as an *alternator*. When used in circuit diagrams its symbol is ─ⓝ─ . An armature, consisting of an armature coil wound upon an iron core, rotates in a magnetic field set up by the field electromagnets. The induced voltage is led to the external circuit through a set of brushes that make a wiping contact with a set of slip rings connected to the ends of the armature coil. (See Figure 11-2.)

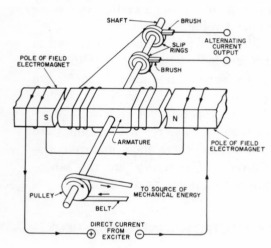

Fig. 11-2.

Simplified illustration of practical a-c generator.

Here we have an improved version of the simple generator illustrated in Figure 7-3. The armature coil consists, not of a single loop, but of many turns of wire wound upon an iron core. The armature is rotated by mechanical energy from some source such as a steam or water turbine. The magnetic field is set up by direct current flowing through the field electromagnets. As in the simple generator, a single cycle is generated as the armature coil makes one complete revolution, passing by a single set of poles (that is—a north pole and a south pole).

Current in this country usually is generated at a frequency of 60 cycles per second. Accordingly, the generator illustrated in Figure 11-2 would have to make 60 revolutions per second (60 rps) or

3,600 revolutions per minute (3,600 rpm). The design of a generator rotating at this speed presents a number of difficulties, particularly if the machine be a large one. Accordingly, we generally seek to reduce the speed of rotation.

You will recall that a cycle is generated as the armature passes a set of north and south poles. If there be only one such set of poles, there can be only one cycle per revolution. But if there be several sets of poles, a cycle will be generated as the armature passes by each set of north and south poles. Accordingly, there will be more than one cycle generated per revolution. Thus, to obtain the 60-cycle current, we would have a generator rotating at less than 3,600 rpm.

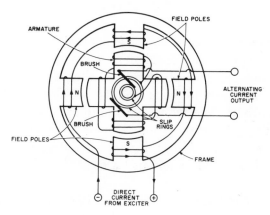

Fig. 11-3. Alternator with two sets of field poles.

In Figure 11-3 you see a generator that has two sets of poles. Note that the field winding is such that north and south field poles are set up alternately. Thus, in a half a revolution the armature rotates past a north and south pole, and a cycle is generated. Accordingly, there are two cycles per revolution. To generate a 60-cycle-per-second current, the armature need rotate only 30 rps, or 1,800 rpm.

Practical alternators may have even more sets of poles, thus permitting slower rotation to produce the desired 60-cycle current. There is a general equation which may be applied here:

$$f = \frac{\text{number of poles}}{2} \times \frac{\text{speed in rpm}}{60}$$

where f is the frequency in cycles per second. If we wish to determine the speed of rotation of an alternator to generate 60-cycle current, we may use the following equation:

$$\text{Speed (rpm)} = \frac{3600}{S}$$

where S stands for the number of *sets* of alternate north and south poles.

Example. How many revolutions per minute must a 6-pole alternator make to generate a 60-cycle current?
Since 6 poles means 3 sets, then

$$\text{Speed} = \frac{3600}{3} = 1200 \text{ rpm.} \quad Ans.$$

Where the currents and voltages generated by the alternator are moderate, we may employ machines similar to those we have just discussed. However, some of our larger alternators are called upon to generate thousands of volts and to set flowing thousands of amperes of current. The wires of the armature coil must be very heavy, as must be their insulation. Thus it becomes quite unwieldy to rotate the armature. Also, the wiping contact between the slip rings and brushes produces serious losses at these high voltages and currents.

On the other hand, the currents and voltages for the field electromagnets are much smaller. Accordingly, it becomes feasible to have the armature remain stationary and to rotate the field coils around it. (You will remember that it makes no difference whether the magnetic field is stationary and the conductor cuts through it, or the conductor is stationary and the magnetic field moves across it.)

The armature (now called the *stator*) is made stationary and the output is taken from the ends of the armature coil by means of heavy, fixed connectors. The mechanical energy is applied to rotate the field coils (now called the *rotor*) inside the armature. The exciting current is applied to the field coils by means of brushes and slip rings.

Our large generating plants generally are of two types. Where falling water is used to drive a relatively slowly rotating water turbine which, in turn, furnishes the mechanical energy to turn the generator, the alternator, too, is of the slow-speed type, employing four or more poles to produce the 60-cycle current. Where fuel (coal, oil, or gas) is burned to produce steam to drive a rapidly rotating steam turbine, which, in turn, rotates the generator, the alternator usually is of the high-speed type, employing only two or four poles.

3. POLYPHASE GENERATORS

Suppose we wind two separate armature coils upon the same core of the generator. Assume that these coils are wound one over the other, but are electrically separate and that each has its own set of slip rings and brushes. As the armature rotates, an alternating voltage will be induced in each coil. Because the coils are wound over each other and rotate together, the voltages induced in them will be in step, or *in phase.*

Now suppose that, instead of winding both coils over each other, we wind them at right angles to each other, as illustrated in Figure 11-4. At the instant armature coil A is cutting the maximum lines of

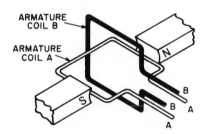

Fig. 11-4.

Two armature coils at right angles to each other.

force (and, hence, its induced voltage is at maximum), armature coil B is not cutting any lines and its induced voltage is at zero. The two induced voltages are *out of phase* with each other. Because the two coils are at right angles to each other (90° apart), the phase difference between the two induced voltages, too, is 90°.

Assume we wind three armature coils upon the same core, each coil being wound 120° from its neighbor. The phase difference between the three induced voltages then is 120°. These relationships are shown graphically in Figure 11-5. In Figure 11-5A you see the graph of the alternating voltage produced by the generator with a single armature coil. Such a generator is called, appropriately, a *single-phase* generator. In Figure 11-5B you see the graph of the

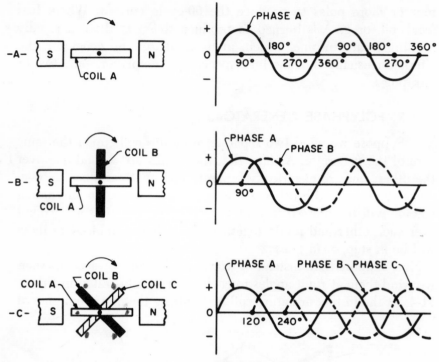

Fig. 11-5. A. Single-phase generator.
B. Two-phase generator.
C. Three-phase generator.

voltages produced by a generator with two armature windings 90° apart (the *two-phase* generator). The voltage of phase B starts 90° behind that of phase A and all the variations of the former are 90° behind those of the latter.

In Figure 11-5C you see the graph of the voltages produced by a generator with three armature windings, each 120° apart (the *three-phase* generator). Voltage of phase B is 120° behind that of phase A, and the voltage of phase C is 120° behind that of phase B.

Generators that have more than one set of armature coils are called *polyphase* generators; the voltages and currents they produce are called *polyphase* voltages and currents. Polyphase generators offer certain advantages, especially when they are called upon to produce power for certain types of a-c motors (which will be discussed later in the book). Most modern polyphase generators are of the three-phase type.

– A –

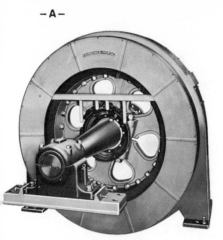

– B –

Fairbanks, Morse & Co.

Fig. 11-6. A. Three-phase alternator designed to operate at 60 cycles.
B. Revolving field of this alternator.

Many industrial machines employ three-phase alternating current. Since each armature coil of a three-phase generator has two ends, we might expect that six lines, two for each coil, would be needed to transmit the three-phase current from the generator to the machine. However, it is possible to join one end of each coil at the generator and then to transmit the current over three lines, one for each phase.

There are two variations of this connection. (See Figure 11-7.) The circuit shown in Figure 11-7A is called a *star*, or *Y*, connection. The one shown in Figure 11-7B is called a *delta* connection.

The three-phase generator usually is operated in a *balanced* condition; that is, the voltage across each armature coil is the same, and so are the currents flowing through the coils. In the Y-connected generator the current in each line is the same as that of the armature coil to which it is connected. It can be proven mathematically that the voltage between any two lines is equal to 1.73 times the voltage across one armature coil.

In the balanced delta-connected generator, on the other hand, the

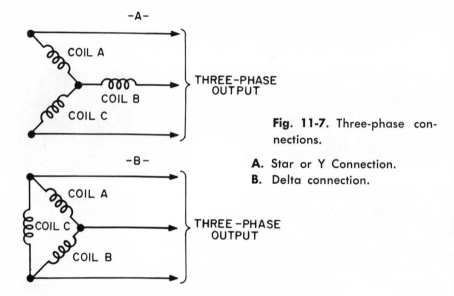

Fig. 11-7. Three-phase connections.

A. Star or Y Connection.
B. Delta connection.

voltage between any two lines is equal to that across any one armature coil. The current in each line, however, is equal to 1.73 times the current in any one armature coil.

B. Direct-current generators

1. THE COMMUTATOR

Although alternating current is used practically everywhere in our country, direct-current generators are required to furnish current for a number of industrial processes such as electroplating and battery charging. Essentially, the direct-current generator resembles the alternator previously described except that it employs a device that mechanically changes the alternating current generated in the armature coil to a direct current which is delivered to the brushes. This device is called a *commutator*.

Look back to the a-c generator illustrated in Figure 11-2. As the armature rotates through one cycle, the current flows first out of one brush and then, a half-cycle later, reverses and flows out of the other brush. If, at the end of each half-cycle, we could transpose the connections between the ends of the armature coil and the brushes, current would always flow out of the same brush. This changeover is performed by the commutator.

Look at Figure 11-8. Note the absence of the slip rings. In their place we have the commutator. This consists of a split metal ring mounted around the rim of an insulator disk. The two halves of the ring are separated from each other by a small gap that usually is filled with mica which insulates one half from the other. Each end of the armature coil is attached to one of these halves and the entire commutator rotates with the armature. The brushes make contact with opposite points on the commutator.

For one half-cycle the direction of the induced voltage in the armature is such as to force electrons to stream out of the negative brush to the external circuit. Then the direction of the induced voltage in the armature is reversed. However, at the same instant, the rotating commutator transposes the connections between the half-rings and the brushes. Accordingly, electrons again stream out of the negative brush. Such a reversal takes place at the end of each half-cycle. Accordingly, the electrons always stream from the negative brush to the external circuit. This is direct current. (When used in circuit diagrams, the symbol for the d-c generator is ⓖ The symbol for the armature, commutator, and brushes is shown as ⭘ .)

The relationship between the induced voltage in the armature and the current flowing from the brushes of the d-c generator can be

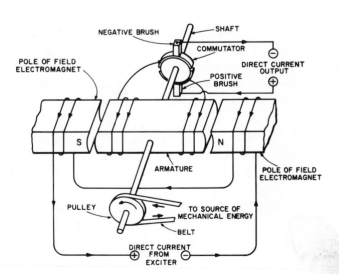

Fig. 11-8.

Simplified illustration of d-c generator.

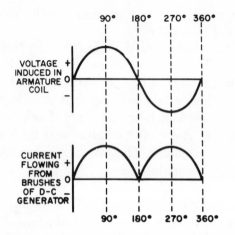

Fig. 11-9.

Graph showing relationship between voltage induced in armature coil and current flowing from brushes of the d-c generator.

shown graphically. (Look at Figure 11-9.) The voltage induced in the armature coil is alternating, just as in the a-c generator. If we consider the current flowing from the brushes of the d-c generator, we see that for the first half-cycle we get a positive loop, just as in the alternator. During the next half-cycle, instead of getting a negative loop (as in the alternator), the commutator action produces another positive loop.

Because the current flow is always in the same direction, it is a direct current. However, as you can see from the graph, it is not a steady direct current but, rather, one that rises and falls. We call such a current a *pulsating direct current.*

As the armature revolves there are two times in each cycle when the brushes are over the gaps between the commutator half-rings. At such times the brushes are shorting these half-rings. Should there be any potential difference between the two half-rings at these instants, sparking will occur. Such sparking eventually wears down both the brushes and the commutator half-rings.

To avoid such sparking, the brushes are so placed with relation to the commutator that the short-circuiting occurs when there is no potential difference between the two half-rings. As shown in Figure 11-10, this is when the armature coil is in the vertical plane and no voltage is being induced.

Now look at Figure 11-11. Here the generator is assumed to be stationary. The magnetic field between the two field poles (as indicated by the dotted lines) is uniformly distributed. The brushes are

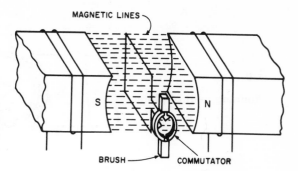

Fig. 11-10.

Brushes are placed so as to short-circuit the commutator half-rings when no voltage is being induced in the armature coil.

set on the commutator so that they cover the gaps when the armature coil is in the vertical plane between the two poles. The plane of the brushes is called the *stationary neutral plane*.

As the generator starts rotating, voltage is induced and current flows through the armature and through the external circuit that is connected to it. As this current flows, however, it sets up a magnetic field around the armature that reacts with the magnetic field of the field coils, distorting this latter field, as shown in Figure 11-12. This action is called *armature reaction*.

The effect of this distortion is to shift the neutral plane in the direction of rotation to a new plane that is called the *running neutral plane*. Since the neutral plane is one in which the brushes may short the commutator half-rings without sparking, we must move the brushes to the running neutral plane, as indicated in Figure 11-13.

If the current drawn from the generator (and, hence, the current flowing through the armature coil) remains constant, all is well. All we need do, then, is to move the brushes to the running neutral

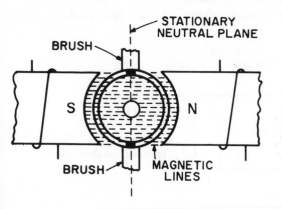

Fig. 11-11.

Stationary neutral plane.

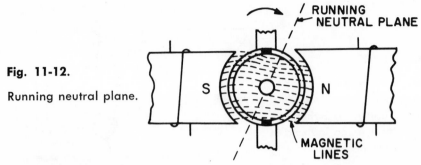

Fig. 11-12.

Running neutral plane.

plane and leave them there. However, the load placed upon the generator generally is a fluctuating one. The variations in current drawn from the generator are reflected in variations in current flowing through the armature coil and, accordingly, in the magnetic field around that coil. These variations in the magnetic field produce varying interference and distortion of the magnetic field produced by the field coils. As a result, the neutral plane no longer is fixed, but varies with the variations of the magnetic fields. Accordingly, the brushes must be adjusted constantly if sparking at the commutator is to be avoided.

To avoid this constant adjustment of the brushes, generators may be fitted with a set of *commutating poles,* as shown in Figure 11-14. These poles are located between the field poles; their windings are in series with the armature coil and the external load. These windings are such that the polarity of each commutating pole is opposite from that of the field pole it follows in the direction in which the armature is rotating.

The effect of the magnetic field of the commutating poles is to offset and neutralize the effect of the magnetic field of the armature coil upon the main magnetic field produced by the field coils. Thus the neutral plane tends to maintain a constant position. As more

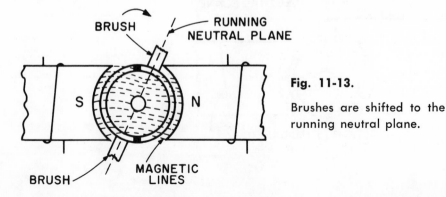

Fig. 11-13.

Brushes are shifted to the running neutral plane.

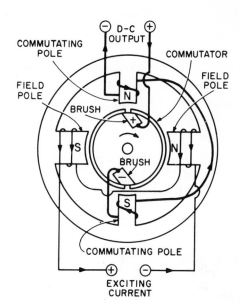

Fig. 11-14.

Generator with com-
mutating poles.

current is drawn from the generator, more current flows through
the armature coil and its magnetic field increases. However, more
current also flows through the windings of the commutating poles
and their neutralizing magnetic fields increase in like degree. When
less current is drawn from the generator, the magnetic fields around
the armature coil and commutating poles both decrease proportion-
ately.

2. MULTICOIL AND MULTIPOLAR GENERATORS

If you examine the graph of Figure 11-9 you will see that the
output of a simple d-c generator (such as illustrated in Figure 11-8)
is a pulsating direct current. Generally, we desire a steadier and
less-fluctuating direct current.

The fluctuations in the output are called *ripples*. We may reduce
the ripple effect by increasing the number of windings, or coils, of
the armature. Look at Figure 11-15A. Here the armature contains
two coils at right angles to each other. The commutator has four
segments, or *bars*. Each coil terminates in two opposite commutator
bars. The two brushes make contact with the two bars that connect
to the ends of the coil which, at that moment, is cutting the mag-

netic lines of force and, accordingly, is producing an induced voltage (in our illustration, coil #1). Coil #2 is not cutting any lines
of force and, hence, is producing no induced voltage.

After 90° of rotation, the coils change places. Now the voltage of
coil #1 has dropped to zero and that of coil #2 has reached a maximum. At the same time the commutator, too, has revolved 90° and
the brushes now make contact with the commutator bars connected
to the ends of coil #2.

The combined effect of the two armature coils is shown graphically in Figure 11-15B. Note that the ripple frequency of the resultant is twice that of each coil and that the output variations from
maximum to minimum are smaller than for each individual coil. The
more coils (and commutator bars) we employ, the smaller will be
the ripple.

Note, in Figure 11-15, that the induced voltage of only the armature coil that connects to the commutator bars in contact with the
brushes is producing a current. The induced voltages (if any) of the
other coils are wasted. Hence, such a system is not practical.

If we were able to connect all the coils in series in such a way

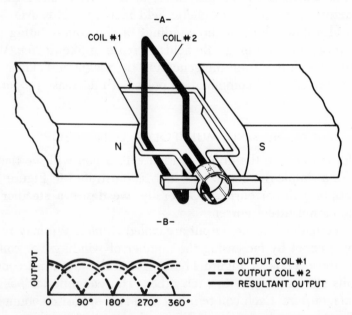

Fig. 11-15. A. D-c generator with two armature coils
B. Graph showing the resultant output.

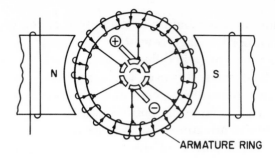

ARMATURE RING

Fig. 11-16. Ring-wound armature.

that the induced voltage of each would add to all the others, we would have a more efficient system. Such an arrangement is shown in Figure 11-16. The armature core is in the shape of a ring and the wire of the armature is wound continuously in the same direction around this ring, the ends being connected together. Hence this is called a *ring-wound armature*. The commutator bars are connected to the winding in such a way that an equal number of turns lie between adjacent bars.

As the armature rotates, current flows through the windings as indicated by the arrows on the wires. If you examine the current flow in the armature winding you will notice it follows two paths. One path is from the top of the ring, through the left-hand winding, to the bottom of the ring. The other is from the top of the ring, through the right-hand winding, to the bottom of the ring. The top and bottom junctions of these paths are the *neutral points* on the armature winding.

The neutral points lie midway between the field poles and correspond to the points on the armature winding where no lines of force are being cut and, hence, where no voltage is being induced. Because of this, the brushes are placed in contact with the commutator bars that correspond to the neutral points on the windings.

Note that the current in both paths of the armature winding flows toward one of these neutral points (in our illustration, the bottom one), which we call the *negative* neutral point. The current flows away from the other neutral point, which is called the *positive* neutral point. The negative brush (marked ⊝) and the positive brush (marked ⊕) make contact with their respective neutral points through the commutator bars. You can see that all the turns of the winding are contributing to the output of the generator and none of the induced voltage is wasted.

As the armature rotates, different portions of the winding will pass the two field poles. However, as the armature revolves, so does the commutator. Accordingly, current will always flow to the negative brush and away from the positive brush.

The ring-wound armature is seldom used in modern generators. For one, the inside portion of the winding, shielded as it is from the magnetic lines of force by the iron of the armature core, produces no induced voltage. Also, it is quite difficult to wind such an armature since it means threading the wire in and out of the core. Most generators, today, employ the *drum-type* armature illustrated in Figure 11-17.

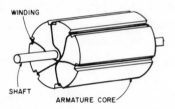

Fig. 11-17.

Drum-type armature.

As the name implies, the drum-type armature is in the form of a cylinder, or drum. The winding lies in slots on the surface of the core and is so arranged that each coil occupies opposite slots on the drum. As in the ring-wound armature, all the coils are connected in series. A single coil generally consists of many turns rather than the single turn shown in the illustration.

Connections to the commutator bars are similar to those for the ring-wound armature and the operation, too, is similar. However, there are no shielded (and, hence, wasted) portions of the winding, and the drum-type armature is easier to wind. The present-day generator employs a drum-type armature with slots for many coils and a commutator with many segments or bars (two for each coil).

The armature winding of the generator is in series with the external load. Thus the current drawn by that load from the generator also flows through its armature winding. Hence, the maximum current that can be drawn from the generator is limited by the amount of current that can flow through the wire of the armature winding without causing it to overheat.

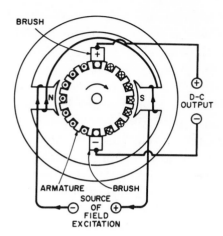

Fig. 11-18.

Two-pole generator.

We can, of course, increase the current-carrying capacity of the armature wires by increasing their size. However, there is a method whereby we can increase the maximum current that can be drawn from a generator without increasing the size of its wires.

Consider the two-pole generator shown in simplified form in Figure 11-18. The drum-type armature is shown in cross-sectional view with the armature wires lying in slots along its surface. [Note that all the wires on the left-hand side of the drum have a dot (•) in their centers, whereas all the wires on the right-hand side have a cross (x) in their centers. This is a method for showing the direction of current flow through a conductor when we look at a cross-sectional view of that conductor. The current is considered as an arrow. If it is flowing out of the page towards you, you see the tip of the arrow, which resembles a dot. If it is flowing away from you, you see the feathered end of the arrow, which resembles a cross.]

There are two neutral points in the armature winding (as indicated by the wires that have neither a dot nor a cross), each lying midway between the two poles. The top one is the positive neutral point and the bottom one is the negative neutral point. The positive and negative brushes make contact with the respective commutator bars that correspond to these neutral points. The armature current, you will recall, flows along two parallel paths through the armature winding. Thus the individual wires of the winding are called upon to carry only one-half of the total armature current.

If we were able to increase the number of parallel paths for the current to follow through the armature winding, we would be able to have a greater total armature current without increasing the size of the wire. This is accomplished by the use of generators having more than two field poles.

In Figure 11-19 you see the simplified drawing of a four-pole generator. Note that the field poles are arranged so that north and south poles alternate. A conductor on the armature undergoes a complete cycle (360 electrical degrees) as it rotates past two opposite field poles. In the case of the two-pole generator, this means a complete revolution. But in the case of the four-pole generator, this means a half-revolution.

Midway between each set of poles are the neutral points. Hence, we have four neutral points—two positive and two negative—and, accordingly, two positive brushes and two negative brushes. If we connect the two positive brushes together and the two negative brushes together, we have *four* parallel paths for the armature current to flow through the armature winding. Thus the individual wires of the winding are called upon to carry only one-fourth of the total armature current.

By increasing the number of field poles, we may have even more parallel paths for the armature current and, hence, a greater total armature current that the wires can safely handle. Generators that are called upon to supply very large amounts of current generally have six or more field poles. Medium-size generators usually have four. Small generators, such as those used in automobiles to charge the storage battery, generally have two.

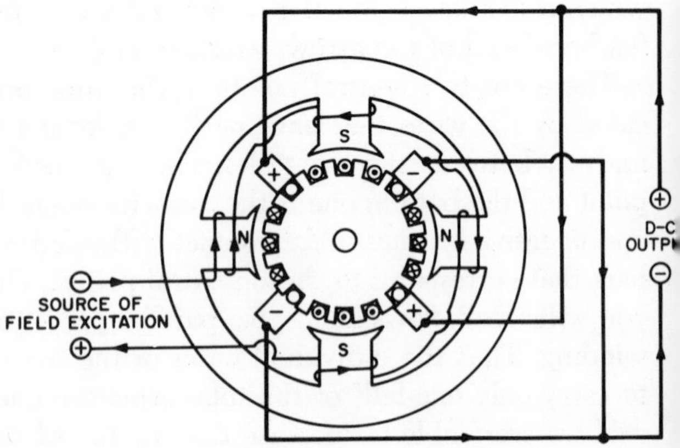

Fig. 11-19.

Four-pole generator.

Fig. 11-20.

Open-type d-c generator.

General Electric Company.

Multipolar generators have another advantage over the two-pole variety. You will recall that when we discussed the alternator we found that increasing the number of field poles increased the frequency of the voltage induced in the armature, the speed of rotation being kept constant. (Remember, the voltage induced in the armature of a d-c generator is of the alternating variety, the commutator changing it to a direct voltage.) Accordingly, the ripple frequency of the output of the d-c generator with many poles is greater than that of the two-pole type. Thus the d-c pulses are closer together and, hence, the output is a steadier direct current.

Even with many coils of armature winding and many field poles, the output of the d-c generator may not be steady enough for certain

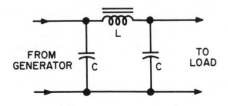

FROM
GENERATOR

L

C   C

TO
LOAD

Fig. 11-21.

Ripple filter.

applications. Accordingly, *filters* may be employed to smooth out the ripple. These filters consist of capacitors and inductors connected as shown in Figure 11-21. The capacitors (C), connected in parallel with the load, oppose changes in voltage. The inductor (L), connected in series with the load, opposes the changes in current. In this way the ripple is filtered out and an almost pure, steady direct current results.

3. TYPES OF DIRECT-CURRENT GENERATORS

a. Separately-excited generators

Just as in the alternator, the direct current used to excite the field coils of the d-c generator may be obtained from storage batteries or from a separate d-c generator. It is usual, in practice, to keep this exciting current at about 5 per cent of the rated current of the main generator. Thus, if the rated current of the main generator is 100 amperes, its field current would be about 5 amperes.

Since the armature windings of any generator are in series with the external load, an increase in current consumption of the load means an increase in the current flowing through the armature windings. Since the resistance of these windings remains constant, this increase in current means a greater IR (voltage) drop, and a decrease in the voltage output of the generator. Conversely, a decrease in load current reduces the IR drop in the armature windings and thus tends to increase the output voltage.

Where the magnetic field of the generator is dependent upon the induced voltage in the armature windings (as in some of the generators we shall discuss a little later) such variations in the armature voltage with variations in the load will, of course, affect the field. In the separately-excited generator, however, the strength of the field does not depend upon the load and, hence, the output voltage of the generator tends to be more constant.

The separately-excited generator is not in wide use today because of the extra cost of batteries or of an exciting generator. Also, the batteries or exciting generator require additional space. However, such a generator may still be used where constant voltage is essential, as, for example, in electroplating. The schematic diagram of a separately-excited generator is shown in Figure 11-22.

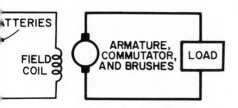

Fig. 11-22.

Schematic diagram of separately-excited d-c generator.

b. Self-excited generators

Inasmuch as the d-c generator delivers a direct current, it becomes obvious that we may use part of the delivered current to excite the field coils. Such generators are called *self-excited* types. There are three general classes of self-excited generators which will be discussed below.

A question should be raised immediately. Since the generator does not generate any current until the armature starts rotating and cutting the magnetic lines of force, and if the field coils do not receive any current until the generator delivers it, from where, then, comes the magnetic flux at the start?

The answer lies in the *residual magnetism* of the field poles. These poles are made of iron and become magnetized as current flows through the field coils. When the generator stops rotating and this current ceases to flow, the field poles lose most of their magnetism. But a certain small amount (the residual magnetism) remains. When the armature starts rotating again, the cutting of the magnetic flux owing to this residual magnetism produces a weak induced current. All this current (or a portion, depending upon the type of generator) is fed back to the field coils, increasing the strength of the magnetic field. As a result, a greater current is generated, more current is fed back to the field coils, and the process continues to build up until the field reaches its normal strength. The entire procedure usually takes about 20 or 30 seconds. Where the generator has been standing idle for a long time, or where the residual magnetism has been lost because of some other effect, it may be necessary to use batteries to furnish field current at the start. Once the generator has started delivering current, the batteries may be removed.

(1) SERIES FIELD GENERATOR

In the *series field* generator, the field coil is connected in series with the armature windings and the load, as shown in Figure 11-23. Here the entire current furnished by the generator flows through the field coils. Accordingly, these coils must be wound with heavy wire. Since the magnetic field depends upon the ampere-turns of these coils, and since the current is large, these coils need have only few turns to obtain the desired magnetic flux.

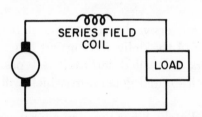

SERIES FIELD
COIL

LOAD

Fig. 11-23.

Series field generator.

You will recall that the output voltage of a generator tends to drop with an increased current drain due to the increased IR drop in the armature. However, an increased drain by the load also increases the current flowing through the series field coil and, hence, the magnetic field is increased. Since there are now more magnetic lines to be cut, the voltage of the generator rises. Thus, increasing the load on the generator causes its voltage to rise.

Conversely, decreasing the load reduces the current flowing through the series field coil. Hence the voltage of the generator drops. You see, then, that the voltage of the series field generator varies with variations in load. It is for this reason that the series field generator is not much used, except in installations where the load can be kept fairly constant.

(2) SHUNT FIELD GENERATOR

In the *shunt field* generator, the field coil is connected in parallel, or in shunt, with the armature windings and the load, as shown in Figure 11-24. The armature current now flows through two parallel paths, one through the load and the other through the field coil. Since the current flowing through the field coil is lost, so far as the generator output is concerned, it is necessary to keep this loss as

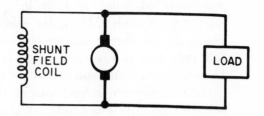

Fig. 11-24.

Shunt field generator.

small as possible. Less than 5 per cent of the armature current generally is fed to the field coil.

To keep the current flowing through the field coil low, the coil must have a high resistance. Hence it is wound with fine wire. However, to have the proper number of ampere-turns to supply an adequate magnetic field, the shunt field coil must have many turns.

As the current drawn by the load increases, the portion reserved for the shunt field coil drops. Hence the magnetic field becomes weaker and the voltage of the generator decreases. Conversely, as the load current decreases, the field current increases, and the generator voltage rises. Thus, you see, the shunt field generator acts opposite to the series field type.

There is a built-in safety feature in the shunt field generator. Should a short-circuit occur in the load, its resistance would drop to practically zero and the current it draws would, accordingly, rise tremendously. With this rise in load current, the field current would drop to practically zero, as would the resulting magnetic field. Since there would be no magnetic lines of force to cut, the generator would cease functioning. Thus, the armature windings are protected against a burn-out which would normally result from the large current.

Note that no such safety factor exists for the series field generator. A short-circuit in its load draws a very large current. This excessive current causes the field to increase and a very large current to flow through the armature windings which may burn out as a result. Practical generators, however, are provided with extra safety devices, such as circuit breakers, to protect them against excessive currents.

(3) COMPOUND GENERATORS

The opposing characteristics of the series field and shunt field generators led, quite naturally, to a type that incorporates the characteristics of both. This is the *compound generator* illustrated in Figure 11-25. This generator has two field coils wound upon each field pole. One is a series coil consisting of few turns of heavy wire. The other is a shunt coil consisting of many turns of fine wire.

With an increase in load current, the series field tends to raise the voltage while the shunt field tends to lower the voltage. By proper design of both types of field coils these tendencies can be made to neutralize each other and the voltage remains fairly constant. Similarly, with a decrease in load current, the series field tends to lower the voltage while the shunt field tends to raise the voltage. Again, these tendencies neutralize each other and, again, the voltage remains constant. Thus the output voltage of a compound generator is essentially constant with variations in load current. It is for this reason that compound generators are in such wide use today.

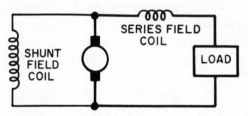

Fig. 11-25.

Compound generator.

As a matter of fact, many generators are designed with the series field coils having a few more turns than is necessary for exact neutralization of the opposing tendencies. Thus, with greater current drain, the voltage of the compound generator tends to rise slightly. This is to offset the increased IR drop in the wires of the line connecting to the load owing to the increased current. Thus the voltage actually applied *at the load* tends to remain constant. Such generators are said to be *overcompounded*.

There are two ways in which we may wind the shunt and field coils upon the pole pieces. In Figure 11-26A you see the *cumulative* winding whereby the polarities of both fields are the same. The behavior of the cumulatively-wound compound generator has been described above.

In Figure 11-26B you see the *differential* winding whereby the polarities of both fields are opposed. Generators of this type are used for special purposes, such as arc welding, where sudden heavy

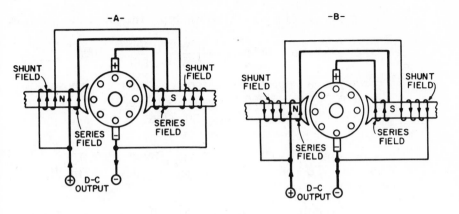

Fig. 11-26. A. Cumulative compound generator.
B. Differential compound generator.

loads may be applied. When such a heavy load occurs, the large magnetic field created by the series winding neutralizes the field created by the shunt winding. As a result, the over-all field is reduced. The armature voltage drops, reducing the armature current and thus protecting the armature winding from overheating. In effect, this acts as an automatic overload control.

C. *Efficiency and regulation of generators*

The power output of the d-c generator normally is rated in watts or kilowatts. In alternating-current circuits, however, the inductance and capacitance of the load affect the phase relationship between the current and voltage and, hence, the power (see Chapter 8, Subdivision C). Since the inductance and capacitance of the load are variable factors that cannot be determined in advance, the power output of alternators usually is rated in volt-amperes (v-a) or kilovolt-amperes (kv-a).

As is true of all machines, the efficiency of the generator is the ratio between the power output and the power input. But note that the input to the generator is the *total* input which includes the power of the machine that drives the generator as well as the power used to excite it (if it is separately excited). If we wish to find the efficiency (in per cent) of a generator, we apply the following formula:

$$\text{Per cent efficiency} = \frac{\text{power output}}{\text{power input}} \times 100.$$

Example. A separately-excited d-c generator whose power output is rated at 1,000 kilowatts is turned by a 1,500-horsepower diesel engine and uses 50 kilowatts to excite its field. What is its efficiency?

Power input = power of diesel engine + power for field excitation. To convert horsepower to kilowatts, multiply by 0.746. Thus,

power of the diesel engine = 1500 × 0.746 = 1119 kilowatts. Therefore,

Power input = 1119 + 50 = 1169 kilowatts.

$$\text{Per cent efficiency} = \frac{\text{power output}}{\text{power input}} \times 100 = \frac{1000}{1169} \times 100$$
$$= 85.5\%. \quad Ans.$$

The efficiency of a good generator generally is between 80 and 95 per cent.

Aside from losses within the source that supplies field excitation (if the generator is separately excited) the losses within a generator fall into three general categories—*mechanical* losses, *copper* losses, and *iron* losses.

Mechanical losses. The largest mechanical losses are caused by friction at the bearings that support the rotating parts and by friction between the brushes and slip rings or commutators. In addition, there is the loss due to wind resistance (called *windage*) encountered by the rotating members. These losses are kept low by proper design of the bearings and rotating parts.

The brushes generally are made of powdered carbon and graphite, held together by some suitable binder. The graphite acts as a lubricant, cutting down friction. In some low-voltage generators (such as the automobile generator that charges the storage battery) powdered copper is added to the carbon and graphite to lower the resistance of the brush.

Copper losses. These losses are due to the power consumed by the heating effect (I^2R) of the current that flows through the wires of the armature and field windings. The wire must be heavy enough to keep this loss at a minimum and to prevent overheating.

Iron losses. These losses are due, essentially, to the fact that the iron armature core and field poles are located within a rapidly changing magnetic field. Thus they are alternately magnetized and demagnetized. Whenever a substance is alternately magnetized and demagnetized, the magnetizing force encounters in the substance a sort of "resistance" which causes the magnetizing effect to lag behind the magnetizing force. This lagging is called *hysteresis.*

The energy loss due to this "resistance" shows up as heat produced within the substance. To minimize the hysteresis loss the armature core and field poles generally are made of soft iron, annealed steel, or certain other alloys that have a high permeability.

In addition to the hysteresis loss there is another caused by the changing magnetic field. The armature core and field poles are conductors and, like other conductors, the changing magnetic field will induce a current within them. This is called the *eddy current* and, since it comes from the generated current and is not available as output, it represents a loss. Eddy current losses are reduced by building up the core and poles of thin sheets, called *laminations,* instead of making them of solid metal. Each lamination is coated with an insulating varnish and so the flow of eddy current is broken up.

Incidentally, great care must be taken to preserve the magnetic flux of the field. The frame of the generator, which supports the field poles, is made of soft iron to furnish an easy path for the circulation of the flux between these poles. The armature and field poles are so mounted that only a very small air gap exists between them. The ends of the poles are curved and flared out to provide a more even distribution of the magnetic flux over the armature.

The mechanical and iron losses tend to remain constant, regardless of variations in the load on the generator. The copper losses, on the other hand, rise rapidly with increases in the load and fall when the load is decreased.

We have seen how the generator voltage tends to drop with an increase in the current drawn by the load, owing to the increased IR drop in the armature winding. There is another cause of voltage drop with increased load. This is the *armature reaction* we discussed earlier. You will recall that as the generator rotates the current that flows through the armature winding sets up a magnetic field that shifts the neutral point from the stationary neutral plane to the running neutral point. The greater the load, and, hence, the greater the armature current, the greater is this shift of plane.

Where the generator is not equipped with a set of commutating poles, we seek to reduce sparking at the commutator by adjusting the brushes according to the shift of the neutral point. This improves commutation, but it also upsets the balance of the armature coils with relation to the brushes. As a result, a certain amount of *demagnetization* takes place which weakens the total magnetic field somewhat, causing a drop in the induced voltage.

The inherent change in the voltage of a generator with changes in load is known as its *voltage regulation*. For rating purposes, we generally take the voltage change between no load and full load. The voltage regulation usually is expressed in per cent as determined by the following formula:

$$\text{Per cent voltage regulation} = \frac{\text{voltage at no load} - \text{voltage at full load}}{\text{voltage at full load}} \times 100.$$

Example. What is the voltage regulation of a generator whose no-load voltage is 110 volts and whose full-load voltage is 100 volts?

$$\text{Per cent regulation} = \frac{110 - 100}{100} \times 100 = 10\%. \quad Ans.$$

The lower the percentage, the better is the generator.

D. Control of generators

We can vary the voltage of a generator in three ways. First, we may change the number of conductors of the armature winding. Increasing the number of conductors cutting a magnetic field, you will recall, increases the induced voltage. Obviously, this method creates mechanical difficulties and, hence, it generally is not used.

Second, we may vary the speed of rotation of the armature. If we increase the rate at which the magnetic lines of force are cut we increase the induced voltage. Because generators usually are designed to be run at a constant speed, this method, too, is not in general use.

The method most frequently used is one that varies the strength of the magnetic field. The greater the number of magnetic lines of force being cut, the greater is the induced voltage. Since the field of the generator is created by current flowing through the field coils, it is quite easy to vary this current and, hence, the magnetic field.

In the alternator, the magnetic field may be varied by means of a variable resistor, called a *rheostat,* placed in series with the field coil and the source of exciting current. (See Figure 11-27.) When the

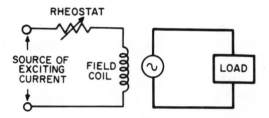

Fig. 11-27.

A rheostat in the field circuit is used to vary the voltage of the a-c generator.

resistance of the rheostat is increased, the field-coil current is lowered. This results in a smaller magnetic field and a decreased generator voltage. Decreasing the resistance of the rheostat increases the field current and, hence, the generator voltage. (The electrical symbol for the rheostat is ‑‑‑ or ‑‑‑ .)

The rheostat may be operated manually. In some installations automatic relays that cut fixed resistors into or out of the circuit are used. These relays are operated by the generator voltage. Should the voltage rise, it operates a relay which inserts a resistor into the circuit, thus reducing the voltage. Should the voltage fall, another relay cuts a resistor out of the circuit. In this way the voltage is kept constant.

For direct-current generators there are several methods for varying the voltage, depending upon the type of machine. If the generator is separately-excited we may use the same system of control as for the alternator.

In the self-excited, series field type, we may place a rheostat in parallel, or in shunt, with the field coil, as shown in Figure 11-28. The current flowing from the generator to the load has two paths to

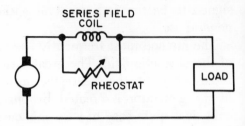

Fig. 11-28.

Voltage control for series field generator.

follow—one through the series field coil and the other through the rheostat. The greater the resistance of the rheostat, the less current will flow through it and the more current will flow through the field coil. Hence, the greater the magnetic field and the larger will be the generator voltage. Reducing the resistance of the rheostat causes less current to flow through the field coil and, hence, the voltage is reduced.

In the shunt field generator we may place a rheostat in series with the field coil, as shown in Figure 11-29. If we increase the resistance of the rheostat, the current through the field coil is reduced. This causes a reduction in the magnetic field and, accordingly, the generator voltage is lowered. Reducing the resistance of the rheostat results in a greater field current, a stronger magnetic field, and a larger voltage.

In the compound generator we may use either or both of the methods of voltage control just described. In all instances the rheostat may be adjusted manually or else automatic control may be achieved by relays that cut resistors in or out of the proper circuits as the voltage rises or falls.

The automobile generator, which supplies direct current to charge up the storage battery, presents a special problem. Because it is

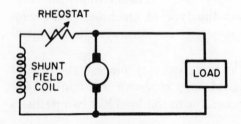

Fig. 11-29.

Voltage control for shunt field generator.

driven by the engine, it does not rotate at a constant speed, as do most other types of generators. Rather, its rate of rotation depends upon the speed of the car. The problem is one of keeping its voltage constant, else it may damage the lights and other appliances. Further, its output current, too, must be kept constant if the storage battery is not to be overcharged or undercharged.

A two-pole, shunt field generator of special design is frequently used. It has three, instead of two, brushes, as shown in simplified form in Figure 11-30. The shunt field coil is connected across the negative and third brushes. Because the third brush is not at the neutral point, the field coil does not receive its full share of field current, as it would were it connected to the positive brush. Hence the magnetic field is weaker and the generator output is lowered.

Fig. 11-30.

Automobile generator with a third brush.

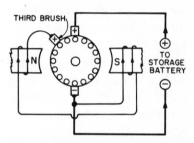

The third brush is movable. The nearer it approaches the positive brush, the nearer it gets to the neutral point, and the greater is the field current. Hence the output of the generator rises. If the brush is moved further away from the neutral point, the output drops. Thus, by adjusting the position of the third brush, we may control the rate at which the generator will charge the battery.

The generator has no commutating poles. Hence, the faster it rotates and the greater the armature current, the greater becomes the armature reaction and the more the output current tends to drop. Because of this, the generator actually produces less current at high speeds than at the normal operating speed of the automobile. This is an advantage since the car usually is driven for longer periods at its normal speed than at high speeds.

There are a number of external devices for regulating and controlling the output of the automobile generator. One such is the *voltage regulator relay* whose circuit is illustrated in Figure 11-31.

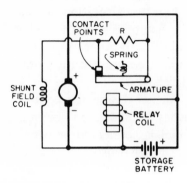

Fig. 11-31.

Voltage regulator relay.

The relay (which will be discussed further later in the book) consists of an electromagnet which, when sufficient current flows through its coil, attracts a soft-iron hinged armature. As this armature moves, it brings together or separates (depending upon the type of relay) a set of contact points, thus closing or opening some circuit of which the contact points are a part. The coil of the electromagnet consists of many turns of fine wire, thus producing a high resistance, and is connected across the line leading from the generator to the storage battery.

Normally, not enough current flows through the relay coil to attract the armature. A spring pulls this armature up and, as a result, a contact point on the armature makes contact with another fixed contact point, shorting out resistor R, which is in series with the shunt field coil. Thus, the full line voltage is applied to this field coil.

Should the voltage rise, however, the armature is attracted and contact between the points is broken. This removes the short across resistor R and its resistance appears in series with the field coil. The magnetic field of the generator is reduced and the voltage falls back to its normal value. At this point, the armature is released and the spring pulls it up, restoring contact between the two points. The resistor is shorted out again.

Another device is the *current limiter relay,* illustrated in Figure 11-32. This resembles the voltage regulator relay except that it is wound with fewer turns of heavy wire (hence low resistance) and is placed in series with the generator and the battery. This time, if

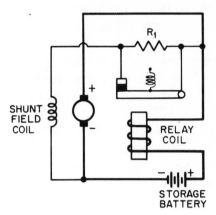

Fig. 11-32.

Current limiter relay.

current increases from normal, the armature is attracted, the contact points are separated, and resistor R_1 is placed in series with the shunt field coil. The output current then drops to normal, at which time resistor R_1 is shorted out again.

While the automobile is in operation, the generator rotates and current is flowing to the storage battery. When the car stops, however, the generator stops as well. However, since it still is connected to the battery, battery current now flows to the generator. This will discharge the battery and may ruin the generator. What we need is some device that disconnects the generator when it stops rotating.

This is the function of the *reverse current*, or *cutout, relay* shown in Figure 11-33. This relay has two coils. One is a heavy-wire winding of few turns in series with the generator, the closed contact points, the relay armature, the ammeter, and the storage battery. The other is a fine-wire winding of many turns in parallel with this circuit.

In Figure 11-33A the circuit is shown while the generator is rotating. When the current flows as indicated by the arrows, the magnetic pulls of both windings aid each other and the armature is attracted, closing the contact points. The ammeter shows that the battery is being charged.

Figure 11-33B shows the current flow the instant the vehicle stops. The generator no longer supplies any current. The battery now starts to discharge (as shown by the ammeter) and the current flows in the opposite direction, that is, in the opposite direction in all portions of the circuit except in the fine-wire winding of the relay. The magnetic fields of both windings now oppose each other. The result is an over-all weakening of the pull on the armature. The spring now is able to overcome this pull and the contacts are separated, opening the circuit from the battery to the generator.

The cutout relay may be used with other than automobile generators. When two generators are connected with their outputs in parallel, all is well as long as their voltages remain the same. Should the voltage of one drop, current from the other would tend to flow into the first. Thus it becomes necessary to cut that one out of the line until its voltage is restored. To do this a cutout relay may be placed in series with each generator.

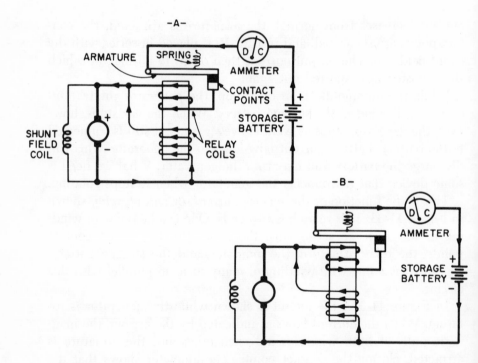

Fig. 11-33. Reverse current, or cutout, relay.

    A. Current flow while generator is rotating and storage battery is being charged.

    B. Current flow the instant generator stops and storage battery starts to discharge.

QUESTIONS

Whenever possible, diagrams should be used to clarify the answers to these questions. These diagrams need not be elaborate, but they should be drawn neatly with the significant portions clearly labeled.

1. What are the four essential parts of an a-c generator?
2. What determines *a*) the voltage of a generator; *b*) the maximum safe current that can be drawn from a generator; *c*) the frequency of the output of an a-c generator?
3. What must be the speed (in revolutions per minute) of a 12-pole a-c generator to produce a 400-cycle-per-second current?
4. What is meant by a *3-phase* a-c generator? What is the phase relationship between currents produced by such a generator?
5. Draw the circuit of the armature of a 3-phase generator wound in *a*) a Y connection; *b*) a delta connection.
6. What are the four essential parts of a d-c generator?
7. Explain the function and operation of the commutator.
8. What is meant by *armature reaction?*
9. Explain the difference between the *stationary neutral plane* and the *running neutral plane* of the d-c generator.
10. Explain the action of the *commutating poles* of a d-c generator.
11. Explain how the ripple in the output of a d-c generator may be reduced.
12. What are two advantages of the *drum-type* armature over the *ring-wound* type?
13. Draw the schematic circuit of a series field d-c generator. What is the effect of an increase in load upon its voltage?
14. Draw the schematic circuit of a shunt field d-c generator. What is the effect of an increase in load upon its voltage?
15. Draw the schematic circuit of a compound field d-c generator. What is the chief advantage of this type generator?
16. A self-excited d-c generator whose power output is rated at 500 kilowatts is turned by a 750-horsepower diesel engine. What is its efficiency?
17. What are the *mechanical* losses in a generator? What steps are taken to reduce them?
18. What are the *copper* losses in a generator? What steps are taken to reduce them?
19. What are the *iron* losses in a generator? What steps are taken to reduce them?

20. What is meant by the *voltage regulation* of a generator?
21. What is the regulation of a generator whose voltage is 220 volts at no-load and drops to 205 volts at full-load?
22. Explain three methods by which the voltage of a generator may be varied. Which method is used most commonly?
23. Explain the use of the *third brush* in controlling the output of an automobile generator.
24. Explain the action of the *voltage regulator relay* of the automobile.
25. Explain the action of the *current limiter relay* of the automobile.
26. Explain the action of the *reverse current relay* of the automobile.

12

Other Types of Generators of Electromotive Force

A. *Chemical type*

1. PRIMARY CELL

In Chapter 11 we learned how the generator converts mechanical energy into electrical energy. You must not get the impression that the generator creates the electrons that constitute the electric current. Actually, the generator creates the electromotive force that sets flowing the billions and trillions of electrons in the circuit itself, just as a water pump creates the pressure that sets flowing the water in the pipes. So we may consider the electrical generator as a sort of electromagnetic "pump."

There are other types of "pumps" that can create an electromotive force. In 1798 Alessandro Volta, an Italian physicist, invented a "chemical pump." He noticed that if two dissimilar metal strips are placed in an acid solution, an electromotive force appears between the two metals. If a conductor connects the two metal strips, electrons will flow through it. Such a "chemical pump" is called a *voltaic cell* in honor of its inventor.

Let us perform an experiment that will duplicate Volta's findings. Pour some hydrochloric acid (a compound of hydrogen and chlorine) into a jar of water. We believe that when hydrochloric acid is placed in water the compound breaks up. The chlorine atom seizes an electron from the hydrogen atom and thus becomes a negative chlorine ion (which appears in Figure 12-1 as Cl^-). The hydrogen atom, having lost an electron, becomes a positive ion (H^+). If, when a substance goes into solution ions are formed, we say that the substance has *ionized* and call the solution an *electrolyte*. Thus the water solution of hydrochloric acid is an electrolyte.

Into this solution insert a strip of copper and one of zinc. Connect a piece of copper wire between the two strips and place an ammeter in the circuit. The meter will show that a current is flowing through the wire from the zinc to the copper strip.

Let us see what happened. When the zinc strip was placed in the acid solution, the zinc started to dissolve—that is, zinc atoms started to leave the strip and enter the solution. As each zinc atom left the strip, however, it left behind two electrons. Thus the zinc atom became a positive zinc ion (Zn^{++}). And the zinc strip, because of the electrons left behind, became negatively charged.

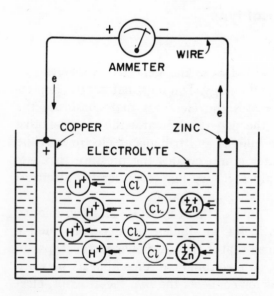

Fig. 12-1.

Voltaic cell.

The positive zinc ions repelled the positive hydrogen ions in the solution toward the copper strip. As each positive hydrogen ion reached the copper, it seized an electron from the strip and, becoming in this way a neutral hydrogen atom, bubbled off into the air. The copper strip, having lost electrons, became positively charged.

Thus a difference of potential (electromotive force) was created between the zinc and copper strips. When connected by a conductor, electrons flowed from the zinc to the copper strip, as indicated by the meter. This process will continue until the entire zinc strip is dissolved.

Almost any two dissimilar metals can be used. A carbon rod may be substituted for the copper strip. Almost any acid may be used for the electrolyte and there are a number of other substances, such as sal ammoniac or lye, that may be used as well. An interesting thing about the voltaic cell is the fact that its electromotive force does not depend upon its size. Making the cell larger increases the amount of current that we may draw from it, but it will not increase the electromotive force or voltage. Its voltage depends, mainly, upon the chemical action and this, in turn, depends upon the materials of the strips (*electrodes*) and upon the substance used for the electrolyte. In the cell we have described, the electromotive force is about one volt.

There are a number of disadvantages to the voltaic cell we have described. For example, when the hydrogen ions reach the copper electrode and take away electrons from it, these ions become neutral hydrogen atoms. You can see them as bubbles around the positive electrode when the external circuit is completed. Some of these hydrogen bubbles tend to cling to the positive electrode, forming a sheath completely surrounding it. After a short time, the action of the cell ceases, owing to the insulating action of the hydrogen bubbles which prevent any new hydrogen ions from reaching the positive electrode. We call this effect *polarization*.

In 1866, Georges Leclanché, a French scientist, using a carbon rod as a positive electrode, overcome the effect of polarization by placing this rod in a porous cup containing manganese dioxide. The porous cup and its material did not prevent the positive hydrogen ions from reaching the carbon rod. But after these hydrogen ions became hydrogen atoms, they combined chemically with the manganese dioxide and thus could not form the insulating sheath around the rod. The manganese dioxide is called, appropriately enough, a *depolarizer.*

The voltaic cell we have been discussing presents another disadvantage. It is a *wet* cell, that is, the electrolyte is a liquid and can be spilled easily. To overcome this defect, the *dry cell* was created. In this cell the electrolyte is a paste, instead of a liquid, and thus cannot be spilled so readily.

Look at Figure 12-2. A zinc can is used as the negative electrode and as a container for the cell. A carbon rod in the center of the cell forms the positive electrode. The space between the zinc shell and the carbon rod is filled with a paste containing *sal ammoniac* (a compound of ammonia and chlorine) which is used as an electrolyte. In addition to the electrolyte, this paste contains manganese dioxide, which is used as a depolarizer, and some material, such as

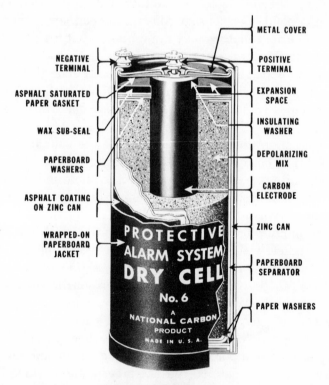

METAL COVER

NEGATIVE TERMINAL

POSITIVE TERMINAL

ASPHALT SATURATED PAPER GASKET

EXPANSION SPACE

WAX SUB-SEAL

INSULATING WASHER

PAPERBOARD WASHERS

DEPOLARIZING MIX

ASPHALT COATING ON ZINC CAN

CARBON ELECTRODE

WRAPPED-ON PAPERBOARD JACKET

ZINC CAN

PROTECTIVE ALARM SYSTEM DRY CELL No. 6 A NATIONAL CARBON PRODUCT MADE IN U. S. A.

PAPERBOARD SEPARATOR

PAPER WASHERS

National Carbon Co., Inc.

Fig. 12-2. Cross-sectional view of dry cell.

sawdust, which is used as a filler. The top is sealed with a cap made of metal, pitch, or sealing wax to prevent the paste from coming out. Immediately below this cap is an air space in which the gases formed by the cell may collect. The entire cell is enclosed in a cardboard case.

Binding posts are attached to the zinc can and to the carbon rod to facilitate connecting the dry cell to an external circuit. The action of this cell is similar to that of the ordinary voltaic cell and it is called a "dry" cell only because the electrolyte is a paste, rather than a liquid. As a matter of fact, should the water of this paste finally evaporate, the cell would cease to function.

The electromotive force that this type of dry cell can produce is approximately 1.5 volts. This voltage remains fairly constant as long as the cell is in good operating condition, regardless of the cell's size. How much current can be drawn from such a cell? The amount of current will depend upon two factors—the resistance of the external circuit and the internal resistance of the cell itself. The greater the external resistance, the less the current drawn from the cell.

If the resistance of the external circuit is reduced to practically zero (we call this a *short circuit*), the amount of current drawn then would be limited by the internal resistance of the cell. (You realize, of course, that the movement of ions within the cell encounters a certain amount of resistance.) This internal resistance depends upon the material and structure of the cell. In general, the larger the size of the cell, the lower the internal resistance, and hence the greater the amount of current that can be drawn. Also, the larger cell has more active material and thus is able to function for a longer period of time than a smaller cell.

Dry cells generally are used for fairly light, intermittent work such as operating door bells or flashlights. If a heavy drain is placed on the cell for an appreciable length of time, its life may be shortened or it may even be ruined. Hydrogen may be formed faster than the depolarizer can consume it and the cell may cease functioning due to polarization. Or else the air space may be too small to contain the excessive amount of gas. As a result, the sides of the cell may split under the pressure, permitting the electrolyte to leak out.

Even when not in use a dry cell has a shelf life of only about one year. Commercial zinc used in these cells contains a small percentage of impurities. When placed in contact with the electrolyte, these impurities form minute cells with the zinc. This is called *local action* and it results in the gradual eating away of the zinc. After about a year's time, holes, through which the electrolyte may leak, are formed in the zinc shell.

In recent years the dry cell has been improved considerably. One such improvement is the so-called *mercury cell*. Here the negative electrode is made of an amalgam of powdered zinc and mercury pressed into shape. The depolarizer is composed of mercuric oxide and graphite powder. The zinc-mercury amalgam cuts down local action and the graphite helps reduce the internal resistance of the cell. Such cells have a considerably longer life than the ordinary dry cell.

In practice, we generally connect two or more cells together to form a *battery*. There are several ways in which these cells may be connected. We may connect them in *series*, that is, with the positive terminal of one to the negative terminal of the other. In Figure 12-3A, a battery of three cells connected in series is illustrated. The electromotive force of each cell is added to that of the others and

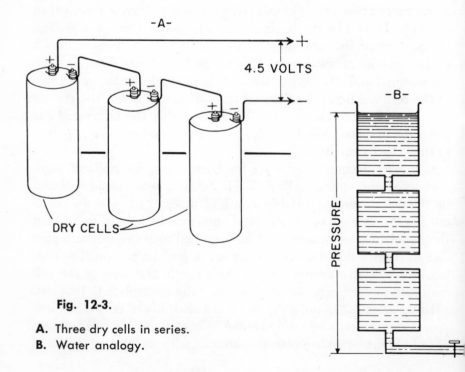

Fig. 12-3.

A. Three dry cells in series.
B. Water analogy.

thus the total electromotive force of this battery is 4.5 volts (3 × 1.5).

You can understand cells in series from the analogy illustrated in Figure 12-3B. Three water tanks of equal size are mounted one above the other and connected together. Each tank adds its pressure to the whole and the total pressure produced by this system is three times that produced by a single tank.

But note that, when the three cells are connected in series, so are their internal resistances. Thus, the internal resistance of the battery is three times that of a single cell. Since both the electromotive force and internal resistance are tripled, the current that can be drawn from this battery is the same as that which a single cell is capable of producing.

The three cells may be joined to form a battery by connecting them in *parallel* (see Figure 12-4A). In this method of connection, all the positive terminals are joined together, and in like manner all the negative terminals. A water analogy is shown in Figure 12-4B.

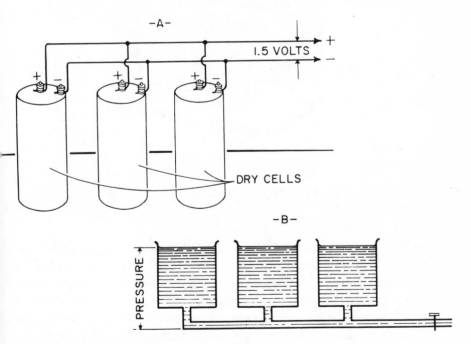

Fig. 12-4. A. Three dry cells in parallel.
B. Water analogy.

Note that the pressure of the system is equal to that of a single tank. The electromotive force of the battery similarly is equal to that of a single cell—1.5 volts.

But note that the internal resistances of all three cells are connected in parallel. Consequently, the total internal resistance of the battery is equal to one-third the internal resistance of a single cell. Since the electromotive force of the battery is equal to that of a single cell and since its internal resistance is only one-third that of a single cell, the current that may be drawn from the battery is three times the current that a single cell may produce.

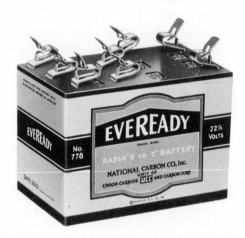

National Carbon Co., Inc.

Fig. 12-5. Dry cell battery of 22½ volts.

Where a large current is desired, the cells are connected in parallel. Where a large voltage is wanted, they are connected in series. Sometimes a number of cells are connected in series to produce a greater voltage, and a number of blocks of such series-connected cells are joined in parallel to produce a higher current. We call such a connection a *series-parallel battery*. In radio work, we often use batteries of 22.5, 45, and 67.5 volts, which are made up of 15, 30, and 45 cells respectively, connected in series.

Cells such as the voltaic cell and the dry cell are called *primary cells* and are a source of direct current. When used in an electrical diagram, the symbol for a cell is ⊣ ⊢ , the small vertical line indicating the negative terminal, and the long vertical line the positive terminal. The symbol for a battery of cells connected in a series is ⊣|ı|ı⊢ .

2. STORAGE CELL

a. The lead-acid cell

In the primary cell chemical energy is converted to electrical energy. In 1859, Gaston Planté, a French scientist, discovered he could convert electrical energy into chemical energy which would be stored in a cell. Then, by connecting this cell to an external circuit, he was able to reconvert the chemical energy to electrical energy as he needed it. In a sense, he was storing electrical energy. Naturally enough, such a cell is called a *storage cell.*

In the Planté storage cell, two lead plates are placed in an electrolyte of sulfuric acid and water. When electrical energy is "pumped" into this cell by connecting the plates to a source of direct current (we call this process *charging*), chemical action converts the surface of one of these lead plates to a negative electrode of spongy lead. The surface of the other is converted to a positive electrode of lead peroxide. The cell then is *charged* and ready to deliver electric current on demand.

When we draw current from the cell (this process is called *discharging*), a chemical action takes place within it which ends with both electrodes becoming converted to lead sulfate. The cell then is *discharged* and no more current may be drawn from it. The cell may be charged again, and the electrodes will be transformed to spongy lead and lead peroxide once more.

In 1881 another French scientist, C. A. Faure, improved the Planté cell by constructing the plates in the form of open metallic grids instead of solid lead sheets. The openings in the grids are filled with the active materials. Thus the spaces of the positive grid are packed with a paste of dark-brown lead peroxide. The spaces of the negative grid are packed with gray spongy lead. (See Figure

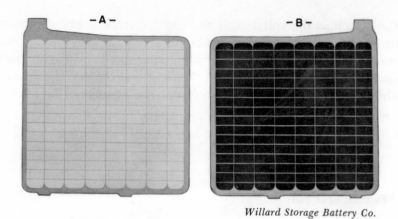

Willard Storage Battery Co.

Fig. 12-6. A. Negative plate of lead-acid storage cell.
B. Positive plate.

12-6.) The advantage of grid-type electrodes is that they are easier to manufacture than those started from solid lead plates.

This kind of storage cell is known as the *lead-acid* type. Its electromotive force when fully charged generally is considered to be two volts, though it is slightly higher when measured at *open circuit*, that is, when it is not connected to an external circuit. When a cell is connected into a circuit and current flows through it, its voltage becomes somewhat lower than its open-circuit voltage because of the *IR* drop due to the cell's internal resistance.

As is true of primary cells, the voltage of the storage cell does not depend upon the size of its plates. However, the larger the plates, the more chemical energy that can be stored in the cell and, hence, the greater the current that can be drawn from it. To increase the effective size of the plates and yet not make the cell too bulky, alternate positive and negative plates are sandwiched together with insulators (called *separators*) of wood, rubber, or other materials between plates (Figure 12-7). The negative plates are connected together, as are the positive plates, producing the effect of a single cell with very large plates. Commercial cells may contain 13, 15, 17, or more, plates. Generally, there is one more negative plate than there are positives. Hence the two outside plates of the stack are negatives.

The capacity of a storage cell is rated in *ampere-hours*. This means that a 120 ampere-hour cell, for example, can deliver, theoretically,

General Motors Corp.

Fig. 12-7. How plates and separators are meshed.

one ampere of current for 120 hours, 120 amperes for one hour, or any other combination of amperes and hours that, when multiplied together, gives 120. However, if the cell is discharged slowly, it may show a capacity greater than the rated 120 ampere-hours. On the other hand, if the cell is discharged rapidly, its capacity is reduced.

The Society of Automotive Engineers has set up a number of methods for determining the capacity of a cell. One of these is the *20-hour rating.* The fully-charged cell is brought to a temperature of 80°F. It is discharged at a rate that, at the end of 20 hours, will drop the voltage of the cell from 2 to 1.75 volts. This rate, multiplied by 20, is the ampere-hour rating of the cell. Suppose the discharge rate is 6 amperes. Then 6×20 is equal to 120 ampere-hours, which is the rating for the cell.

Storage cells generally are connected in batteries, the chief use for which is in the automobile. Such batteries usually are of the 6-volt and 12-volt types. Thus, three similar cells are connected in series to form the 6-volt type and six cells are series-connected for the 12-volt type.

The battery container usually is made of hard rubber or some other material that is able to withstand mechanical shock, extremes of heat and cold, and is resistant to the action of the acid electrolyte. A separate compartment is provided for each cell and each compartment has space at its bottom for any sediment that may drop from the plates. Each set of plates of the cells has a heavy lead terminal post and these posts are connected in series (that is, the positive terminal of one cell to the negative terminal of its adjacent cell) by means of heavy lead connectors. (See Figure 12-8.)

Each cell compartment has a cover, usually of molded hard rubber. Openings are provided in these covers for the two terminal posts and for a vent. Each vent has a plug so constructed that the electrolyte cannot splash out, although gases may escape from the cell. The joints between covers and containers are sealed with an acid-resistant compound.

Discharging the battery. Let us see what happens as we draw current from a fully-charged battery. The positive plates consist of grids containing lead peroxide. The negative plates contain spongy lead. The electrolyte is a solution of sulfuric acid and water.

If we compare concentrated sulfuric acid with an equal volume of water, we find the acid is 1.834 times as heavy as the water. We say that the *specific gravity* of the concentrated sulfuric acid is 1.834. As we add water to the sulfuric acid, the specific gravity of the solu-

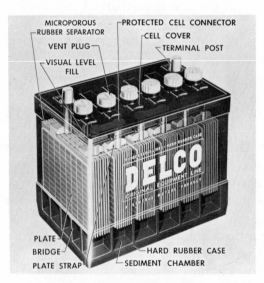

General Motors Corp.

Fig. 12-8. "Phantom" view of the structure of lead-acid storage battery with six cells.

tion goes down. The specific gravity of the electrolyte of a fully charged storage battery should be approximately 1.280.

We may measure the specific gravity of a liquid quickly by means of a *hydrometer* (Figure 12-9). This consists of a glass barrel and bulb syringe for sucking up a sample of the liquid. Inside the barrel is a sealed glass float that is weighted at one end to make it float upright. The depth to which the float sinks in the liquid indicates the relative weight of the liquid compared to water and thus gives us a measure of the specific gravity of the liquid. If the float sinks low in the liquid (Figure 12-10A), the specific gravity is low. If it floats high (Figure 12-10B), the specific gravity is high. A paper scale inside the float indicates the specific gravity of the solution if we note the mark that is level with the surface of the liquid.

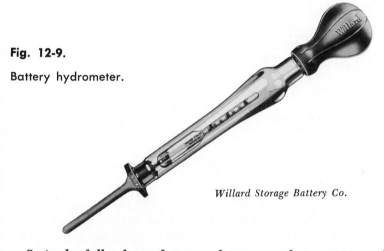

Fig. 12-9.

Battery hydrometer.

Willard Storage Battery Co.

So in the fully-charged storage battery we have positive plates of lead peroxide and negative plates of spongy lead immersed in an electrolyte of sulfuric acid and water. In this solution some of the sulfuric acid ionizes into positive hydrogen ions and negative sulfate ions. As the battery is discharged by connecting it to an external circuit, the following chemical reaction takes place:

Positive plate. Lead peroxide + sulfuric acid + hydrogen ions ⟶

lead sulfate + water.

Negative plate. Lead + sulfate ions ⟶ lead sulfate.

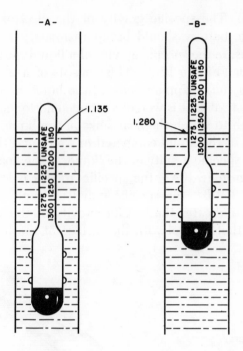

Fig. 12-10.   A. Low float means low specific gravity.

B. High float means high specific gravity.

You see that on discharge both plates tend to turn to lead sulfate. The more current we draw from the battery, the more lead sulfate is formed. When enough lead sulfate forms on the plates, the chemical action ceases and the battery goes dead. It is completely discharged.

Note, too, that water is produced on discharge. The more we discharge the battery, the more water is formed and the lower the specific gravity of the electrolyte becomes. By means of a hydrometer we can measure the specific gravity of the electrolyte and thus determine how much charge is left in the battery. The following table may be used:

1.280 specific gravity.............. 100% charged
1.250 specific gravity.............. 75% charged
1.220 specific gravity.............. 50% charged
1.190 specific gravity.............. 25% charged
1.160 specific gravity.............. Very little useful capacity left
1.130 specific gravity.............. Discharged

When the specific gravity of the electrolyte is measured, its temperature must be taken into account. The volume of the electrolyte expands when it is heated and contracts when it is cooled. When expanded, owing to heat, it will not raise the hydrometer float as high and this will cause the reading to be too low. When it is cooled, the volume shrinks and causes the float to rise higher and thus read too high.

At ordinary temperatures it usually is not necessary to correct a hydrometer for the temperature effect, but at extremes of temperature the correction may be important. The correction chart shown in Figure 12-11 may be employed. If 80°F is taken as normal, the temperature correction amounts to about 0.004 specific gravity for each 10°F change in temperature. Thus, if the temperature of the electrolyte is 60°F, we must subtract 0.008 from the hydrometer reading. If the temperature is 100°F, we must add 0.008 to the reading.

Now, how much current can we draw from a battery? As much as the battery can furnish without dangerous overheating. For ex-

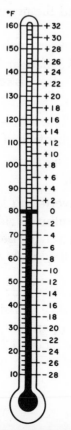

Fig. 12-11.

Temperature correction of specific gravity.

ample, the starting motor of an automobile may require more than 300 amperes! Because of its low internal resistance, the lead-acid storage battery can furnish such currents. But only for a few seconds at a time. Then it must be recharged.

If the battery is discharged excessively, too much lead sulfate is formed, clogging the pores of the plates and making recharging increasingly difficult. Also, the excess lead sulfate in the plates raises the internal resistance of the cell, thus lowering its voltage. The specific gravity of the electrolyte, too, is reduced by the water that is formed, and this lowers the cell's voltage even more. A lead-acid storage cell must not be discharged beyond the point where its voltage falls to 1.75 volts.

Charging the battery. The storage battery is a direct-current device. When it runs down and must be recharged, the recharging current must come from a direct-current source, such as a d-c generator. If only alternating current is available, it must be rectified to a direct current before being applied to the battery. During the charging period the positive terminal of the source must be connected to the positive post of the battery and the negative terminal of the source to the negative post.

You will recall that as the battery discharges, both the positive and negative electrodes tend to turn to lead sulfate and the specific gravity of the electrolyte is lowered. As the battery is recharged, the following chemical reaction takes place:

Positive plate. Lead sulfate + water + sulfate ions $\longrightarrow$
lead peroxide + sulfuric acid.

Negative plate. Lead sulfate + hydrogen ions $\longrightarrow$
lead + sulfuric acid.

Note that the positive electrode is reconverted to lead peroxide and the negative electrode to lead. Because sulfuric acid is produced on charging, the specific gravity of the electrolyte rises. When this specific gravity reaches its maximum and will go no higher, the battery is fully charged.

At what rate can the storage battery be recharged? At as high a rate as the battery can take without excessive "gassing" or heat. When the battery is being recharged, only a portion of the current goes to re-forming the electrodes. The rest acts to break up the water of the electrolyte into hydrogen and oxygen gases. This is called *electrolysis*. During recharge a certain amount of "gassing" is normal. But when the charging rate becomes too high, the "gassing" becomes excessive. The vigorous bubbling action loosens the active material of the grids (especially at the positive plates). The loose particles fall to the space at the bottom of the compartments. If enough sediment collects there, it may short-circuit the plates of the cells, making the battery inoperative.

Too great a charging rate may produce excessive heat. This will cause plates to buckle and a short-circuit may occur. Also, the water of the electrolyte will be dissipated by electrolysis and evaporation, raising the concentration of the sulfuric acid left behind. The strong acid then may char the separators, especially if they are made of wood. The temperature of the electrolyte should not be permitted to rise above 110°F.

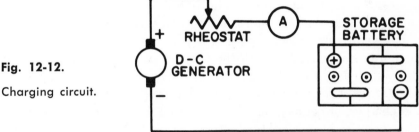

Fig. 12-12.

Charging circuit.

There are a number of methods for charging a storage battery. (See Figure 12-12.) A d-c generator is connected in series with a rheostat, ammeter, and the battery to be charged. Note that the positive brush of the generator goes to the positive post of the battery and the negative brush is connected to the negative post. The generator and battery are in opposition. Thus, if current is to be fed to the battery, the voltage of the generator must be high enough to overcome the opposing electromotive force of the battery, its internal resistance, and the resistance of the rheostat and ammeter.

A rule-of-thumb method for determining the rate of charge is to allow 1 ampere for every positive plate of a single cell. Thus, if the cell contains 13 plates, six of them will be positives. The rheostat is adjusted until the ammeter shows 6 amperes flowing into the battery.

When the battery is in its most discharged state, most of the charging current will go to re-form the plates and very little "gassing" will occur. But as the battery acquires a charge, the "gassing" increases. The rate of charge then must be reduced by introducing more resistance into the circuit by means of the rheostat. When the "gassing" becomes quite heavy and cannot be reduced, and the specific gravity of the electrolyte shows no further increase, the battery is fully charged.

When the battery is being charged, the vents must be open so that the gases may be able to escape. Otherwise, the case may be cracked or the battery otherwise damaged. The mixture of hydrogen and oxygen gases is explosive and care must be taken not to ignite it.

Another method for charging the battery is to start with a very high rate of charge for a short time and taper off to a small finishing charge. This will not damage the battery as long as "gassing" and heat are not excessive. Chargers of this type often have built-in devices, such as fans, to cool the battery. The advantage of this method is that the charging time is greatly reduced.

If several batteries are being charged at once, they may be connected in series, that is, with the positive post of one connected to the negative post of its neighbor. This leaves one positive and one negative post for connection to the charging circuit. The voltage of the charger, of course, must be high enough to overcome the back electromotive force of all the batteries in series. When a low-voltage, high-current charger is used, the batteries are connected in parallel, that is, with all the positive posts connected together and all the negative posts so connected. The positive terminal of the charging circuit connects to the positive posts of the batteries and the negative terminal connects to the negative posts.

After charging is completed, water should be added to compensate for that lost by "gassing" and evaporation. The level of the electrolyte should be about one-half inch above the tops of the plates. If water is not added, the excessive concentration of sulfuric acid may char the separators, or the battery may be otherwise damaged. Only distilled water or pure water that is free of minerals or sediment should be used. Otherwise, a coating may be deposited on the plates, ruining the battery.

b. The Edison storage cell

There are several different kinds of storage cells. One is the *lead-*

acid cell employed in most storage batteries. Another is the *Edison cell* invented by Thomas A. Edison around 1908.

In the Edison cell the positive plate consists of a number of perforated steel tubes welded together. Each tube is filled with nickel peroxide. The negative plate is constructed of many small, perforated steel pockets. Each pocket is filled with pure powdered iron. (See Figure 12-13.) As in the lead-acid cell, alternate positive and negative plates, separated by rubber insulators, are stacked together. All the positive plates are connected together, as are all the negative plates. The electrolyte is a solution of potassium hydroxide in water. The perforations in the tubes and pockets of the plates are to permit the electrolyte to get at the active ingredients.

The assembled plates are housed in a nickel-plated steel container. A steel container is used because there is no acid to attack it. Indeed, the potassium hydroxide of the electrolyte helps protect the container from corrosion. The positive and negative posts extend from the top of the container through insulated bushings. A vent is provided through which gases may escape and through which dis-

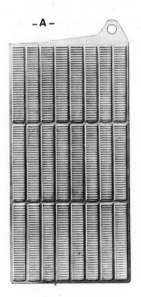

Thomas A. Edison, Inc.

Fig. 12-13. A. Negative plate of Edison storage cell.
B. Positive plate.

tilled water may be added as needed. No sediment space is required at the bottom of the container because none of the active material can flake off the plates.

The chemical action that takes place in the cell is somewhat complicated. In brief, as the cell is discharged, the nickel peroxide of the positive plate is changed to nickel oxide and the iron of the negative plate is converted to iron oxide. When the cell is charged, the nickel oxide is reconverted to nickel peroxide, and the iron oxide to iron. The electrolyte undergoes no change. We may illustrate the chemical process as follows:

Cell Charged

Nickel Peroxide + Iron + Potassium Hydroxide + Water $\rightleftarrows$

Cell Discharged

Nickel Oxide + Iron Oxide + Potassium Hydroxide + Water

(The arrows $\rightleftarrows$ indicate that the chemical action is reversible.)

The Edison cell produces an electromotive force of approximately 1.2 volts when fully charged and falls to 0.9 volts when discharged. It has a higher internal resistance than the lead-acid cell and, hence, cannot furnish as high a current. Because of this, the Edison battery is not used to operate the starting motor of the automobile. Because of its lower voltage, five cells are connected in series to form a 6-volt battery.

Charging an Edison battery is similar to the charging of a lead-acid type, except that an Edison battery can stand an overcharge without damage, provided that there is no frothing and that the temperature of the electrolyte does not rise above 115°F. For ordinary purposes, it is best to charge the Edison cell at its *normal* rate which is about one-fifth of its rated capacity. Thus, if the battery is rated at 150 ampere-hours, then its normal charging rate will be about 30 amperes.

Since the electrolyte undergoes very little change in its specific gravity, a hydrometer is not suited for checking the battery for charge. Instead, a voltmeter may be employed to determine whether the cells are up to their rated voltages.

c. Care and use of the storage battery

The storage battery should be kept clean and dry, and all corrosion must be removed. Water and dirt on the top of the battery

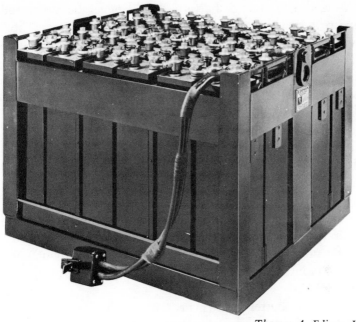

Thomas A. Edison, Inc.

Fig. 12-14. Thirty-cell Edison storage battery.

may cause leakage which will slowly drain the battery. When the battery is being charged, the gas bubbles carry with them a fine spray of acid which is deposited on the terminals and other nearby objects, causing corrosion. During the charging period the vents should be kept open to permit the escape of gases. Be sure to keep an open flame away from these explosive gases.

Be sure that the electrolyte always is about one-half inch above the tops of the plates. If the electrolyte falls too low, it generally is because water has evaporated or has been "gassed" out. This results in a too-high concentration of the acid and the separators may be damaged as a result. Also, the tops of the plates may be changed to a crystalline type of lead sulfate that defies recharging and causes the active materials to fall out of the grids.

If the electrolyte falls too low, add distilled water or pure water that is free from metallic salts. Unless the electrolyte has been spilled, sulfuric acid (for the lead-acid battery) or potassium hydroxide (for the Edison battery) should never be added.

The lead-acid storage battery should never be permitted to remain in a low-charge state for any length of time. The specific gravity of the electrolyte should not be permitted to go below about 1.225 (for standard electrolytes). If it remains in this low-charge state, crystalline lead sulfate will form. Since this lead sulfate occupies a larger volume than the material from which it is formed, the plates may buckle, the separators may be damaged, and active material may be dislodged from the grids. Besides, if enough of this lead sulfate forms on the plates, the battery cannot be recharged. If the battery is to remain idle for an extended period, it will slowly discharge itself and, therefore, it must be recharged from time to time.

Another danger to low-charge batteries is that of freezing at low temperatures. Whereas the electrolyte of a fully-charged battery (specific gravity of about 1.280) will freeze at about $-90°F$, the freezing point of an electrolyte with a specific gravity of 1.150 is about $+5°F$.

The Edison battery, however, will not be damaged if permitted to stand in a low-charge state. Besides, its electrolyte undergoes very little change, regardless of the state of the battery, and its freezing point is well below any temperature likely to be encountered.

Too-high temperatures should be avoided. The temperature of the electrolyte should never be permitted to rise above $110°F$ (for the lead-acid battery) or above $115°F$ (for the Edison battery). Excessive temperatures generally are produced by charging at too high a rate. Plates may be buckled, separators damaged, and active materials dislodged from the plates. In tropical climates it is customary to employ an electrolyte in the lead-acid battery that has a specific gravity of about 1.210 and to charge the battery at a rate lower than normal.

Both the lead-acid and Edison batteries may be discharged at as high a rate as the battery can deliver. But in the lead-acid type the overdischarge may be maintained only for a very short time and the battery must be recharged immediately. Otherwise, the excess lead sulfate may clog the pores of the plates, cause them to buckle, or otherwise damage them.

Too high a charging rate (that is, too many amperes) is to be avoided. This is not serious for the Edison battery, provided the heat does not become excessive. But in the lead-acid type serious damage may result from the excessive heat and "gassing." Over-charging (that is, continuing to charge the battery after it has re-ceived all the charge it can hold) should also be avoided. Plates may be damaged and the separators may be charred by the over-concentration of acid. The Edison battery, however, is not damaged by an overcharge.

The lead-acid storage battery has a number of advantages over the Edison type. It has a greater voltage per cell so that only three cells are required for a 6-volt battery, whereas a similar Edison bat-tery must have five cells. In addition, the internal resistance of the lead-acid cell is lower than that of the Edison cell. This means that the lead-acid battery can deliver a higher current on demand.

The voltages of all batteries drop in cold weather. But the voltage of the Edison cell drops more than that of the lead-acid cell. Be-cause of this, the lead-acid battery is better suited for cold-weather operation. Another advantage is that the initial cost of the lead-acid battery is less than that of an equivalent Edison type.

The higher initial cost of the Edison battery, however, is some-what offset by the fact that this type of battery is much easier to maintain. It can stand idle for long periods without damage, regard-less of its charge. It can be overcharged or undercharged without harm. Its life is much longer than that of the lead-acid type.

The Edison battery is much more rugged than the lead-acid type and is lighter in weight than an equivalent lead-acid battery. It can-not produce acid fumes that corrode nearby objects. It can with-stand high temperatures better than the lead-acid type and cannot freeze in cold weather. The lead-acid battery will not freeze only if it is at least three-quarters charged.

Remember that the storage battery does not store electricity. It converts electrical energy to chemical energy which is stored in its cells. Upon demand, it reconverts its chemical energy to electrical energy. Thus the battery is useful wherever electricity is generated for future use. In general, the storage battery may be employed wherever a low-voltage, high-current, direct-current source is re-quired.

Its chief use is in the automobile to provide current for starting, ignition, lights, radio, heater, and so forth, when the engine is stopped. When the engine is running it operates a direct-current generator that takes over the duties of the battery. In addition, the generator charges up the battery so that it will be ready when needed. Lead-acid batteries are used here because of the high starting current they can deliver.

Storage batteries are used to furnish power to electric motors that operate electric trucks and other types of vehicles, such as mine locomotives and submarines. When the submarine is submerged it cannot use engines that consume the air. Hence it runs on electric motors operated by storage batteries. On the surface, however, the submarine is run by diesel engines. These engines also operate a d-c generator that recharges the batteries. (Atomic-powered submarines do not use batteries for motive power since the reactor that furnishes the heat for the turbines does not exhaust the air.)

Storage batteries are used for lighting purposes in remote rural areas where there are no power lines. The batteries are kept in charge by means of a d-c generator usually driven by a gasoline engine. In d-c areas, storage batteries are used to "iron out" fluctuations in the power lines. Batteries, whose voltages are equal to that of the line, are connected with their positive terminals to the positive side of the line and their negative terminals to the negative side. This is called "floating." So long as the voltage of the line is maintained, nothing happens. But if the line voltage drops, the batteries discharge into the line, bringing its voltage back to normal. When, as a result of discharge, the battery voltage falls, the line current recharges it. Storage batteries are also used for standby service if power lines fail.

Storage batteries, especially the Edison type, are used where a steady, reliable d-c source is required, as in telephone, alarm, and railway-signalling systems. Batteries are used, too, where an extremely steady d-c source is needed, as for sound recording.

Where low weight and high currents are essential, as in the automobile storage battery, thin Faure-type plates are employed. Many plates can be sandwiched into a small space and practically the entire plate consists of active material. However, such plates wear out rapidly. The normal life of an automobile battery is under two years.

Where the batteries are stationary and the maximum-current requirements are not so great, Planté-type plates, formed from solid lead sheets, may be employed. Such plates, though heavier, last considerably longer than Faure-type plates. Sometimes a compromise is made. Deterioration is greater at the positive plate. Accordingly, the battery may employ Planté positive plates and Faure negative plates.

A relatively recent addition to the storage-battery field is the *nickel-cadmium storage battery*. In appearance it resembles the Edison battery. The pockets of its positive plates are filled with nickel hydroxide and those of its negative plates with cadmium oxide. The electrolyte is potassium hydroxide.

This battery has virtually all the advantages of the Edison battery plus the additional advantage of a lower internal resistance. Hence it is able to furnish the higher current required for engine-starting purposes. Its chief disadvantage is its higher initial cost compared to the lead-acid battery.

B. *Piezoelectric type*

We have seen how the generator converts mechanical energy into electrical energy. But this is an indirect action. It requires magnetic energy as an intermediate step between the mechanical energy applied to the generator and the electric current flowing from it.

We have, however, a method for converting mechanical energy directly into electrical energy. Certain crystals, such as Rochelle salts and quartz, have the property of generating an electromotive force when they are compressed. The voltage generated depends upon the degree of compression. This is known as the *piezoelectric effect*.

For example, the Rochelle salt crystal is often employed in *phonograph pickups* to convert the variations in the grooves of a phonograph record into a varying electrical voltage. See Figure 12-15. The phonograph needle is held firmly against the crystal. As it passes through the grooves of the record, the needle is vibrated from side to side by the variations in the grooves. These vibrations are transmitted to the crystal as variations in pressure. As a result, a varying voltage is generated by the crystal, which, when it is amplified and fed into a loudspeaker, produces sound.

The interesting thing about the piezoelectric effect is that it is reversible. A mechanical strain applied to opposite faces of the crystal will generate a voltage—that is, it will set up an electrostatic field between the two faces. Conversely, if a voltage is applied to electrodes on two parallel faces of the crystal, a mechanical strain occurs in the crystal.

Webster Electric Co.

Fig. 12-15. Phonograph pickup using a piezoelectric crystal.

This property of a quartz crystal may be employed to generate the high-frequency alternating currents that are used in radio transmitters. Flat metal electrodes are placed against two opposite parallel faces of the crystal. A voltage placed across these electrodes produces a mechanical strain in the crystal. This strain, in turn, produces an electrostatic field which, in turn, again produces a strain. This process goes on.

You may understand this better, perhaps, if you review the action in a parallel-resonant circuit (see Chapter 9, Subdivision D, 4, b). There an electrostatic field alternately changes to a magnetic field and back again. In the quartz crystal the electrostatic field alternately changes to a mechanical strain and back again.

At the natural frequency of the mechanical vibrations of the crystal, the two actions may be made mutually self-sustaining by bringing in sufficient electrical energy to replenish the energy that is lost as heat during each cycle. The effect of the crystal, then, is to produce an oscillating voltage whose frequency is determined by the natural frequency of the crystal. This frequency, in turn, is determined by the mechanical structure of the crystal. Quartz crystals can be cut whose natural frequency may be thousands, and even millions, of cycles per second. When used in this way, the crystal, with its associated circuit, is known as a *crystal oscillator*.

C. *Thermoelectric type*

At many generating plants, coal or oil is burned under boilers to produce steam to operate steam turbines. These turbines, in turn, rotate generators that produce electricity. Thus heat energy is changed to electrical energy. But it is an indirect process.

In the eighteenth century, Alessandro Volta, the inventor of the voltaic cell, discovered a curious phenomenon. He found that if two dissimilar metals are placed in contact with each other, one of the metals will become slightly negative and the other slightly positive. In other words, a potential difference appears between the two. We call this *contact potential.* He further found that the contact potential is affected by the metals used and the temperature of the junction between them.

Today, we believe that the contact potential is produced because of the free electrons present in the metals. These free electrons move from one metal to the other but, depending upon the metals used, can cross more readily in one direction than in the other. The metal receiving the most free electrons will then become negative. The other, because of its deficiency of electrons, becomes positive.

In 1822, Thomas J. Seebeck, a German physicist, taking a tip from Volta's observations about the effect of temperature on contact potential, developed the *thermocouple.* This consists of two dissimilar metal strips, joined at one end. When the joined ends are heated, a small direct voltage appears between the cool unjoined ends of the strips. The magnitude of this voltage depends directly upon the difference in temperature between the heated and cool ends of the thermocouple. The use of the thermocouple for electrical and temperature measurement has been discussed in Chapter 10, Subdivision B, 2.

A number of thermocouples may be joined to produce a *thermopile,* which is an extremely sensitive detector of heat rays. (See Figure 12-16.) As many as several hundred thermocouples may be joined in series (only three sets are shown here) and encased in a container that is open at one side. One set of junctions is kept cool by placing it at the back of the container. The other set of junctions is exposed to heat rays entering through the opening. A horn,

Fig. 12-16.

Thermopile.

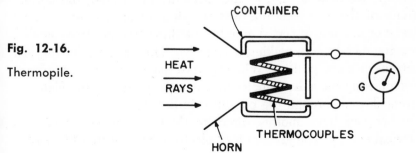

mounted at the open side, acts as a sort of funnel to catch more of the heat rays and thus increase the voltage generated across the open ends of the thermopile. A sensitive galvanometer is used to measure this voltage.

In 1883, Thomas A. Edison, while experimenting with his incandescent lamp, noticed a peculiar effect. His lamp consisted of a filament within a glass bulb from which all the air had been removed. When an electric current was passed through this filament, the resistance it encountered caused the filament to glow, producing light.

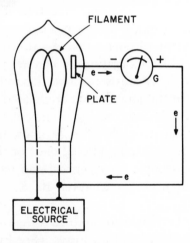

FILAMENT

PLATE

e →

G

+ —

e ↓

← e

ELECTRICAL SOURCE

Fig. 12-17.

Circuit used by Edison.

In this particular lamp, Edison had sealed in a metal plate. (See Figure 12-17.) When he connected a sensitive galvanometer between the plate and one side of the filament, the instrument showed that a small current was flowing through it from the plate to the filament. Edison was unable to explain the presence of this current.

Today, we believe that, as the filament was heated, the normal activity of the free electrons was speeded up until some of them were shot out into space. A number of these free electrons landed upon the metal plate, making it negative. The filament, having lost electrons, became positive. When the external circuit was completed by connecting the galvanometer between the plate and the filament, current flowed through the circuit as indicated.

So here we have another direct method for converting heat to electrical energy. The giving off of electrons by a heated filament is called *thermionic emission*. Most of the electron tubes used in radio, television, and similar devices operate on this principle. We will discuss this matter further later in the book.

D. *Photoelectric type*

Electrical energy is transformed into light energy in the electric lamp. Can light energy be changed back to electrical energy? The first clue came in 1887 when Heinrich Hertz, the German scientist who is known as the "father of radio," discovered that, for a given electromotive force, an electric spark will jump across a larger gap if this gap is illuminated by ultraviolet light than if the gap is left in the dark.

The second clue came about a year later when Wilhelm Hallwachs, another German scientist, found that ultraviolet light falling upon a negatively-charged metal plate caused it to lose its charge. If the plate was charged positively, there was no apparent change. The final clue came about ten years later when Joseph J. Thomson, the famous English scientist, discovered that ultraviolet light falling upon a metallic surface caused it to emit electrons.

Here was the reason for the behavior of Hertz's spark gap. The presence of the emitted electrons (from the metal balls between which the spark jumped) reduced the effective resistance of the gap and thus the spark was able to jump across it more easily. Also, if a negatively-charged plate emitted electrons, it lost its negative charge. If, on the other hand, the plate was charged positively, the loss of electrons would merely increase the charge.

The emission of electrons under the impact of light energy is called *photoelectric emission*. The more intense the light, the more electrons are emitted by the exposed metal. Although most metals will emit electrons when their surfaces are exposed to ultraviolet light, two other German scientists, Julius Elster and Hans Friedrich Geitel, discovered that some metals, such as sodium, potassium, and certain others, will emit electrons when exposed to ordinary visible light rays and infrared rays as well.

This is the principle of the *phototube* illustrated in Figure 12-18. A half-cylinder of metal (called the *cathode*) is coated on its inner surface with some emissive substance such as potassium or cesium.

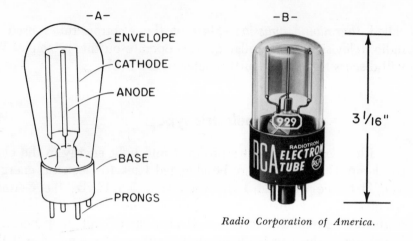

Radio Corporation of America.

Fig. 12-18. A. Phototube, showing its parts.
B. Commercial phototube.

A thin metal rod (called the *anode*) is placed along the central axis of the cathode. Both the cathode and anode are enclosed in a glass envelope from which the air has been evacuated and which is set in a bakelite base. Connections are made to the anode and cathode by means of prongs mounted in the base.

There are two reasons for evacuating the air from the envelope. First, we wish the emitted electrons to have an unimpeded path from the cathode to anode without colliding with air molecules. Second, the emitting surface must be absolutely clean. Air would soon corrode the surface and impair the action of the tube.

To keep out unwanted light, the inner surface of the envelope may be masked, except for a small, circular window facing the inner surface of the cathode through which the light may enter. Or else a shield with a similar window may be placed over the entire tube.

As light strikes the inner surface of the cathode, electrons are emitted; and the greater the intensity of the light, the stronger is the emission. Some of these electrons strike the anode, making it negative. The cathode, having lost electrons, becomes positive. If a microammeter is connected between the two, current will flow through the meter from anode to cathode.

If a battery is placed in the external circuit as illustrated in Figure 12-19, a positive charge will be placed on the anode. This will

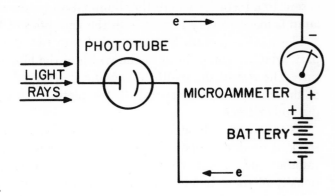

Fig. 12-19.

Phototube circuit.

attract more of the emitted electrons and a larger current will flow through the external circuit. (The symbol for the phototube is ⊸( )⊢ . The half-circle stands for the cathode; the bar is the anode.)

Here, then, is a device that converts light energy directly into electrical energy. The numerous applications of the phototube are as simple as they are ingenious. For example, a beam of light at one side of a room may be focused to strike the cathode of a phototube at the opposite side. Electrons are emitted and the flow of current is amplified until it is large enough to close an electromagnetic relay. If a fire breaks out and smoke fills the room, the light beam is obscured and the current in the phototube circuit drops. This causes the relay to open and an alarm is sounded.

A similar setup may be used as a burglar alarm, except that an invisible ultraviolet ray will be used instead of a visible light ray. When the beam is interrupted by the body of the burglar passing through it, an alarm will be given. Similar circuits may be employed for counting and sorting purposes where the interruption of the light beam operates a counter or some other device. Since the current flowing in the external circuit of the phototube will vary directly as the intensity of the light striking the tube, a meter in that circuit will indicate the intensity of the light.

Perhaps the most ingenious application of the phototube is to reproduce the sound from sound-on-film motion pictures. The original sound enters a microphone, producing an electric current that varies directly with the frequency and loudness of the sound. This current is sent to a recorder where the illumination produced by an electric lamp is made to vary in step with the variations of the current.

The motion picture film is divided into two unequal parts. One part, which occupies most of the width of the film, contains the picture. The rest of the width of the film is reserved for the recording of the sound that corresponds to the picture. This portion is called the *sound track*.

As the varying light from the lamp strikes the unexposed sound track, it produces, upon development, a series of dark bands whose number corresponds to the frequency of the original sound. The density of these bands depends upon the loudness of the sound.

In the projector, a light shines through the pictures on the film, projecting them on the screen. At the same time, another light shines through the sound track of dark bands and falls upon a phototube. Since the film is moving, the light entering the tube will be interrupted at a frequency corresponding to the number of bands on the film, which, as you know, corresponds to the frequency of the original sound. The intensity of the light reaching the tube will vary with the density of the bands, which corresponds to the loudness of the original sound. Consequently, a varying beam of light, whose variations correspond to the frequency and to the loudness of the original sound, enters the phototube. As a result, a varying current will flow in the tube. The current is amplified and passed into a loudspeaker, which reproduces the original sound that entered the microphone.

Fig. 12-20.

Photronic cell.

Weston Instruments Div., Daystrom, Inc.

Another device for converting light to electrical energy is the *photronic cell,* which consists of an iron disk, one side of which is covered with a thin layer of selenium. This layer then is sprayed with a transparent film of a conducting lacquer and contact is made to the lacquer coating by means of a metal ring. The iron disk forms one electrode of the cell and the selenium layer, through the lacquer and metal ring, the other. The whole is enclosed in a case of glass and plastic (see Figure 12-20).

Light, passing through the transparent layers and striking the selenium, causes some of its electrons to break away and move to the iron disk, thus giving the latter a negative charge. The selenium, having lost electrons, acquires a positive charge. The potential difference between the iron and selenium is proportional to the intensity of the light striking the latter.

The cell can be connected directly to a sensitive meter and the intensity of the light can be measured. Such a cell and meter constitute the *exposure meter* used in photography to measure the intensity of illumination to determine the proper exposure for the film. (See Figure 12-21.)

Weston Instruments Div., Daystrom, Inc.

Fig. 12-21. Front and rear views of exposure meter.

E.   *Solar and atomic types*

Where appreciable quantities of electrical power are required, the mechanical generators described in Chapter 11 are generally employed. To a lesser degree, primary and storage cells are used also. The power output of the other devices described in this chapter, on the other hand, is extremely small. Hence these devices are not used as suppliers of power but, rather, for certain applications, examples of which have been given. It well may be, however, that at some future date these devices may be developed to the point where they are able to supply appreciable electrical power.

There are two more types of generators of electromotive force that have been developed recently—the *solar cell* and the *atomic cell*. Although the power output of these cells still is small, the promise of things to come they have given has excited the imagination of all scientists.

Our sun constantly radiates enormous quantities of heat and light energy to the earth. Numerous, and, so far, fairly unsuccessful attempts have been made to harness these energies. The phototube is able to convert the light to electrical energy. But it is able to deliver as power only about 0.5 per cent of the light energy it receives.

The scientists at the Bell Telephone Laboratories have developed a solar cell that is about 20 times as efficient as the phototube. It consists of a thin wafer of silicon to which has been added a minute amount of arsenic. An extremely thin layer of silicon containing a trace of boron is deposited on one surface of the wafer. Leads connected to the wafer and layer complete the cell. (See Figure 12-22.)

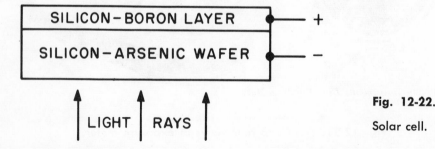

Fig. 12-22.

Solar cell.

The free electrons find it easier to travel from the layer to the wafer. Thus the wafer becomes negative because of the accumulation of free electrons and the layer becomes positive because of their loss. A contact potential, which soon reaches a stable value, is established between them. This contact potential is quite small. But when sunlight strikes the clear surface of the wafer, many more electrons are freed to travel from layer to wafer. The action of the solar cell is somewhat similar to that of the *transistor*, which will be described later in the book.

In practice, a number of cells are placed side by side to form a battery. The whole is enclosed in a transparent plastic case to protect it from damage and corrosion. Such a battery is capable of producing electric power from sunlight at the rate of 90 watts per square yard of illuminated surface.

Fig. 12-23. Hitching solar batteries to telephone system at Americus, Georgia.

Bell Telephone Laboratories.

In a recent successful test the solar battery was used to supply electricity to a telephone system. A battery consisting of 432 individual cells was mounted on a pole and exposed to sunlight. On a bright day it generated 10 watts. Part of the electricity went to the telephone system and the rest was used to charge up a storage battery. This storage battery was a reserve to be used at night or on cloudy days when the sun was obscured.

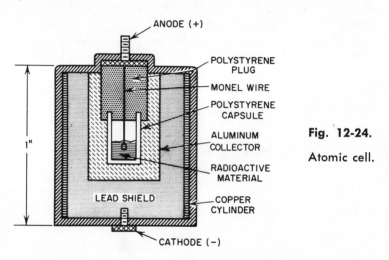

ANODE (+)

POLYSTYRENE PLUG

MONEL WIRE

POLYSTYRENE CAPSULE

ALUMINUM COLLECTOR

RADIOACTIVE MATERIAL

LEAD SHIELD

COPPER CYLINDER

1"

CATHODE (−)

Fig. 12-24.

Atomic cell.

Solar batteries are used, too, to generate electricity to power the various instruments carried by the man-made earth-circling satellites. These satellites contain many solar cells that convert the energy from the sun to electricity.

Atomic energy can be used to generate electricity. In the atomic reactor the tremendous heat produced by the fissioning atoms is employed to convert water to steam. This steam, in turn, drives the steam turbines that cause large generators to rotate, thereby producing great quantities of electrical power.

Where very small quantities of power are desired, *atomic cells,* using different principles, may be employed. For example, in the cell illustrated in Figure 12-24 a small amount of radioactive material is enclosed in a capsule of polystyrene, an insulator. As electrons emitted by the radioactive source penetrate the walls of the capsule, they are absorbed by the aluminum collector surrounding it and flow through the lead shield around the aluminum collector to the cathode (−) terminal.

At the same time, the radioactive source, having lost electrons, acquires a positive charge. This charge is carried to the anode (+) terminal by means of the monel wire. Hence the cathode terminal obtains a negative charge and the anode terminal a positive charge. If an external circuit is connected between these terminals, current will flow.

In another type of atomic cell a small amount of another radioactive material, Polonium 210, is sealed in a small capsule. The polonium is in contact with the "hot" junctions of a number of thermocouples while the "cold" junctions are located outside the container. A temperature difference of about 450°F. thus produced between the hot and cold junctions generates a voltage that causes a current to flow through the device.

Still another type utilizes the radiations from a radioactive source to cause certain chemicals, called *phosphors*, to glow. The light from these phosphors energizes a phototube, thus producing a small electric current.

The current delivered by such cells is quite small. However, since radioactive material is a by-product of the atomic reactor, such materials will become readily available as atomic power is developed. And some of these materials are capable of emitting electrons for thousands, and even millions, of years. No wonder the future of the atomic cell is bright!

QUESTIONS

Wherever possible, diagrams should be used to clarify the answers to these questions. These diagrams need not be elaborate, but they should be drawn neatly with the significant portions clearly labeled.

1. Explain the action of a voltaic cell using electrodes of zinc and copper and hydrochloric acid as an electrolyte.
2. Draw the cross-sectional view of a dry cell, indicating its principal parts. Explain the use of each such part.
3. What determines the voltage of a cell? What determines the maximum current that can be drawn from a cell?
4. Draw the electrical circuit of twelve 1.5-volt dry cells connected in series-parallel to produce a 6-volt battery.
5. Describe the structure of a lead-acid storage cell.

6. Describe the chemical action that takes place in a lead-acid storage battery during *a*) the charging period; *b*) the discharge period.
7. Explain how the hydrometer can be used to indicate the amount of charge in a lead-acid storage battery.
8. How is the capacity of a storage battery rated? Explain the meaning of the rating.
9. How are batteries charged? What precautions should be observed when charging a battery?
10. If a lead-acid storage battery is to stand idle for a long time, what precautions must be taken? Explain.
11. Describe the structure of an Edison storage cell.
12. Describe the chemical action that takes place in an Edison storage battery during *a*) the charging period; *b*) the discharge period.
13. Can a hydrometer be used to indicate the amount of charge in an Edison storage battery? Explain.
14. Explain the advantages of the Edison storage battery over the lead-acid type. Explain its disadvantages.
15. What is meant by the *piezoelectric effect?*
16. Explain the action of a *thermocouple.*
17. What is meant by *photoelectric emission?*
18. Explain the action of the *phototube.*
19. Explain the action of the *photronic cell.*
20. Explain the action of the *solar cell.*
21. Explain the action of the *atomic cell.*

Practical
Applications
of Electricity

13

Applications
Depending Upon
the Thermal Effect

In this and in the following chapters of this section, we shall discuss the application of electric current at home and in industry; applications that make possible our present-day civilization. Obviously, it is impossible to consider in one book all such applications. Instead, we shall choose only the examples that are most frequently encountered and that are representative of an entire class.

To facilitate our discussion, we shall group these applications according to the electrical effects they employ. The effects of electricity, you will recall, are *thermal, luminous, chemical,* and *magnetic.* For some of these applications, more than one effect may be employed. However, for the purpose of grouping, we shall consider the effect that is most pertinent to the particular application. In this chapter we shall consider applications that depend, primarily, upon the heating effect of the electric current.

As you know, a current flowing through a conductor encounters resistance and, as a result, the conductor is heated by the current flow. Thus electrical energy is converted to heat energy. The common unit of electrical energy is the *wattsecond* or *joule* (Chapter 3, Subdivision B, 5). The common unit of heat energy is the *calorie*. The calorie is the amount of heat necessary to raise the temperature of a gram of water 1°C. In 1840 James Joule, an English physicist, found that one wattsecond of electrical energy was equivalent to 0.24 calorie of heat energy.

There is another unit of heat energy frequently used—the *British thermal unit* (abbreviated *Btu*). This unit is the amount of heat required to raise the temperature of one pound of water 1°F. One British thermal unit is equal to 252 calories and is the equivalent of 1,050 wattseconds of electrical energy.

> *Example.* How many calories of heat are produced by a current of 10 amperes flowing through a resistor of 5 ohms for 5 minutes? How many British thermal units?
>
> Heat (in calories) = 0.24 × (Current)² × Resistance × Time
> (in seconds)
>
> = 0.24 × (10)² × 5 × 5 × 60 = 36,000 calories.   *Ans.*
>
> 1 Btu = 252 calories
> $$\frac{36,000}{252} = 142.8 \text{ Btu.} \quad Ans.$$

A. Devices employing heating elements

Although, under certain circumstances, the heating effect of the electric current may be considered an unavoidable evil that wastes power, nevertheless, for some devices, such as the electric stove, flatiron, toaster, waffle iron, heating pad, and many others, it is highly desirable. The basic principle of all these devices is the same. Current is passed through a high-resistance *heating element,* thus producing the required heat.

The heating element must be a conductor that has sufficient resistance so that a reasonable length may be employed to change large amounts of electrical energy to heat energy. At the same time it must have a melting point high enough to withstand the heat produced. Further, it must be able to withstand the oxidizing effect of the air at high temperatures.

Generally, we use an alloy of nickel and chromium, called *ni-chrome,* which has a resistance more than 50 times that of copper of equivalent size. The heating element may be made of either nichrome wire or ribbon wound on some insulating material that is able to withstand the heat. Where a long length of wire is required to produce the necessary resistance, it may be made into a long coil and this coil then is wound on the insulating form. (See Figure 13-1.)

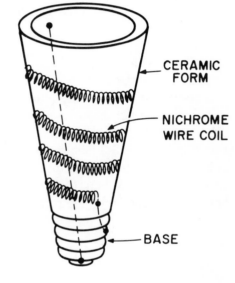

Fig. 13-1.

Heating element of electric room heater.

The heating element illustrated is of a type used in certain kinds of *electric room heaters.* The nichrome coil is wound in a spiral on a ceramic form. The entire heating unit screws into a socket mounted in the center of a metallic parabolic reflector. The reflector is used to concentrate the heat rays and direct them forward.

Another device using a heating element is the *electric soldering iron* illustrated in Figure 13-2. The heating element is wound with nichrome wire on a ceramic spool. It is inserted into a metal tube, or barrel, that is set in a wooden handle. The heat of the element is transferred to a copper tip and the soldering is done with the hot tip. The wires connecting the element to the power line usually are asbestos-covered since the ordinary cotton-and-rubber insulation cannot withstand the heat well.

The *immersion heater* is merely a variation of the soldering iron.

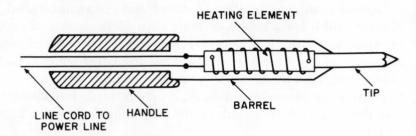

Fig. 13-2. Electric soldering iron.

A similar heating element is completely sealed in a metal tube. The heat from the element makes the tube hot, and when the whole is immersed into a liquid, the liquid is heated.

The *electric flatiron* is another typical household device utilizing the heating effect of the electric current. Its heating element is illustrated in Figure 13-3. Nichrome ribbon is wound on a form made of mica or some other insulating material that is able to withstand the heat produced. When the heating element is connected to the house mains, the nichrome ribbon becomes red-hot, heating the iron.

Fig. 13-3.

Heating element of electric flatiron.

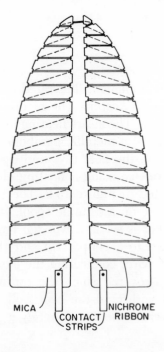

Example. An electric flatiron operating from 120-volt house mains is rated at 720 watts. What is the resistance of the heating element?

$$P \text{ (watts)} = E \text{ (volts)} \times I \text{ (amperes)}$$

$$720 = 120 \times I$$

$$I = \frac{720}{120} = 6 \text{ amperes}$$

$$R \text{ (ohms)} = \frac{E \text{ (volts)}}{I \text{ (amperes)}}$$

$$R = \frac{120}{6} = 20 \text{ ohms.} \quad \textit{Ans.}$$

Some of the more expensive flatirons can be adjusted to produce varying degrees of heat for ironing different types of materials. This is accomplished by means of a *thermostat* that automatically breaks the circuit and shuts off the iron when the proper temperature is reached. If the iron becomes too cool, the thermostat closes the circuit and the iron heats up again.

The thermostat operates on the principle that different metals have different rates of expansion on heating and contraction on cooling. For example, brass expands and contracts more than iron. If a strip of brass is securely fastened on top of a similar strip of iron and the whole heated, the brass strip will expand more than the iron one,

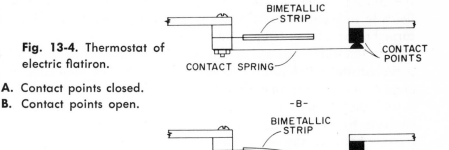

Fig. 13-4. Thermostat of electric flatiron.

A. Contact points closed.
B. Contact points open.

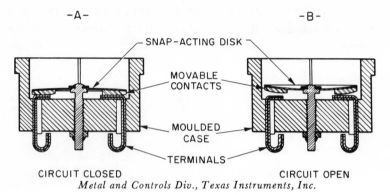

-A-   -B-

SNAP-ACTING DISK

MOVABLE
CONTACTS

MOULDED
CASE

TERMINALS

CIRCUIT CLOSED   CIRCUIT OPEN

Metal and Controls Div., Texas Instruments, Inc.

Fig. 13-5. A. Cross-sectional view of the Klixon switch closed.
B. Klixon switch open.

forcing the bimetallic strip to curve downward. If the bimetallic strip now is cooled, the brass, contracting more than the iron, will cause the strip to straighten.

In the flatiron the bimetallic strip is mounted so that it curves downward when heated. (See Figure 13-4.) When the proper heat has been attained, the strip will have bent sufficiently to separate a set of contact points that are in series with the heating element of the iron. Current ceases flowing through the iron. As the iron cools, the bimetallic strip resumes its horizontal position, the contact points touch once more, and current again flows through the iron. In this way, the temperature is kept fairly constant.

The thermostat may be adjusted by means of a screw that presses down on the bimetallic strip from above. The screw is operated by a knob on the iron. As the screw forces the bimetallic strip closer to the contact spring, less heat is required for the strip to bend sufficiently to separate the contact points. Consequently, the iron is turned off at a lower temperature.

An interesting variation of the thermostat shown in Figure 13-4 is the *Klixon switch* illustrated in Figure 13-5. The bimetallic element consists of a springy disk. Normally, the curvature of this disk is such that the movable contacts fastened to it touch a set of fixed contacts, thus completing the circuit. As the disk is heated, the difference between the expansions of the two metals of which it is composed causes the disk to curve in the opposite direction, thus separating the contacts and opening the circuit.

Because of the springiness of the disk, the action is not gradual. The disk snaps from one curvature to the other when its temperature reaches a certain predetermined level. When the temperature falls to another predetermined level, the disk snaps back to its original curvature.

Such switches frequently are mounted inside the housing of electric motors to prevent overheating. The switch is connected in series with the motor and the power line. Normally, the switch is closed. But should the temperature within the motor housing rise to a dangerous level, the switch opens the line circuit, thus stopping the motor. When the temperature drops to a safe level, the disk snaps back to its original curvature, and the motor may resume its rotation. Some switches contain a reset button that can be used manually to reverse the curvature of the disk from its "off" position to its "on" position.

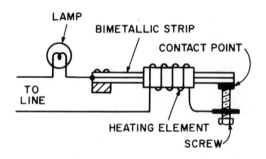

Fig. 13-6.

Electric flasher.

The thermostat can be combined with a heating element to make a *flasher*, a sort of time switch that automatically turns some device, such as an electric lamp, on and off at regular intervals. (See Figure 13-6.) The bimetallic strip is mounted so that it curves upwards when heated. An insulating material is placed over a portion of the strip and over this the nichrome wire is wound to form a heating element.

A contact point is attached to the bottom of the free end of the bimetallic strip and a screw is so mounted that it normally makes electrical contact with this point. When the flasher is placed in the circuit, current flows from the line, through the heating element to the screw, to the contact point, through the bimetallic strip, through the lamp (or any other device that is to be turned alternately on and off), and back to the line. Because the circuit is complete, the lamp lights.

However, the heater element is heated by this flow of current. This causes the bimetallic strip to become warm. After a short period of time, determined by the physical and electrical characteristics of the flasher, the bimetallic strip becomes warm enough to curve upwards. This causes the contact between the contact point

Westinghouse Electric Corp.

Fig. 13-7. Several of many electrical appliances using a heating element.
    A. Electric toaster.
    B. Electric fry pan.
    C. Electric warming pad.

and the screw to be broken. The circuit is opened and the lamp goes out.

Since there now is no current flowing through the heating element, the bimetallic strip starts to cool. When it has cooled sufficiently, the strip straightens, and the contact point touches the screw again. The circuit is completed, current flows, and the lamp lights again. Then the whole cycle is repeated.

The *electric toaster* contains two heating elements somewhat similar to the type used in the flatiron, mounted vertically, with a space between them into which a slice of bread may be inserted. Some toasters also have a thermostat that controls the degree of toasting and a clockwork mechanism that pops the bread out when it has been heated sufficiently. The *electric stove* is equipped with a somewhat similar heating element, generally arranged in the form of a circle or disk upon which a pot may be placed.

B. *Fuses*

Consider the electrical wiring in the walls of your house. Suppose that some electrical device that is connected to this wiring becomes defective and develops a *short circuit* (that is, the resistance of the device drops to approximately zero). Under such circumstances, the current that will flow through the wiring will become very large. The heat produced by this current may make the wires red-hot and the house may be set on fire.

To avoid this catastrophe, we need some device that automatically will break the wiring circuit when too much current flows through it and before the wires can become hot. This device is the *fuse.* It consists of a strip of metal that will melt at a comparatively low temperature, placed in series with the wiring circuit. Generally, the fuse is made of zinc or of an alloy of tin and lead. Because its resistance is higher than that of copper, it heats more quickly than the wires. Because of its low melting point, it will melt before the wires become too hot.

One form of fuse (Figure 13-8A) is made of porcelain or some other insulating material, and resembles the base of an ordinary incandescent lamp. The strip of fuse metal is inside this porcelain cup and connects between the bottom contact and the shell contact.

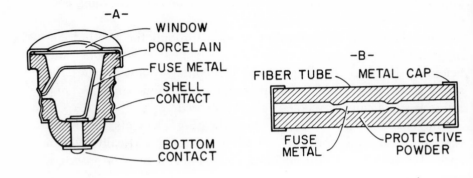

Fig. 13-8. A. Plug fuse.
B. Cartridge fuse.

This fuse, which is called a *plug fuse*, screws into an ordinary lamp receptacle and is connected in series with the house wiring circuit at the point where this circuit connects to the outside mains (generally at the watthour meter). A window of glass or mica prevents the spraying of hot metal when the fuse melts, or "blows," and permits visual observation of its condition.

Another type of fuse is the *cartridge fuse* (Figure 13-8B). The fuse metal is contained in a fiber tube. Contact is made through metal caps at each end of the tube. A special receptacle is required for this fuse. Usually, the tube is filled with a protective powder that helps to break the circuit quickly, preventing current from flowing in an arc between the unmelted portions of the fuse metal when the fuse is blown. As is true of the plug fuse, this type, too, is placed in series with the house wiring circuit.

Fuses are rated by the number of amperes of current they will pass without melting. Thus, for example, a 15-ampere fuse will permit 15 amperes of current to flow through it. Should the current rise a little above 15 amperes, the fuse will carry the overload for a short time without blowing. But if a large overload occurs, the fuse quickly melts before the house wires become hot. It is a safe rule to use fuses rated no higher than 15 amperes for ordinary home use, except in certain special installations where extra-heavy wires are employed.

In addition to protecting house wires, fuses may be used in series with any electrical device to protect it against a too-high current. In each instance the fuse must be rated to blow when the current becomes higher than that which the device being protected can safely carry.

There are times when a momentary overload may blow a fuse needlessly. For example, when a motor is started it draws a heavier current than when it is running steadily. Thus, a certain type of motor operating on a line that is fused for 15 amperes may draw 25 amperes at start. Within a few seconds it reaches the normal running speed and the current drain drops to below 15 amperes. The momentary overload cannot harm the house wires nor the motor. But the fuse may have blown.

To avoid this needless blowing of fuses, a special *slow-blowing fuse* has been developed. It consists of a fuse strip and a *thermal cutout* in series. The thermal cutout is a device similar to the flasher previously described. For the motor under discussion, the fuse strip is rated to blow on currents above 25 amperes. The thermal cutout is designed to open the circuit on currents above 15 amperes.

Should a dangerous overload occur and the current go above 25 amperes, the fuse strip will blow at once, opening the circuit. However, the normal starting current of the motor would not be high enough to melt the strip. As for the cutout, the 25-ampere starting current would be great enough to cause it to open. However, the cutout cannot operate quickly. It takes a certain length of time for its element to heat up. Before it has a chance to do so, the motor will have reached its normal running speed and the current will have dropped to below 15 amperes. Hence the cutout remains closed. Should the running-speed current of the motor rise above 15 amperes because of some defect and this excessive current be maintained for more than a few seconds, the thermal cutout will open the circuit.

Although fuses are essential to open the circuit on overload and thus prevent fires and protect valuable appliances or instruments, there are certain drawbacks. Once blown, the fuse must be replaced. Hence there are the cost and the nuisance of replacement. It is for these reasons that the *circuit breaker* frequently is used instead of a fuse.

There are several different types of circuit breakers. However, we

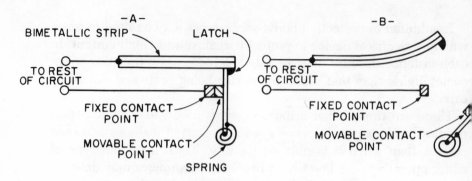

Fig. 13-9. Thermal circuit breaker.

A. Circuit closed.

B. Circuit open.

shall describe here one that operates upon the thermal principle. Look at Figure 13-9. A latch at the end of a bimetallic strip holds fixed and movable contact points in contact with each other, despite a spring that would separate them. Since the circuit breaker is in series with the rest of the circuit, as long as the contact points are together, the circuit is closed.

Should an overload occur, the excess current flowing through the bimetallic strip would heat it beyond normal. As a result, the end of the strip would curve upwards. This would release the latch and the spring would pull the contact points apart, thus breaking the circuit. Once the current stopped flowing, the strip would cool and become straight again. However, the contact points would remain separated. After the cause of the overload had been determined and corrected, the circuit breaker would be relatched (generally by pushing a button that brings the contact points together) and it would be ready for operation once more.

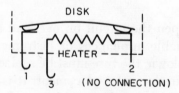

Fig. 13-10.

Thermal circuit breaker using a Klixon disk.

Metal and Controls Div., Texas Instruments, Inc.

There is a variation of the thermal circuit breaker that employs a Klixon bimetallic disk. (See Figure 13-10.) Here, a heater is inserted so that the line current flows through it and the switch, which normally is closed. As the current rises to a dangerous level, the heat produced by the heater becomes great enough to cause the disk to change its curvature, thus opening the switch and stopping the flow of current. The circuit breaker may be reset by means of a manually-operated button that changes the curvature of the disk, thus closing the switch again.

C.   *Infrared lamp*

You are aware that the incandescent-filament lamp (which will be discussed in greater detail later in the book) emits heat as well as light. The heat energy given off by the lamp is known as *infrared*, or *radiant-heat, rays.* These rays are similar to the ordinary visible light rays, except that they are invisible to the human eye.

The heat of the infrared rays is used in a number of industrial processes. For example, when the paint has been sprayed on automobile bodies, these bodies are moved slowly through large chambers, which are lined with banks of infrared lamps. These lamps resemble the ordinary incandescent-filament type, except that they are designed to produce a larger percentage of infrared rays. As a result of the heat produced, the automobile bodies emerge from these chambers with the paint dry and hard, eliminating the need for the

Fig. 13-11. Infrared lamps drying paint on automobile bodies. Floor conveyor lines bring the car through the drying oven in about seven minutes.

General Motors Corp.

long waiting period normally required to dry the paint. In addition to its industrial applications, the infrared lamp often is used at home to supply heat for the relief of pain due to neuritis and arthritis.

D. *Welding*

There are many occasions when we wish to join two pieces of metal together. There are a number of methods for doing this. We may bolt or rivet them together. Certain metals may be soldered together. Another method is to *weld* them by heating the metals at their junction until they melt and fuse together.

Welding may be accomplished by a number of methods. One is through the use of an oxyacetylene blowtorch. The heat is produced by burning a mixture of oxygen and acetylene gases. There also are two types of electrical welding. One type makes use of the resistance of the metal itself to produce the heat required for the weld. The other utilizes the heat of the electric arc.

Resistance welding generally is used for joining metal sheets. The two sheets are placed so that the edge of one overlaps the edge of the other. (See Figure 13-12A.) Two heavy copper electrodes are placed firmly at either side of the sheets at the point where the joint is to be made. An extremely heavy current flows between the electrodes and, as a result, the higher resistance of the sheet metal pro-

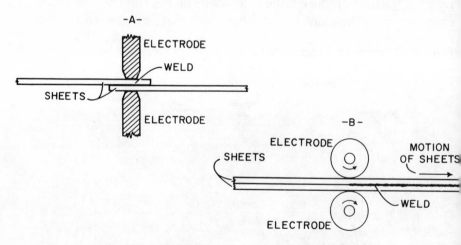

Fig. 13-12. Electrical resistance welding.
A. Spot welding.
B. Seam welding

duces enough heat to melt the metal at the junction of the two sheets. At the same time, a heavy pressure is applied between the electrodes, forcing the sheets together and forming the weld. Then the electrodes are moved to another spot along the seam where another weld is made. We call this *spot welding*.

If we wish to make a continuous weld along the seam, we may use electrodes in the form of rollers (Figure 13-12B). As the sheet metal is moved between these rollers, a continuous weld is formed. We call this *seam welding*. The electrodes often must be water-cooled to keep them from overheating.

Resistance welding requires extremely large currents. Up to 100,-000 amperes may be employed, depending upon the nature of the materials to be welded. Pressures applied to the electrodes at the instant of weld may reach 30,000 pounds. The voltages required, though, are small—from one to two volts. A step-down transformer (which will be discussed later in the book) usually is employed to produce the required current. Sometimes, a large capacitor is charged up from a direct-current source and then permitted to discharge instantaneously through the electrodes.

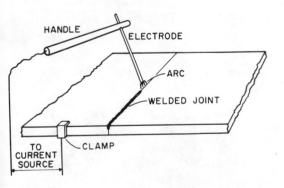

Fig. 13-13.

Electric arc welding.

In *arc welding*, the work to be joined forms one electrode. (See Figure 13-13.) A rod of carbon, tungsten, or some other metal, forms the other electrode. This rod is touched to the work, completing the circuit. Then the rod is withdrawn slightly, forming an intense electric spark, or *arc*. The arc heats the edges of the metals until they melt and flow together. The rod is moved slowly along the seam and the arc follows.

Sometimes a carbon or tungsten rod is employed as the electrode. More frequently, however, a rod of the same material as the work is used and, as this rod becomes hot, it melts and contributes some of its metal to help make the joint. Frequently, a second similar rod, called a *filler rod,* is inserted into the arc to add its metal to the joint as it melts. The rods generally are coated with various chemicals, which aid the welding by preventing oxidation of the material of the joint.

The current required for arc welding need not be as large as that used for resistance welding. Generally, about 20 amperes are employed, although at times as much as 1,000 amperes may be required. The voltage, however, must be relatively high in order to form the arc—from 15 to 50 volts. Current may be supplied from a generator, from storage batteries, or from a step-down transformer.

General Electric Company.

Fig. 13-14. Arc welding.

Not all materials may be arc-welded satisfactorily. The intense heat produced may damage the structure of certain steel alloys. Aluminum, too, presents a difficulty because it oxidizes so readily, especially at high temperatures. The oxide coating prevents the formation of a satisfactory weld. This problem was solved by enclosing the work in an envelope of hydrogen or ammonia gas. The gas envelope keeps the air away from the aluminum, preventing the formation of the oxide coating.

The welding of magnesium presented a unique problem. This metal burns fiercely at the temperatures obtained by the arc. The problem was solved by enclosing the work in an envelope of helium gas which keeps out the air and prevents the magnesium from burning.

Resistance welding is faster than arc welding and the lower heat it produces does not heat up the material as much. Arc welding, however, can be used for joining heavier pieces of metal, such as building beams and ship plates. The welder must wear special goggles to protect his eyes from the ultraviolet rays and the intense light produced by the electric arc.

E. *Electric ovens and furnaces*

The ordinary household *electric oven* consists of a metal box with flat, nichrome-wire heating elements along the inner sides of the top and bottom. An adjustable thermostat usually is incorporated to keep the heat in the oven constant at any desired temperature. The *electric kiln* used for baking ceramic objects is constructed in similar fashion, except that the box usually is made of some heat-resistant material such as fire brick.

On the other hand, the electric *resistance furnace,* which is used to melt metallic materials, does not employ this kind of a heating element. Instead, a high current is passed through the material to be melted and the resistance of the material to this current produces the required heat. (Look at Figure 13-15.) The furnace is a box made of some heat-resisting material, such as fire brick. The material to be melted is placed in a heavy, graphite crucible which is set in the furnace. Since graphite is a conductor of electricity, the crucible acts as one of the electrodes. The circuit is completed

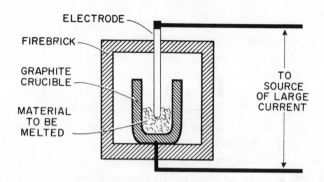

Fig. 13-15. Electric resistance furnace.

by inserting another electrode, usually a heavy carbon rod, through the top of the furnace to make contact with the material in the crucible. Furnaces of this type may reach a temperature of 2,200°C.

A similar device is the electric *arc furnace* which employs the heat of an electric arc, rather than the heat produced by resistance. This furnace resembles the resistance furnace, except that after the carbon electrode touches the material in the crucible, it is withdrawn slightly to form an electric arc. This arc produces a heat that may reach 3,500°C. It is used in the manufacture of steel and for the heating or melting of other metals. It may be used to heat materials other than metal, provided such materials are conductors of electricity. For example, carborundum usually is made in an arc furnace.

F. *Inductive and capacitive heating*

The most recent advances in electrical heating utilize alternating currents of extremely high frequencies—often millions of cycles per second. Suppose that we placed an iron bar inside a coil of wire through which an alternating current is flowing. The iron bar becomes magnetized and, as the alternating current flows through the coil, the molecules of the iron are agitated in step with the alternations of current. Because of the "internal friction" encountered by these molecules, the iron bar becomes warm. If the current flowing through the coil is large, and its frequency is high, the iron bar may become red-hot in a very short time.

Even if a nonmagnetic conductor were placed in the coil, it would become hot owing to the resistance encountered by the flow of current that is induced within it. This is the principle of *inductive heating.*

Nonconductors, too, can be heated by high-frequency alternating current. The dielectric of a capacitor is heated as the metal plates on either side are charged by an alternating current. The reason is that the electrons of the atoms of the dielectric are repelled from the negative plate and attracted toward the positive one (Figure

Fig. 13-16. Tapping a 70-ton electric arc furnace used in manufacturing steel.

American Iron and Steel Institute.

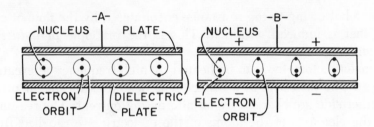

Fig. 13-17. Illustration of the theoretical effect of charged plates on the orbits of electrons in the dielectric.
A. Uncharged plates.
B. Charged plates.

13-17). Hence, the orbits of the electrons around the nuclei are distorted. As alternating current flows to the plates, their polarities change in step with the alternations of current. Consequently, the electron orbits of the dielectric are distorted first toward one plate, and then toward the other. If the current is large and its frequency is very high, the "internal friction" encountered by these changing orbits may cause a large rise in the temperature of the dielectric in a very short time. This is the principle of *capacitive heating*.

Inductive and capacitive heating present a number of advantages. Heat is created simultaneously throughout the body, instead of going from the outside in, as with other types of heating. For example, plywood is made by gluing several sheets of wood together. Previously, it was made by placing a layer of glue between the sheets of wood and inserting the sandwich thus formed between steam-heated plates in order to melt the glue. Not only did it take days for the heat of the steam to penetrate the wood, but even so, the glue would tend to harden unevenly. For this reason, plywood generally was limited to a thickness of about one inch.

Today we use capacitive heating. The wood-glue sandwich is placed between two metal plates, acting as the dielectric of a capacitor. The plates are connected to a high-power source of high-frequency alternating current and a job that used to take days is performed in hours. The heat is uniformly distributed, hence the glue hardens evenly. And there is no limit to the size or shape of the plywood.

The penetrating power of inductive heating is utilized in the diathermy machine, which doctors use for applying heat inside the body to produce certain therapeutic effects. This machine is a gen-

erator of high-frequency alternating current. The current flows
through a coil of wire that is placed around the portion of the body
to be heated. In this way, the inside portion of the body may be
warmed although the skin remains cool.

One advantage of inductive heating is that a high heat may be
produced very quickly. For example, sheet iron is coated with tin to
prevent corrosion. When the tin is deposited on the iron sheet, there
are many minute spots where the iron is exposed. By passing the
sheets of coated metal through the coil of an inductive heating de-

Fig. 13-18. Brazing a carbide tip on a tool with a five-kilowatt
high-frequency inductive heater.

General Electric Company.

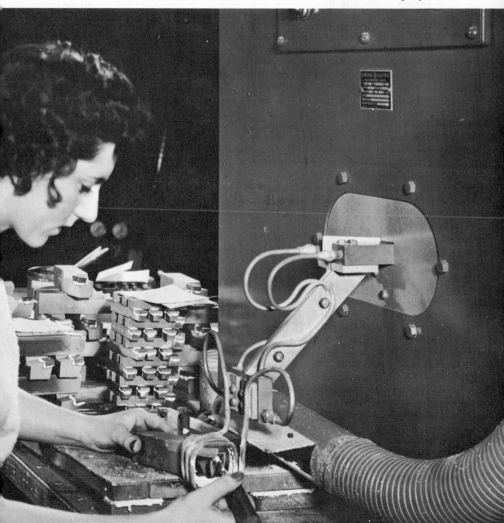

vice, the tin is melted and flows evenly over the entire sheet, covering the exposed spots. So quickly is the heat created, that the sheet may move through the coil at a speed of 1,000 feet per minute!

Another advantage of inductive and capacitive heating is the fact that the heat may be localized in a very small area. For example, the teeth of a gear wheel may be heated red-hot for tempering purposes, while the body of the wheel remains cool and retains its toughness. If we were to attempt to heat the teeth by ordinary means, the entire wheel would be heated.

Finally, by means of capacitive and inductive heating, we can accomplish feats of heating that ordinarily would be impossible. Consider the case of the electron tube where it is desired to heat metal parts enclosed in a glass bulb without melting the glass. The entire tube is placed in the coil of an inductive-heating device. Although the metal parts become red-hot, the glass bulb is unaffected and remains cool. Incidentally, we may heat the glass while the metal remains unaffected, by placing the tube between the plates of a capacitive-heating device.

We have just touched upon the possibilities of inductive and capacitive heating. New applications are discovered each day. The high-power, high-frequency alternating current is produced by generators employing electron tubes. Such generators will be discussed in the next section.

QUESTIONS

Wherever possible, diagrams should be used to clarify the answers to these questions. These diagrams need not be elaborate, but they should be drawn neatly with the significant portions clearly labeled.

1. **The heating element of an electric stove operating on a 240-volt line has a resistance of 48 ohms. How many calories of heat are produced by this heating element in one-half hour? How many British thermal units?**

2. **A 600-watt heating element of an electric stove that operates on a 120-volt line was accidentally inserted into a stove operating on a 240-volt line. Explain the result.**

3. **An electric stove has two types of heating elements. One produces a higher heat, the other a lower heat. Which element has the higher resistance? Explain.**

4. Explain the structure of a *thermostat* and show how it can be used to regulate the heat of an electric iron.

5. Explain what is meant by a *short circuit* and why it is dangerous.

6. A 120-volt line in a house is protected by a 15-ampere fuse. Attached to this line is a television receiver rated at 330 watts, a light fixture using a three-way lamp rated at 100-200-300 watts, and other light fixtures employing six 100-watt lamps and four 60-watt lamps. It is desired to add to this line another light fixture containing one 100-watt lamp and two 60-watt lamps. Can this be done safely? Explain.

7. Explain the action of the *thermal circuit breaker.*

8. Explain the *resistance-welding* process.

9. Explain the *arc-welding* process.

10. Explain the structure and operation of the *resistance furnace.*

11. Explain the structure and operation of the *arc furnace.*

12. Explain the principle of *inductive heating.* What are its advantages over ordinary heating methods?

13. Explain the principle of *capacitive heating.* What are its advantages over ordinary heating methods?

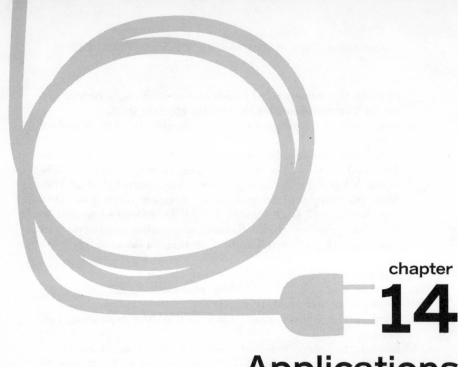

chapter

14

Applications
Depending Upon
the Luminous Effect

A. Incandescent-filament lamp

In Chapter 5, Subdivision B, we saw how Edison heated a carbon filament by passing a current through it until it became incandescent. The temperature of the carbon filament at that point was approximately 1,350°C. Because the melting point of carbon is about 3,500°C., there was no danger that the filament would melt.

Although the carbon-filament lamp was used for many years, it nevertheless suffered from several serious defects. True, the filament did not burn up or melt. But some of the carbon was evaporated from the hot filament. When this carbon vapor came in contact with the cooler inner surface of the glass bulb, it condensed. In this way, an opaque layer of carbon was gradually deposited on the inner surface of the bulb, cutting down the amount of light that could pass through. Moreover, the carbon filament was quite brittle and easily broken by vibration. A search, therefore, was made for a filament that would not evaporate so easily, and one that was not so brittle as carbon.

The search centered on a metal called *tungsten* which melts at about 3,300°C. and does not evaporate so readily as does carbon. However, tungsten was too brittle and could not be drawn out into a thin filament.

In 1910, William D. Coolidge, an American scientist, discovered a process by means of which tungsten could be made extremely ductile and thus be drawn into fine filaments. These filaments are used in lamps today instead of carbon. Because the tungsten filament does not evaporate so readily, it can be heated to a greater temperature than a carbon filament. Tungsten filaments are heated to about 2,100°C. The result is a more intense and whiter light than that produced by carbon-filament lamps.

It is necessary to explain why the tungsten filament at 2,100°C. produces a more intense and whiter light than does the carbon filament at 1,350°. If we heat an iron bar to about 525°C., it will become red-hot and emit a red light. If we raise the temperature to about 1,000°, the light will be yellow. At 1,200° the bar glows white-hot and white light is emitted. Thus, as the temperature is increased from 525° to 1,200°, the color of the emitted light shifts from red to white. After that, increasing the temperature causes the emitted light to be whiter and more intense.

Were it not for the fact that evaporation of the filament would be increased, the tungsten filament could be heated still more and thus produce a more intense light. To reduce the evaporation and permit a greater heat, Irving Langmuir, another American scientist, introduced a certain amount of inert gas, such as nitrogen or argon, into the bulb. This gas is introduced at a pressure of about 5 pounds per square inch. When the filament is heated, the pressure of the hot gas rises to about 15 pounds per square inch. Increasing the pressure reduces the rate of evaporation. Because the gas is inert, the filament does not burn up.

The presence of the gas, however, tends to cool the filament by conducting some of its heat to the glass bulb by means of convection currents. To compensate for this undesirable effect, the filament is constructed as a tight coil of fine wire and thus can be concentrated into a small space. This results in greater heat and more brilliant light. (See Figure 14-1.) This is the type of lamp most commonly used today. The coiled tungsten filament is supported by two wires that are sealed into the base of the glass bulb. These wires carry the current to the filament. One wire is attached to the metal shell of the base. The other goes to the bottom contact. When the lamp is screwed into a socket, the shell and the bottom contact are connected to the source of electric current. The inner surface of the glass bulb generally is frosted to diffuse the light in order to reduce glare. The filament of such a lamp operates at about 3,000°C., producing a white light of great intensity.

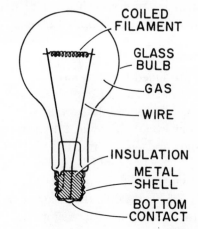

Fig. 14-1.

Modern type of incandescent-filament lamp.

We may measure the light intensity of any lamp by comparing it with some standard. Such a standard of light intensity is the *candlepower*. This is the light intensity of a burning standard candle, which is made to certain chemical and physical specifications and which burns at a specified rate. If a lamp produces a light that is, say, 40 times as intense as the light of the standard candle, the lamp is said to produce *40 candlepower* of light. Some of our larger searchlights may produce a light intensity of millions of candlepower.

Westinghouse Electric Corp.

Fig. 14-2. Some special types of incandescent-filament lamps.

You may have noticed that our ordinary electric lamps are rated in *watts* instead of candlepower. Since we pay for the electricity used to operate these lamps by the number of watts per hour that they consume, such a rating is more practical. Thus you will find carbon lamp produced about ⅓ candlepower per watt. The non-gas-filled tungsten lamp produced about 1 candlepower per watt. The gas-filled lamp produces about 1⅓ candlepower per watt.

B.   *Arc lamp*

We have learned that the passage of an electric current may heat a gas to incandescence. This is the principle underlying the *carbon-arc light* (Chapter 5, Subdivison B). The temperature of the carbon arc may reach as high as 3,500°C., producing a brilliant white light. In addition to this visible light, the carbon arc produces large quantities of infrared and ultraviolet rays.

Although capable of producing an intense white light, the carbon-arc lamp was abandoned in favor of the more practical incandescent-filament lamp for ordinary lighting purposes. One reason was that the carbon-arc lamp required more manipulation—the tips had to be brought together and separated to start the arc. Another reason was that, as the carbon rods burned away, the arc became longer and longer, until finally the gap between the tips was too great for the current to bridge, and the lamp would become extinguished. It is true that mechanical devices were invented to feed the carbon rods automatically, but they merely introduced further complications. The carbon rods required frequent replacement. The flame of the burning carbon vapor produced a flickering light and had to be protected against gusts of wind. Moreover, the ultraviolet rays it produced were harmful to the eyes. (Fortunately, ordinary glass can stop these ultraviolet rays.) For all these reasons, the carbon-arc lamp is used today only for special purposes, such as in motion-picture projectors and for certain photographic work where the strong ultraviolet rays are desired.

A new arc lamp has been developed recently that uses *zirconium* metal instead of carbon. The heat of the arc causes the metal to form a small pool, and the passage of current heats the molten metal to about 3,600°C. The result is a dazzling white light that is about 20 times as bright as can be produced by a comparable tungsten-filament lamp.

C. Vapor lamp

We have seen how light is produced by heating a solid, a liquid, or a gas to incandescence. What causes this light was, for many years, one of nature's deepest secrets. But with the development of the electron theory of the structure of matter we began to get some of the answers.

All atoms, you will recall (Chapter 1, Subdivision B, 1), contain a central nucleus around which revolve electrons in various orbits or shells. The electrons of the outer shell are most loosely held and, in certain types of atoms, may be detached quite easily. The electrons of the inner shells, however, being closer to the nucleus, are held more firmly. Now, should a certain amount of energy, such as heat energy, be applied to the atom, one or more electrons contained in an inner shell may be forced to leave that shell and jump to an outer one. We say that the atom is *excited*.

The displaced electron has acquired extra energy. However, the attraction of the nucleus soon pulls the displaced electron back to its normal position. As the electron falls back, it loses its extra energy. It is this extra energy that is given off in the form of light.

There are other methods besides the use of heat to excite atoms, and modern lighting techniques are relying more and more on these other methods to produce illumination. Let us turn again to the electron theory. The normal atom is neutral, that is, there are as many electrons in its shells as there are protons in its nucleus. Since the negative charge on the electron is equal and opposite to the positive charge on the proton, these charges neutralize each other. Should a neutral atom lose an electron, it becomes a positive ion. Should it gain an electron, it becomes a negative ion.

We know that opposite charges attract each other. If we were to place a positively charged electrode to one side of a neutral atom and a negatively charged electrode at the other side, nothing would happen, since the neutral atom is attracted to neither the positive nor negative electrode. If, however, the charges on the electrodes were to be made sufficiently strong, an electron from the outer shell of the atom would be attracted to the positive electrode. This loss of an electron would convert the atom into a positive ion. Hence the ion would be attracted to the negative electrode.

The speed of the electron to the positive electrode is very great, as fast as 1,000 or more miles per second. Thus, although the weight of the electron is extremely small, should it strike another atom in its flight, the force of the impact might knock an electron free from that atom. This new free electron then would rush toward the positive electrode. The remainder of the atom, having become a positive ion, would be attracted to the negative electrode. This process is cumulative, and soon there would be a stream of electrons speeding toward the positive electrode and a stream of positive ions rushing to the negative one.

The ion moves more slowly than does the electron. But the ion's mass is so much greater than the mass of the electron that the force of the impact between it and a normal atom may also knock an electron loose. Thus the movement of the ions, too, adds to the number of free electrons and ions produced. This process is known as *ionization*.

What happens when a positive ion and an electron meet in flight? Since they are oppositely charged, they attract each other. The ion combines with the electron and becomes a normal atom once more, until another collision ionizes it again.

Should a free electron succeed in reaching the positive electrode, it is drawn off into the external electrical system. Should a positive ion reach the negative electrode, it receives an electron there and becomes a normal atom again. The whole process is then repeated.

But what has all this to do with light? Well, when a positive ion combines with an electron to become a normal atom, light energy may be emitted. Again, the impact of collision between a normal atom with a speeding electron or ion may cause the atom to lose an electron (ionization), or the impact may cause one of the atom's electrons to jump from an inner shell to an outer one (excitation). In

Fig. 14-3.

Neon lamp.

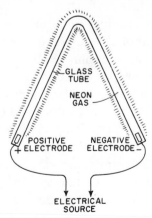

the latter case, you will recall that the attraction of the nucleus quickly pulls the displaced electron back to its original position. As the electron falls back to its normal shell, light energy is emitted.

It is this principle upon which the familiar "neon lamp" operates (see Figure 14-3). A glass tube is bent into the desired shape. A metal plate, or electrode, is sealed into each end. The air is evacuated from the tube, and in its place neon gas at low pressure (about $\frac{1}{40}$ atmospheric pressure) is introduced. An electrical source capable of placing a charge up to 15,000 volts is connected to the electrodes. The neon gas near the electrodes becomes ionized. This ionization almost instantly extends throughout the tube as a result of collisions between the electrons and ions and the normal gas atoms. Light is produced as the excited atoms return to their normal states, and as ions recombine with electrons to become normal atoms once more.

If the gas in the tube were not at reduced pressure, there would be too many atoms present. The electrons and ions could not travel very far before colliding with normal atoms. The longer the electrons or ions travel without collision, the greater is their acceleration, the greater is their speed, and, hence, the greater the force of impact on collision. If the collisions take place too soon, the force of impact may not be great enough to ionize the normal gas atoms.

The electrical source is generally a *step-up transformer* (this will be discussed later in the book) which changes the 120-volt, 60-cycle alternating current obtained from the house mains in most localities to the 15,000 volts required to operate the neon lamp. This source periodically reverses the charges on the electrodes, usually 120 times per second. As a result, the electrons and ions change their directions of flow at this rate. This change, however, does not affect the light produced.

Other gases besides neon may be used in these lamps. Each gas produces light of characteristic color. Neon produces a reddish light. Helium produces a pinkish light; argon produces a bluish-white light; mercury vapor produces a greenish-blue light. The gases may be mixed to produce combinations of colors, and colored glass tubes may be used to produce additional color effects.

The mercury-vapor lamp is of particular interest. In addition to visible light, it also emits powerful ultraviolet rays. Normally, these rays cannot penetrate the glass tube. But if this tube be made of fused quartz or of certain recently developed types of glass, the ultraviolet rays can pass through readily.

Ultraviolet rays tan the skin and are believed to be beneficial in moderate quantities. However, when the body is exposed to the mercury-vapor lamp, glass goggles should be worn to protect the eyes from the ultraviolet rays. Ultraviolet rays can destroy bacteria, and mercury-vapor lamps are used for this purpose in air-conditioning units, refrigerators, food counters, and other similar installations. They are also used in the treatment of certain skin diseases.

Ultraviolet light is also used to produce Vitamin D, the "sunshine" vitamin, in certain foods. Thus, milk, for example, has its Vitamin-D content increased by exposure to mercury-vapor lamps.

Photographic film is particularly sensitive to ultraviolet rays. For this reason, mercury-vapor lamps are used for lighting purposes in photographic studios. However, because such lamps are weak producers of red light, neon lamps usually are used in conjunction with them to compensate for this defect.

Lamps such as we have described here are called *vapor lamps* and have a number of advantages over the incandescent-filament types that we have previously discussed. First of all, lamps that operate by ionization produce a "cool" light. Whereas the incandescent lamps operate at temperatures as high as 3,000°C., the heat produced by the glowing gas in the neon-light type of lamp may be only 140°.

Second, whereas filament lamps can produce only a yellowish-white light, vapor lamps can produce light of a great number of colors. In this way, they lend themselves readily to many decorative and novel effects.

Another advantage of the vapor lamp is the fact that illumination is produced over a large area, instead of in a concentrated point as in the case of the incandescent filament. Consequently, glare and shadows are reduced.

Finally, a greater proportion of the electrical power is converted to light energy in the vapor lamp than is converted in the incandescent lamp, which uses a major part of the power to heat the filament. This means that more light per watt is obtained from the vapor lamp, or, in other words, more candlepower per dollar is produced.

The vapor lamps we have been describing, however, suffer from a serious disadvantage. Whereas the incandescent-filament lamps may operate directly from the 120-volt house mains available in most parts of the country, the vapor lamps require a high voltage across the electrodes, often as high as 15,000 volts. This requires a special device, such as the transformer, to convert the 120-volt current to the required voltage. It would be very convenient if the vapor lamp could operate at lower voltages.

One lamp that can operate at a lower voltage is the "night light" illustrated in Figure 14-4. Two electrodes, consisting of halves of a

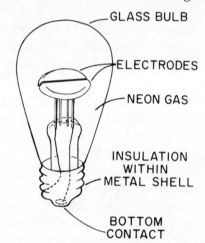

Fig. 14-4.

"Night light."

split metal disk separated by a small gap, are sealed in a small glass bulb. The air is evacuated and neon or argon gas is introduced at reduced pressure. The lamp terminates in a screw base which fits an ordinary lamp socket. The 120-volt mains are connected to this socket and, through it, to the electrodes.

When the current is turned on, the gas near the electrodes becomes ionized. The electrons stream to the positive electrode, and the positive ions travel toward the negative electrode. When these ions reach the negative electrode, they each receive an electron and become normal atoms again. In the process, light is produced. In this way, the negative electrode is covered by a glow of light.

Since the type of electricity commonly used in this country reverses the charge on the electrodes 120 times per second, the glow of light which surrounds the negative electrode will alternately change from electrode to electrode at this rate. Since the eye cannot detect this change, both electrodes will appear to glow.

Lamps of this type use very little current, and the light produced is quite feeble. They are used where little illumination is needed, as in a child's bedroom at night. Hence the name "night light."

Another vapor lamp that is widely used for highway lighting is the *sodium-vapor lamp,* one type of which is illustrated in Figure 14-5. A specially shaped set of electrodes and a coil of tungsten wire (*heater*) are sealed in a glass bulb. The air within the bulb is evacuated and a small amount of neon gas under reduced pressure and some metallic sodium are introduced. The entire bulb then is inserted into a vacuum flask, somewhat similar to a Thermos bottle. This flask, however, is not silvered and will transmit light.

Electric current is passed through the tungsten coil which is in the heater circuit. As current flows through the coil, it becomes hot. The heat energy excites the tungsten atoms sufficiently to cause a large number of electrons to fly off.

By means of a second circuit (the *ionizing circuit*), a negative charge is placed on the coil and a positive charge is placed on the positive electrodes. The electrons emitted by the hot coil speed toward these positive electrodes. In passage, the electrons collide with the atoms of neon gas, causing them to become ionized.

The heat produced by this ionization soon causes the metallic sodium to vaporize, and the bulb quickly fills with the sodium vapor. As a result of collisions between the speeding electrons and ions and the sodium-vapor atoms, the latter, too, become ionized and excited. As these sodium-vapor ions collect electrons and become

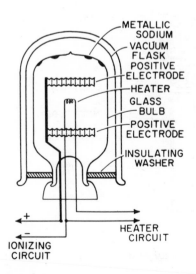

METALLIC
SODIUM
VACUUM
FLASK
POSITIVE
ELECTRODE
HEATER
GLASS
BULB
POSITIVE
ELECTRODE
INSULATING
WASHER

+

—

HEATER
CIRCUIT

IONIZING
CIRCUIT

Fig. 14-5.

Sodium-vapor lamp.

normal atoms once more, or as the excited sodium-vapor atoms return to their normal states, a characteristic yellow light of high intensity is produced.

The vacuum flask that surrounds the bulb is used to prevent the sodium vapor from cooling and condensing. Both the heater and the ionizing circuit use low-voltage current, eliminating the need for devices such as the high-voltage transformer.

The advantage of the sodium-vapor lamp over the ordinary incandescent-filament lamp is evident from the fact that the former may produce 5 candlepower per watt, compared with 1.3 candlepower per watt for the filament lamp.

A somewhat similar type of lamp is the *mercury-vapor lamp* illustrated in Figure 14-6. Here the inner tube contains a few drops of mercury and a little argon gas. The starting voltage is applied between the starting probe and the upper electrode and causes the argon gas between them to ionize. Very little current flows from the probe to the electrode at any time because of the high resistance in series with the probe.

The flow of current through the gas produces sufficient heat to vaporize the mercury, forming mercury vapor which fills the inner tube. The ionizing voltage, applied between the upper and lower electrodes, causes the mercury vapor to ionize, thus producing an intense greenish-blue light.

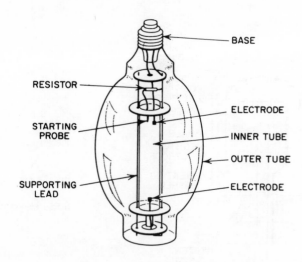

Fig. 14-6. The mercury-vapor lamp.

D. *Fluorescent lamp*

Perhaps the greatest advance in recent years in the science of illumination is the development of the *fluorescent lamp*, which was introduced about 1938. This lamp resembles the mercury-vapor lamp which we have discussed on page 290, except that the inside of the glass tube is coated with certain chemicals, called *phosphors,* that glow (*fluoresce*) when struck by the ultraviolet rays produced by the mercury vapor.

Different phosphors glow with different colors. Cadmium borate glows with a pinkish light; zinc silicate produces a green light; calcium tungstate produces a blue light; and magnesium tungstate produces a bluish-white light. By combining these and other phosphors, light of other colors may be produced.

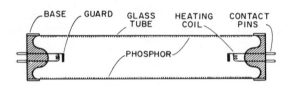

Fig. 14-7. Fluorescent lamp.

The fluorescent lamp is illustrated in Figure 14-7. A tungsten filament is sealed into each end of a long glass tube whose inner surface is coated with a suitable phosphor. The air in the tube is pumped out and, in its place, a little argon gas and a few drops of mercury are introduced.

First, current is passed through the filaments and the heat produced vaporizes the mercury, filling the tube with mercury vapor. Then a relatively high voltage is placed across the tube, using the filament in each end as an electrode. The argon gas ionizes first and then the mercury vapor, producing ultraviolet rays. These rays strike the phosphor coating, causing it to glow and produce visible light. When the lamp starts to glow, the filament circuit is opened. The heat produced by the ionization of the gases is sufficient to keep the mercury vaporized. Note that the filaments are not required to produce any light; they act as heating coils and as electrodes for the high-voltage ionizing circuit.

Note the *guards* that are placed over the heating coils. As the speeding electrons and ions strike, the force of impact may be great enough to damage the coils. Therefore, guards of heavy wire are placed in front of the coils to absorb the shock.

From the the above description, you can see that the fluorescent lamp requires two circuits. One is the *filament* circuit which remains closed only long enough for the filaments to heat and vaporize the mercury. Then this circuit is broken. The other is the *high-voltage* circuit which places a high voltage across the electrodes to ionize the mercury vapor in the tube.

The filament circuit is controlled by a *thermal switch,* illustrated in Figure 14-8. The switch contains a resistor that heats when the main switch is closed and current flows through it. The current that flows through the resistor also flows through the filaments of the lamp, causing them, too, to become heated. The heat from the resistor causes a nearby bimetallic strip to bend, separating a pair of contact points that normally touch each other. As these contact points separate, they open the filament circuit.

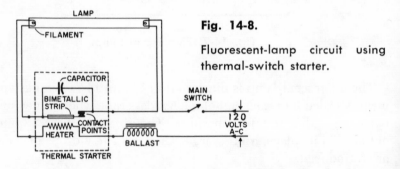

Fig. 14-8.

Fluorescent-lamp circuit using thermal-switch starter.

Note the capacitor that is connected across the contact points. Its function is to reduce sparking across these points as they are separated. Were the capacitor not there, the electrical pressure would cause current to arc across the slight gap formed as the contact points start to separate. This arcing would ionize the air and form a path over which the current would continue to flow, even after the contact points were a considerable distance apart. Because of the capacitor, however, the electrical pressure is used in charging the capacitor rather than in forming the arc, and sparking is reduced.

The thermal switch and its capacitor generally are enclosed in a small, cylindrical, metal can. This unit is called the *starter*. Most fluorescent lamps today employ the *glow-type* starter illustrated in Figure 14-9. Here, the movable and fixed contact points are enclosed in a small, glass bulb containing argon gas. The movable contact point is attached to a bimetallic strip and, normally, the two

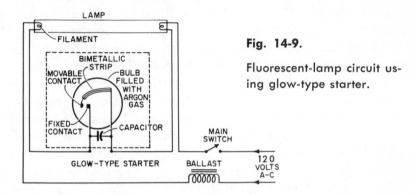

Fig. 14-9.

Fluorescent-lamp circuit using glow-type starter.

points are separated. When the main switch is closed, the 120-volt current ionizes the gas in the bulb and, as a result, a small current flows between the two contact points. The flow of this current produces heat, which causes the bimetallic strip to bend until the points touch each other. When this occurs, the flow of current through the gas ceases, but now current flows through the closed contact points and through the filaments of the lamp.

Because the current has ceased flowing through the gas, the bimetallic strip cools off and moves to separate the contact points once more, thereby opening the filament circuit. However, enough residual heat remains to keep the points closed long enough for the filaments to vaporize the mercury in the lamp.

Note that the fluorescent lamp is connected in shunt across the starter. Once the lamp is started and current flows through it, the voltage across the starter drops to too low a value to cause the argon gas in its bulb to glow. Hence the contact points remain separated and the filament circuit of the lamp remains open.

Now let us consider the high-voltage circuit. Note the *ballast* in series with the lamp and starter. The ballast consists of many turns of fine wire on an iron core. Because of its self-induction, a high counter electromotive force is generated at the instant that the contact points of the starter separate and break the circuit. This high voltage is applied across the filament electrodes of the lamp, ionizing the mercury vapor. Once this ionization starts, current will continue to flow through the lamp, even though the voltage across the electrodes is sharply reduced.

After the ionization has started, the ballast performs a second function. You will recall that this ionization tends to grow and, unless it is checked, the flow of current through the lamp may become great enough to wreck it. But the ballast acts as a safety device. Due to its self-induction, the counter electromotive force that it generates keeps the current flowing through the lamp within safe limits.

You will note that the fluorescent lamp is, essentially, an alternating-current device. It is possible, however, to use such a lamp on direct currrent. The high-voltage surge set up at the moment the contact points are separated will be produced by either type of current. However, the protective action of the ballast is absent since there is no counter electromotive force generated when a steady direct current flows through it. For this reason, a resistor must be connected in series to perform the current-limiting action. Because of the power loss in this resistor, fluorescent lamps do not operate as well on direct current as they do on alternating current.

There are a number of reasons why the fluorescent lamp is rapidly replacing the incandescent type. First, the fluorescent lamp gives more light per watt. For example, the white-light fluorescent lamp produces about 2.5 candlepower per watt. Consequently, it is cheaper to operate than the incandescent-filament type which produces about 1 candlepower per watt. Then, the light of the fluorescent lamp is "softer" and produces less glare. This is because the illumination comes from a long line of light, rather than from a concentrated filament. Again, the number of colors that can be produced and the various shapes in which the lamp can be formed make the fluorescent lamp more suitable for decorative purposes than the incandescent lamp. Further, the light from the so-called "daylight" fluorescent lamp more nearly approaches natural daylight. The lamp operates at a lower temperature than the incandescent lamp. The incandescent lamp operates at about 3,000°C. and produces a yellowish-white light. The fluorescent lamp produces a whiter light and its temperature is less than 50°. To produce light of a color similar to that produced by the fluorescent "daylight" lamp, the incandescent filament would have to be heated to over 6,000°C.! Finally, the life of the fluorescent lamp is several times longer than

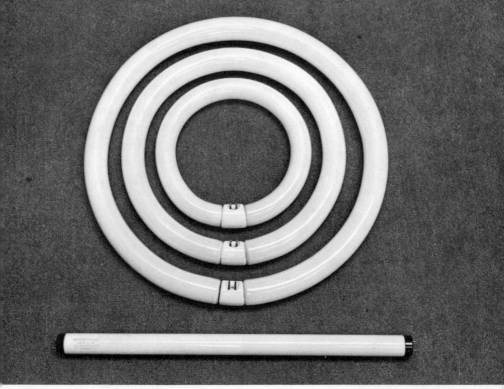

Fig. 14-10. Fluorescent lamps are made in various shapes and sizes.

that of the incandescent type. This is because the former does not have a filament that operates continuously at high temperature.

Fluorescent lamps may be obtained in sizes ranging from six inches to over four feet in length. In addition, they are made in various forms such as straight tubes, circles, and semicircles. Thus they lend themselves to various decorative designs.

E. *Illumination*

If you wish to see an object—for example, the page of this book—it is not enough that the lamp be bright. Enough of its light must fall on the page to make the page bright enough to be read. When we talk of *illumination,* we are concerned with the amount of light falling upon each unit area of the illuminated object.

The illumination of an object depends upon how close it is to the source of illumination. We know that when we want to see better, we go "nearer to the light." The illumination of an object at a distance of one foot from a light source of one candlepower is *one foot-candle,* which is the unit of illumination. If, instead of a standard candle, we use, say, a 100-candlepower lamp, the illumination on the object at a distance of one foot would be 100 foot-candles.

However, if we hold the object 2 feet away from the 100-candlepower lamp, the illumination would not be 50 foot-candles, as you might expect, but rather, 25 foot-candles. You will see this more clearly if you examine Figure 14-11.

Fig. 14-11.

Diagram illustrating the inverse-square law of illumination.

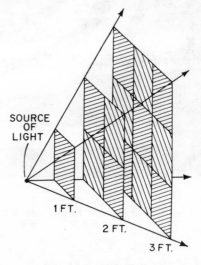

Assume that the source of light is a 100-candlepower lamp. A one-foot-square screen, one foot away from the source, receives a certain amount of light from the lamp. If, now, this screen is removed, since light rays travel in straight lines, the same amount of light would cover 4 square feet of a second screen 2 feet removed from the source. Similarly, the same amount of light would cover 9 square feet of a screen 3 feet removed from the source.

The illumination of the first screen is 100 foot-candles. At the second screen (2 feet from the source) the same amount of light is spread over 4 square feet. Hence, the light falling upon each unit area of the second screen, its *illumination,* is only one-fourth that of the first. That is, the illumination is 25 foot-candles. The same amount of light, falling upon the third screen (3 feet from the source) is spread over 9 square feet and the illumination now is only one-ninth, or 11⅑ foot-candles.

Note that at twice the distance from the source, the illumination is one-quarter as great. And at three times the distance from the source the illumination is only one-ninth as great. Thus the illumination varies inversely as the square of the distance from the source. This is known as the *inverse-square law of illumination.*

Thus, for proper illumination, we need not only a source of proper intensity, but we also need to have the object close enough to the source so that adequate illumination falls upon it. Or, if the object is further from the source of light, this source must be made more intense to furnish the proper illumination.

Illumination engineers have set certain standards of illumination for various types of activities. Thus, libraries and classrooms should have an illumination of at least 15 foot-candles at the desks. Manufacturing plants need from 15 to 50 foot-candles at the machines, depending upon the type of work done. These are minimum standards and greater illumination is desirable.

There is another factor in illumination. If the source of light is too concentrated, the reflection from a bright surface, such as the page of this book, may produce a glare which will strain the eye and cause fatigue. Hence, it is better if the light comes from a large surface rather than from a small point. That is why the long fluorescent lamp is superior to the small incandescent-filament lamp. In addi-

Fig. 14-12.

Light meter.

Weston Instruments Div., Daystrom, Inc.

tion, modern homes use indirect lighting, whereby the light is directed against the white ceiling and then is reflected from this large surface to the rest of the room.

There are a number of methods used for measuring illumination. The simplest method, perhaps, is to use a photronic cell such as described in Chapter 12, Subdivision D, and a microammeter. The combination of cell and meter form a *light meter*. This light meter is placed where we wish to measure the illumination and the light is permitted to fall upon the cell. The greater the intensity of illumination, the greater will be the voltage generated by the cell, and more current will flow through the meter. This meter is calibrated directly in foot-candles.

F. *House wiring*

Most household appliances are constructed to operate at 120 volts. Accordingly, the household mains are 120-volt lines. (Although we usually refer to the household mains as 120-volt lines, the electricity may be supplied at 110, 115, or 117 volts, depending upon the locality.)

Electrical appliances are connected in parallel across the line. Thus the voltage across each appliance remains the same—120 volts. The current flowing through the line will depend, of course, upon the sum of the currents drawn by each appliance. If this current exceeds the rating of the fuse, the latter "blows," opening the circuit and cutting off all the appliances on that particular line.

You can see, therefore, that it is not wise to connect all the appliances to a single line. What we need are two or more lines. Of course, we may bring these extra lines into the house, using two wires for each line. Thomas Edison invented a *three-wire system* whereby two lines can be brought in, using only three wires instead of four.

Look at Figure 14-13. Here we have two 120-volt direct-current generators connected in series (positive brush to negative brush). The voltage across both outside wires is 240 volts. The voltage from either outside wire to the center one is 120 volts. Thus we have two 120-volt lines with only three wires.

We can accomplish the same thing with alternating current by

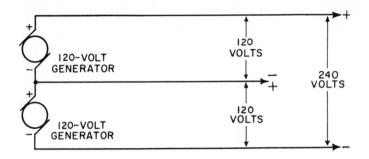

Fig. 14-13. Three-wire system for direct current.

means of a *transformer*. This device will be discussed in detail a little later in the book, but for our purposes here, it consists of an input coil or winding of wire (called the *primary winding*) that is magnetically coupled to an output winding (the *secondary winding*). When an input voltage is applied to the primary winding, an output voltage appears across the secondary winding. The ratio between the input and output voltages is directly proportional to the ratio between the number of turns of the primary and secondary windings.

Thus, if the secondary winding has one-tenth the number of turns of the primary winding, the secondary voltage will be one-tenth that of the primary voltage. This is an example of a *step-down transformer*. If the secondary winding has ten times the number of turns of the primary winding, the secondary voltage will be ten times the primary voltage. This is a *step-up transformer*.

High-voltage current is sent from the power plant by means of overhead or underground wires to a step-down transformer located near the house. Assume this voltage is 2,400 volts. If a ten-times step-down transformer is employed, the output voltage will be 240 volts. If the output winding is *center-tapped* (that is, a connection, or *tap*, is made to the center of the winding), the voltage between either end of the winding and the center tap will be 120 volts and the voltage across the entire secondary winding will be 240 volts. (See Figure 14-14.) Note that, except that alternating current is involved, the result is the same as in the direct-current system illustrated in Figure 14-13.

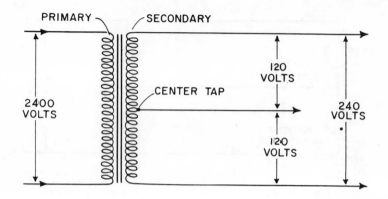

Fig. 14-14. Three-wire system for alternating current.

Since the center wire (which sometimes is called the *neutral* wire) of this system is at a potential that is halfway between $+120$ volts and -120 volts, it must always be at zero potential or voltage. Since the ground, too, is at zero voltage, the neutral wire may be connected to ground and no current will flow from that wire to the ground connection. Connecting the neutral wire to the ground introduces a safety factor, as we shall see presently.

Figure 14-15 shows a typical household installation. The connection from the neutral wire to ground generally is made just before or just after the wires enter the side of the house. After the three wires enter the house, a fuse (whose symbol is $\sim$) is placed in

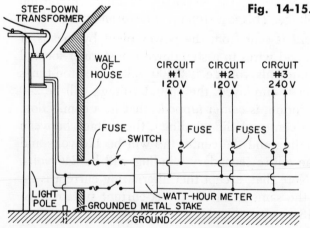

Fig. 14-15. Wiring diagram showing how current is brought into a house.

series with each outer wire (often called the "hot" wires or leads). A *two-pole switch,* to be used to break the circuit, if desired, is placed in series with the "hot" leads. (This switch is called the *main switch* and the fuses that precede it are known as the *main fuses.*) Then all three wires are attached to the *watthour meter* which indicates the electrical power consumed in the house.

As the three wires emerge from the watthour meter, one 120-volt circuit is taken off between one of the "hot" leads and the neutral wire. A second 120-volt circuit is taken off between the other "hot" lead and the neutral wire. If a 240-volt circuit is required, as, for example, if an electric stove is to be operated, a third circuit is taken off from the two "hot" leads.

If any connection to the neutral wire should accidentally be touched to ground (*grounded*), no current will flow because both points are at the same potential. But should one of the "hot" leads, or any connection to it, become grounded, there is a 120-volt difference of potential that will cause current to flow. If the resistance of the grounded circuit is very low, sufficient current may flow to heat the wires and set the house afire. For this reason, fuses must be placed in all the "hot" leads.

A typical wiring circuit is shown in Figure 14-16. As the 120-volt line enters the room, it divides into two parallel circuits. One circuit runs along the bottom of the room and connects to a number of base

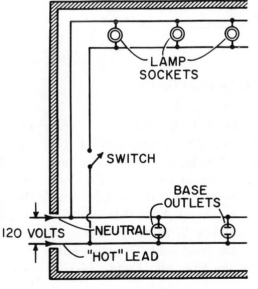

Fig. 14-16.

Wiring diagram showing how current is brought into a room.

outlets. Note that all these outlets, and hence all appliances connected to them, are in parallel.

The other circuit runs up the wall. About four feet above the floor, the "hot" lead is broken and a switch is inserted in series with it. The circuit then is connected with a number of lamp sockets. These lamp sockets, too, are connected in parallel. Closing the switch connects all the lamps; opening it turns them all off. Note, however, that the switch does not affect the base outlets.

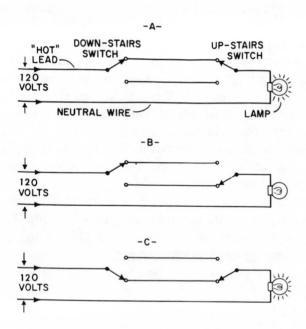

Fig. 14-17. Two-way light circuit.

An interesting lighting circuit is illustrated in Figure 14-17. A flight of stairs may be illuminated by a lamp located at the top of the stairs. Suppose that you wish to be able to turn the lamp on and off at both the top and the bottom of the stairs. The "hot" lead is broken at both ends of the stairway. Two *single-pole, double-throw switches* are inserted, one at each break. Note that a third wire must be connected between the switches. With the switches in the position shown in Figure 14-17A, the lamp is lit. Throwing either switch to its opposite position turns the lamp off (Figure 14-17B). When the lamp is off, throwing either switch to its opposite position causes the lamp to light again (Figure 14-17C). In this way, the lamp may be turned on and off from either the top or the bottom of the stairs.

Because of the danger of fire from faulty installation, house wiring is carefully regulated by a code drawn up by the National Board of Fire Underwriters and by local ordinances. The wires must be heavy enough to carry the current without undue heating, they must be insulated adequately, and they must be installed properly so that there is no danger of insulation failure or of wires breaking.

The permanent wires in the home generally are solid, made of copper, and lightly coated with tin to facilitate soldering. They are insulated with a coating of rubber or some plastic material, and the whole wrapped in cotton braid that has been impregnated in some fire-resistant material. Where heavy currents are to be carried, the insulation may be of asbestos.

The size of the wire is determined by its cross-sectional area measured in *circular mils*. A *mil* is $\frac{1}{1,000}$ of an inch. To obtain area in circular mils, the diameter of the wire, in mils, is squared. Thus, a wire whose diameter is 80 mils (0.080 inch) has a cross-sectional area of 6,400 circular mils.

To avoid the use of large numbers, standards have been set up whereby small numbers are assigned to wires of definite size. One such standard which is widely used is the American Wire Gage (AWG), formerly known as the Brown & Sharp Gage (B & S). A #10 wire, for example, is one having an area of 10,380 circular mils. The #12 wire has an area of 6,530 circular mils. (See Appendix C.)

House wires are color-coded for easy identification. The neutral wire always is colored white. The "hot" wire may be black or red. Where a three-wire system is used, the neutral wire is white, one "hot" wire is black, and the other is red.

When the wiring is exposed, the wires may be held in place by means of porcelain knobs or cleats. Many localities require that such exposed wires be enclosed in thin steel tubing, called *conduit*. Where the wiring must pass through the narrow space inside walls or between a ceiling and the floor above it, flexibility is required. Accordingly, a flexible, steel-armored cable, called *BX*, may be employed. This cable consists of the insulated wires wrapped in fire-

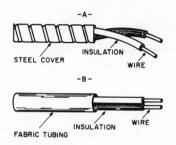

Fig. 14-18. A. BX cable.

B. Nonmetallic sheathed cable.

resistant paper and the whole enclosed in metal strip wrapped spiral-fashion. See Figure 14-18. Sometimes a *nonmetallic cable,* consisting of the insulated wires in braided fabric tubing, is used.

The wire connecting the various appliances to the electrical outlets generally is flexible and is made of a number of thin copper strands twisted together so that the equivalent of about a #18 wire is formed. It then is covered with a rubber or plastic insulation. Two such insulated wires are wrapped with cotton or silk to form a single lead, one end of which is attached to the appliance, and the other end terminates in a two-pronged plug that fits into the electrical outlet. Sometimes two rubber-covered wires are merely attached to each other to form a lead that is known as "zip cord." Where the appliances are heat producers, such as flatirons or toasters, asbestos insulation is employed.

QUESTIONS

Wherever possible, diagrams should be used to clarify the answers to these questions. These diagrams need not be elaborate, but they should be drawn neatly with the significant portions clearly labeled.

1. In an incandescent-filament lamp, what is the relationship between the light produced and the temperature of the filament?
2. What is the function of the inert gas introduced into the bulb of the incandescent lamp?
3. In terms of the electron theory, explain the operation of the neon-type vapor lamp. How are different colored lights obtained?

4. Give three uses for the *mercury-vapor lamp.*
5. In the *night light* illustrated in Figure 14-4, will one or both plates "light up" if the lamp be used on *a*) alternating current *b*) direct current? Explain.
6. Explain the operation of the fluorescent lamp in terms of the electron theory. How are different colored lights obtained?
7. Explain the function and operation of the *glow-type starter* in the fluorescent-lamp circuit.
8. Explain the functions of the *ballast* in the fluorescent-lamp circuit.
9. Draw the circuit of a fluorescent lamp using a glow-type starter. Label all parts.
10. What are the advantages of the fluorescent lamp over the incandescent-filament type? What are its disadvantages?
11. An engineer, measuring the illumination of a room, found that at a distance of 1 foot from a light source, the illumination was 1,000 foot-candles. What would be the illumination 5 feet from the source?
12. What components of the house wiring system are ordinarily connected *a*) in series; *b*) in parallel?

chapter

15

Applications
Depending Upon
the Chemical Effect

The chemical applications of the electric current are based upon the movement of ions through a liquid toward charged electrodes (see Chapter 4, Subdivision B). For example, let us examine a commercial method of obtaining chlorine gas.

We start with ordinary table salt (sodium chloride) which is a compound consisting of one atom of sodium and one atom of chlorine. When the salt is dissolved in water, it ionizes, breaking up into positive sodium ions and negative chlorine ions. Two electrodes are placed into the solution and these electrodes are connected to a source of direct current. The positive sodium ions are attracted to the negative electrode and the negative chlorine ions move toward the positive electrode.

When a positive sodium ion reaches the negative electrode, it receives an electron and becomes a neutral, or uncharged, sodium

312

atom. Similarly, when a negative chlorine ion reaches the positive electrode, it surrenders its negative charge to the electrode and becomes a neutral chlorine atom. The neutral sodium atom combines with the water of the solution, but the neutral chlorine atom, being a gas, bubbles off and is collected. This process of passing electric current through a chemical compound and breaking it down is called *electrolysis*. Note that direct current must be used to attract ions of only one kind to each electrode. The electrodes generally are made of carbon or platinum so that they may resist any chemical action.

If we wish to recover the sodium, we cannot use a water solution of sodium chloride since the sodium atom formed at the negative electrode reacts with the water to form sodium hydroxide. Instead, we use molten salt. The molten salt ionizes and, since there is no water, pure sodium is collected at the negative electrode.

A similar method is used to obtain metallic magnesium. Pure magnesium chloride, obtained from sea water, is melted and a direct current is passed through it. The pure magnesium is collected at the negative electrode.

Electrolysis is used to break down water, which is a compound of hydrogen and oxygen, into its two component gases. The difficulty here, however, is that pure water is not an electrolyte and will not conduct electricity. An indirect method must be employed, therefore.

A little sulphuric acid is added to the water. Each molecule of this acid contains two hydrogen atoms combined with a group of atoms consisting of one sulfur atom and four oxygen atoms. This group of atoms is called the *sulfate* portion (whose chemical symbol is SO_4). As each molecule of sulfuric acid dissolves in the water, it breaks down into two positive hydrogen ions (H^+) and one sulfate ion bearing two negative charges (SO_4^{--}).

The hydrogen ions are attracted to the negative electrode where each ion obtains an electron and becomes a neutral hydrogen atom. Hydrogen is a gas and it is collected as it bubbles off around the negative electrode. The negative sulfate ion is attracted to the positive electrode where it becomes neutral by surrendering its two excess electrons. It immediately reacts with the water around it, forming sulfuric acid as it combines with the hydrogen of the water. The oxygen remaining when the hydrogen of the water combines with the sulfate portion is released as a gas, which is collected as it bubbles off around the positive electrode.

The newly formed sulfuric acid ionizes once again and the entire process is repeated. The sulfuric acid in the solution remains constant, but the water is used up. Since each molecule of water contains two atoms of hydrogen and one atom of oxygen, twice as much hydrogen gas is produced.

Electrolysis is also used to extract metallic aluminum from its ore. Vast quantities of aluminum exist in the crust of the earth, generally in the form of an oxide called *bauxite*. Yet, it was so difficult to extract the metal from its ore that for many years aluminum remained a precious metal. Today, thanks to a process invented in 1886 by an American, Charles Martin Hall, aluminum costs but a few cents a pound.

The key to the problem was in finding a way to change the bauxite ore into a liquid so that it could ionize. It does not dissolve in water. Nor can it be melted readily, since its melting point is about 2,000°C. Hall discovered that bauxite will ionize in molten *cryolite*, a mineral composed of sodium, aluminum, and fluorine, which melts at about 1,000°C.

The bauxite is dissolved in molten cryolite and the solution is placed in a carbon-lined iron box which acts as the negative electrode (see Figure 15-1). The positive electrode consists of several

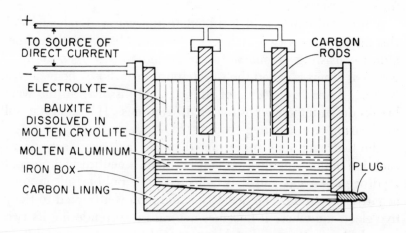

Fig. 15-1. How aluminum is obtained by electrolysis.

Fig. 15-2. Interior view of an aluminum smelting works, showing a row of electrolytic cells in operation.

carbon rods that dip down into the electrolyte. The negative oxygen ions are attracted to the positive carbon rods. There they surrender their negative charges and become neutral oxygen atoms. The positive aluminum ions migrate to the negative electrode. There they receive electrons and become neutral aluminum atoms. The molten aluminum collects at the bottom of the box. From time to time, it is drained off by removing the plug or by siphoning off the molten metal.

A variation of the electrolysis process, called *electroplating*, is used to deposit a metal coat on the surface of some object. For example, suppose we wish to deposit a copper coat on a piece of iron. A compound of the metal to be deposited—in this case, copper sulfate—is dissolved in water. As it dissolves, it forms positive copper ions and negative sulfate ions. If a direct current is passed through the solution, the copper ions will be attracted to the negative electrode and the sulfate ions to the positive one.

The object to be plated is made the negative electrode. As the positive copper ions reach this electrode, they obtain electrons and become neutral copper atoms. These atoms adhere to the electrode and the object thus becomes coated with a fine, uniformly distributed copper plate.

The negative sulfate ions migrate to the positive electrode, which may be a carbon rod. There the ions become neutralized as they yield up their excess electrons, and they immediately react with the hydrogen of the water to form sulfuric acid, releasing oxygen in the process. Hence the electrolyte gradually changes from copper sulfate to sulfuric acid as the copper is deposited on the negative electrode.

In practice, the positive electrode usually is made of a bar of pure metal of the type being deposited—in this example, copper. Now, as the sulfate ion is neutralized, it reacts with the copper instead of the water, forming fresh copper sulfate. Thus the copper sulfate of the electrolyte is replenished and the process may continue until the entire copper electrode is "eaten away."

Since the object to be plated forms the negative electrode, it must be a conductor of electricity. However, nonconductors may be plated, too, if they first are covered with a coating of powdered graphite. This graphite adheres to the object and, since it is a conductor, the metal plate will be deposited on its surface.

Almost any metal can be used for plating. Nickel, cadmium, and chromium frequently are deposited for protective purposes. Silver and gold, too, are used for plating, but they generally are employed for decorative and ornamental purposes rather than for protecting the surface of the object from the air.

Only direct current may be used. This current usually is supplied by storage batteries or direct-current generators. A great deal of skill is necessary to form a satisfactory plate. The current and temperature of the electrolyte must be carefully controlled if a smooth, durable plate is to be obtained.

Electroplating enters into the manufacture of books. As you know, printing is accomplished by the use of type. The metal em-

International Silver Company.

Fig. 15-3. Electroplating spoons. The spoons move around the tank, keeping the solution agitated and assuring an even distribution of silver during plating. The length of time the pieces remain in the tank and the amount of electrical current used determines the thickness of the silver deposited on spoons.

ployed for type generally is an alloy of lead, antimony, and tin. Although a large number of impressions can be taken from such type, it is relatively soft. If several hundred thousand copies are to be printed, such type metal would soon wear out. Accordingly, we must print a book like this one from a harder metal.

The ordinary type is arranged to form a page. Then a special kind of wax is poured over it. When this wax hardens and is peeled off, it bears an impression of that page. The wax then is coated with graphite to make it a conductor and becomes the negative electrode of a copper electroplating setup. When the copper plate becomes about as thick as an ordinary visiting card, it is peeled off the wax. We thus have an impression of the page in copper, which is a good deal harder than type metal. The copper sheet is backed by a layer

Fig. 15-4.

Electrotype.

about an inch thick of a special metal alloy to give it stiffness. The page is printed from this copper sheet.

This process is called *electrotyping*. A similar process is used for making phonograph records. The sound to be recorded is converted into vibrations of a sharp needle as it passes over the surface of a wax disk. This wax disk, which bears the impression of the vibrations of the needle, then is coated with graphite and electroplated. The metallic coating, which is stripped off the wax disk, bears these impressions, too. This plate, which is called the *master copy,* then is suitably backed to give it stiffness; duplicate records are made by pressing against it disks of a special composition, such as shellac or plastic. The impressions on the master copy are transferred to the duplicate records somewhat in the fashion that the impressions of the type are transferred to paper.

The electroplating process may be used for purposes other than coating some object. For example, copper obtained directly from its ore may contain certain impurities. First it is dissolved in sulfuric acid, forming copper sulfate. This copper sulfate solution will, of course, still contain these impurities.

This solution is the electrolyte. A thin sheet of pure copper forms the negative electrode. The positive electrode consists of a slab of the raw, impure copper. As a direct current passes through the solution, pure copper will be deposited on the negative electrode, which will grow in size. The copper of the positive electrode will react with the sulfate ion, forming copper sulfate and thus replenishing the solution. The impurities sink to the bottom of the tank as a sort of mud or sludge. This process is called *electrolytic refining*.

Fig. 15-5. Lifting a load of cathode (negative) copper electrodes from electrolytic refining tanks.

The Anaconda Company.

QUESTIONS

Wherever possible, diagrams should be used to clarify the answers to these questions. These diagrams need not be elaborate, but they should be drawn neatly with the significant portions clearly labeled.

1. In terms of the electron theory, explain the electrolysis of water.
2. Describe and explain how metallic aluminum is extracted from its ore.
3. In terms of the electron theory, explain the electroplating process.
4. Explain how electrotypes are made.
5. In terms of the electron theory, explain the electrolytic refining of copper.

16

Applications Depending Upon Magnetic Effect

As current flows through a coil of wire, a magnetic field is built up around the coil. This magnetic field can be employed in several ways. It can be used to magnetize magnetic materials and attract them to the coil. This is the principle behind devices such as the lifting magnet, relays, and many others. Or the magnetic field can be used to induce an electromotive force in a conductor that happens to cross the field. This is the principle behind the generator (which was discussed in Chapter 11) and the transformer.

A third use for the magnetic field is to produce mechanical motion. This is the principle behind the electric motor, which will be discussed in the next chapter.

A. *Electromagnets, relays, and sucking coils*

Where large quantities of magnetic materials, such as scrap iron, iron sheets, iron castings, are to be moved, the *lifting magnet*

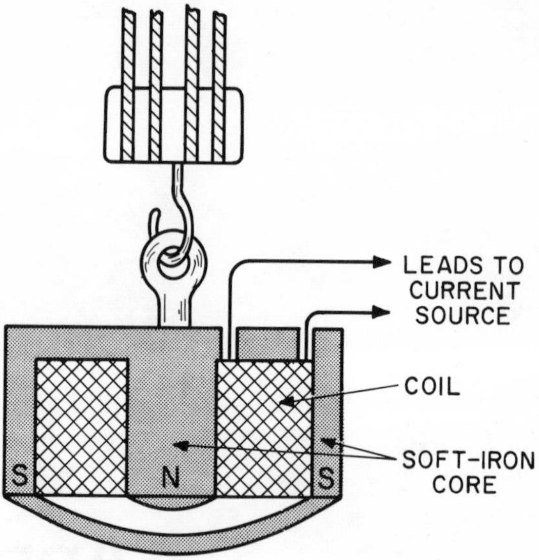

Fig. 16-1.

Cross-sectional view
of lifting magnet.

LEADS TO
CURRENT
SOURCE

COIL

SOFT–IRON
CORE

(illustrated in Figure 16-1) generally is employed. This is a large electromagnet made up of a coil of wire and a soft-iron core. This core not only passes through the center of the coil, but also surrounds the outside. Thus, when a direct current is sent through the coil, the effect is that of a number of U-magnets arranged in a circle with all their north (or south) poles at the center. Not only does this produce a concentration of the magnetic force, but also the coil is protected from outside damage.

In Chapter 5, Subdivision D, 2, we learned that the strength of the electromagnet depends upon the number of turns of the coil and the current flowing through them, as well as the material and shape of the core. Accordingly, electromagnets that must lift tons of material at a time are constructed with many turns of wire heavy enough to carry safely the large currents required. Such lifting magnets generally are equipped with portable d-c generators that furnish the required current. Of course, the electromagnet does not lift the load. It merely holds it fast while a motor-driven crane lifts both magnet and load.

Another use for the electromagnet is in the *electric bell* illustrated in Figure 16-2. The electromagnet consists of two coils of wire on a U-shaped soft-iron core. These coils are wound in opposite directions so that, as current flows through them, a north and south pole appear next to each other, thus concentrating the magnetic field.

The soft-iron armature is mounted on a flat spring and so placed that, normally, the two contact points touch each other. If a source of direct current is connected to the binding posts, current flows through the coils of the electromagnet, through the two contact points, through the armature spring, and back to the source. As it does so, however, the electromagnet is activated, attracting the armature. As the armature is pulled toward the electromagnet, the contact points are separated, breaking the circuit. This causes the electromagnet to release the armature and its spring forces it back to its normal position. The contact points touch and the circuit is completed again. The entire cycle repeats itself, the armature vibrates back and forth, and the hammer attached to this armature repeatedly strikes the gong.

The source may be several dry cells which are connected to the binding posts through a pushbutton, a sort of switch. Note that the direction of current flow makes no difference so far as the operation

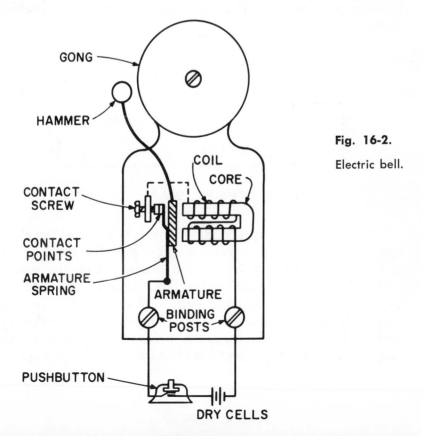

Fig. 16-2.

Electric bell.

of the bell is concerned. Accordingly, the bell will operate on alternating current as well as on direct current. For a-c operation we generally use a *bell-ringing transformer* which steps the 120-volt line down to about 6 volts.

Some of the most interesting applications of the magnetic effect of the electric current are in the field of communications. Man constantly seeks to extend both the distance over which he is able to transmit intelligence and the speed with which it is sent. Yet, up to the nineteenth century, messages sent by sight or sound signals were limited to a few miles. Longer distances could be covered only through the use of the mail or by personal messengers.

With the invention of the electromagnet, however, a new field was opened. An electromagnet can be operated from any distance, provided we have wires long enough and an electromotive force strong enough to send the current through the wires. If we connect the battery and the switch that opens and closes the circuit to one end of the wires, and the electromagnet to the other end (Figure 16-3), a current will flow through the electromagnet as the switch is closed. As a result, a soft-iron armature is attracted to the electromagnet.

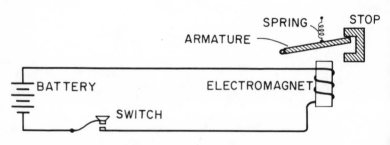

Fig. 16-3. Simple one-way telegraph circuit.

When the switch is opened, the circuit is broken and the electromagnet loses its attractive force. A spring pulls the armature back. A U-shaped metal stop is provided against which the armature strikes. Thus, as the switch is closed, the armature is pulled down until it strikes against the bottom arm of the stop. When the switch is opened, the spring pulls the armature up until it strikes the upper arm of the stop. As the armature strikes the stop, it produces a metallic click. So, if the switch is closed and opened, we hear two clicks—once when the armature strikes the bottom arm, and again when it strikes the upper arm.

The interval of time elapsing between the two clicks at the electromagnet end of the line is determined by the length of time the switch at the other end is kept closed. If the switch is closed for a short period, the interval between clicks is short. If it is closed for a long period, the interval between clicks, too, will be long.

Here, then, is a method for transmitting intelligence over wires. All we must do is arrange a code composed of short intervals between clicks, called dots (.), and long intervals between clicks, called dashes (−). For example, the letter *A* may be sent as *dot dash* (. −); the letter *B* as *dash dot dot dot* (− . . .); and so forth. Because the current flows through the wires at a speed nearly equal to that of light (186,000 miles per second), messages can be sent instantaneously as far as we can string our wires and send current through them.

This is the principle of the *telegraph*. Although scientists all over the world had been working on the problem, its invention generally is credited to an American, Samuel F. B. Morse, in 1837.

The telegraph circuit, in simplified form, is illustrated in Figure 16-4. Each end of the circuit contains a switch (called a *key*) and an electromagnet-armature-stop combination (called a *sounder*). Note that the keys, electromagnets, and battery are connected in series.

Normally, both keys are kept closed. When the operator at one end of the line wishes to send a message, he opens his key, thus breaking the circuit. When he closes his key, both sounders operate. In this way, the message is sent. After he is through, he closes his key again.

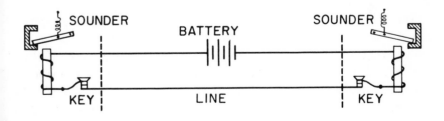

Fig. 16-4. Simple two-way telegraph circuit.

No sooner had man learned how to send intelligence over the long wires of the telegraph circuit, when the next step was suggested. Was it possible to send the spoken word over such wires? Men like Charles Boursel of France and Philip Reis of Germany had some good ideas, but it remained for an American, Alexander Graham Bell, to invent the first practical *telephone* in 1876.

Speech originates with the vibrating vocal cords in the human throat. As these cords vibrate back and forth, they alternately compress and expand the air in front of them. These alternate compressions (*condensations*) and expansions (*rarefactions*) travel through the air in the form of a sound wave.

There are two factors that determine the intelligence carried by the sound wave. The tone or pitch of the sound is determined by the *frequency* of the sound wave, that is, by the number of condensations and rarefactions per second. The intensity or loudness of the sound is determined by the *amplitude* of the sound wave.

At the transmitting end of the telephone, the sound wave enters a *microphone* where the variations of the sound wave produce corresponding fluctuations in an electric current. One type of microphone commonly used in the telephone consists of a large number of small carbon granules loosely packed in a cup between two carbon plates (Figure 16-5). The back plate is firmly held in place, but the front one can move back and forth. This movable carbon plate is fastened to a thin, flexible diaphragm that is held firmly at its rim.

Suppose, as in Figure 16-5A, that a rarefaction of the sound wave approaches this diaphragm. Because of the low pressure produced by this rarefaction, the diaphragm bulges out, carrying with it the movable carbon plate. As a result, the carbon granules are more loosely packed than before. When a condensation approaches the flexible diaphragm (Figure 16-5B), the latter is pushed in and the carbon granules become more tightly packed.

The electrical resistance between the two carbon plates through the carbon granules depends upon how tightly the granules are packed. If they are packed loosely, the resistance is greater. If they are packed tightly, the resistance is smaller. Thus the granules form a variable resistor whose resistance depends upon whether a rarefaction or a condensation of the sound wave approaches the diaphragm.

Now, suppose that we apply a steady direct current across the

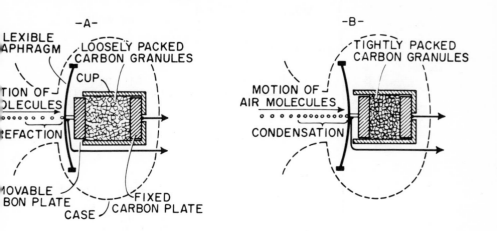

Fig. 16-5. Carbon-granule microphone, showing the effects of rarefactions and condensations of the sound wave.

two carbon plates. The current will remain steady so long as the carbon granules are not disturbed. But if a rarefaction approaches the diaphragm, the resistance of the granules increases. As a result, the current drops. As a condensation approaches the diaphragm, the resistance decreases and the current rises. You can see this relationship in the graphs of Figure 16-6.

Here, then, is a method for superimposing intelligence upon an electric current. If the sound wave produced by the human voice strikes the diaphragm, its condensations and rarefactions will be impressed upon the electric current. We call this process of superimposing intelligence on the electric current *modulation,* and say that *the sound wave modulates the electric current.*

The modulated current, carrying the intelligence superimposed on it, can be sent along wires to a distant point. The next problem to be solved is how to remove the intelligence from the current. This is the function of the *telephone receiver.*

In the telephone receiver a permanent magnet is so placed that it attracts a thin, flexible, iron diaphragm that is held along its rim. (See Figure 16-7.) A coil is placed over one end of the magnet and it is so wound that, as current flows through this coil, a magnetic

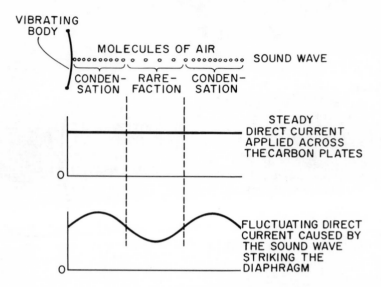

Fig. 16-6. Graphs showing how the sound wave modulates the electric current.

field is set up opposed to that of the permanent magnet. The diaphragm, then, is attracted with a force that is the resultant of the magnetic field of the permanent magnet and the opposing field of the coil. The current that flows through this coil comes from the microphone.

If a steady current flows through the coil, the resultant pull on the diaphragm, too, will be steady. However, if a fluctuating current flows through the coil, its magnetic field will fluctuate with the variations in current. Thus, the resultant pull on the diaphragm will fluctuate in step and, accordingly, the diaphragm will vibrate back and forth. The vibrating diaphragm will set in motion the air next

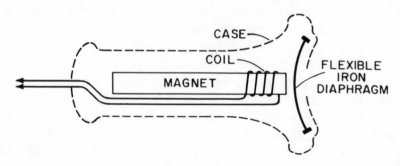

Fig. 16-7. Telephone receiver.

to it and a sound wave will be produced. Since the vibrations of the diaphragm are in step with the variations of the original sound wave, the sound wave it produces will be identical with the original.

The intelligence carried by the sound wave can be stored in a magnetic wire or tape for future reproduction by means of the *magnetic recorder* invented by Valdemar Poulsen, a Danish scientist. In this device the sound wave strikes a microphone, producing a fluctuating current, as in the telephone. This fluctuating current is made to flow through the coil of an electromagnet (the *recording coil*), thus producing a magnetic field that fluctuates in step with the variations of the current.

An unmagnetized wire made of some magnetic material passes through this magnetic field at a uniform rate. As it does so, the wire becomes magnetized to a degree depending upon the strength of the magnetic field at that particular instant. Since the magnetic field is a

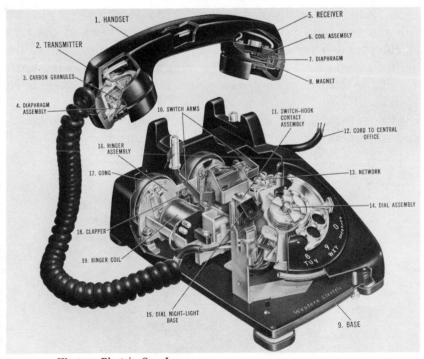

Western Electric Co., Inc.

Fig. 16-8. Cutaway view of modern telephone showing transmitter, receiver, dialing, and ringing apparatus.

fluctuating one, various portions of the wire are magnetized to a greater or lesser degree, depending upon the strength of the field at the instant each portion is passing through. Thus the intelligence contained in the sound wave is transferred into a corresponding magnetic pattern in the wire.

In modern practice, a magnetic tape is used instead of the wire. This tape usually is made of paper and is coated with some plastic material. Imbedded in this plastic is a layer of finely-divided magnetic material, such as iron powder. In its unmagnetized state, the molecules of iron are arranged helter-skelter. But as they pass through the magnetic field, they are lined up, as shown in Figure 5-9B, and held in position by the plastic coating.

To reproduce the sound, the tape bearing the magnetic pattern is made to pass at the same uniform rate through a second coil of wire (the *playback* coil). As the magnetic fields surrounding the magnetized particles of the tape cut across the conductors of the coil, a current is induced in that coil. This induced current will vary in step with the variations in strength of the magnetic fields of the tape which, you will recall, vary in step with the intelligence of the original sound. Passing this varying induced current through a device similar to the telephone receiver causes the original sound to be reproduced.

With reasonable care, a recording can be reproduced many thousands of times. If we wish to erase the recording from the tape, all

Webster Electric Co.

Fig. 16-9. Magnetic tape recorder.

we need do is to pass the tape through the magnetic field produced by a high-frequency alternating current flowing through another coil (the *erase* coil). As a result, the magnetic molecules will become arranged in a helter-skelter pattern once more. The tape then is ready to receive a new recording.

The electromagnet may be used to protect electrical circuits against overloads and underloads. For example, look at the illustration of an *overload circuit breaker* shown in Figure 16-10. Current

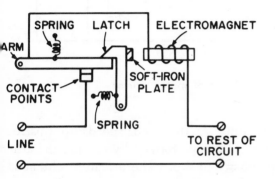

Fig. 16-10.

Overload circuit breaker.

flows from the line, through the contact points, through the movable arm, through the coil of the electromagnet, through the circuit being protected, and back to the line. As a normal amount of current flows through the electromagnet, its attraction for the soft-iron plate attached to the latch is overcome by the pull of the spring and, hence, the latch remains in place. However, should the current rise to a dangerous value, the pull of the electromagnet is increased and the soft-iron plate and latch are pulled over to the right. This releases the arm whose spring pulls it upward. The contact points are separated and the circuit is broken, thus protecting the rest of the electrical circuit. This circuit remains open until the cause of current rise is corrected and the circuit breaker is relatched.

Sometimes a current drop (underload) may become dangerous. For example, in certain types of electric motors (as you will learn later in the book) a sharp drop in the current flowing through the field may damage the motor unless the line current is disconnected immediately. Accordingly, the *motor starter* (illustrated in Figure 16-11) is employed.

This motor requires that at the start a certain resistance be placed

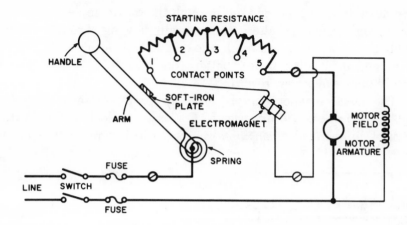

Fig. 16-11. Circuit of motor starter.

in series with the motor armature. As the motor speeds up, this resistance is reduced gradually. This is performed by moving the arm clockwise from contact point #1 to #5. (The armature circuit is shown in heavy lines.)

Note that as the arm reaches contact point #1, the motor field circuit is completed and current flows through the electromagnet which is in series with it. When the arm reaches contact point #5, all the resistance has been cut out of the armature circuit. Current in the field circuit flows from the line, through the arm, through the resistors, through the electromagnet, through the motor field, and back to the line. The soft-iron plate attached to the arm rests against the electromagnet and is held by it.

If, for any reason, the current in the field circuit should drop sharply, the electromagnet becomes weaker. Now the spring on the arm is powerful enough to pull the arm all the way back to the left. This opens the line and the motor is protected.

The *relay* is an electromagnetic switch that is used to open or close electrical circuits by remote control. Look at Figure 16-12A. The relay consists of an electromagnet and its switching mechanism, made up of a soft-iron armature and its arm, and a set of contact points mounted on flat springs. Note that there are two distinct circuits. One is the *control* circuit consisting of the switch, battery A, and the coil of the electromagnet. The other is the *controlled* circuit made up of the two contact points, battery B, and the bell. Note, too, that, as represented in the illustration, both circuits are open.

As the switch in the control circuit is closed, the electromagnet becomes energized and attracts the soft-iron armature. As this armature is attracted, its arm presses against the contact spring. The contact points are forced together, thus closing the controlled circuit. As a result, the bell starts ringing.

See how this circuit can be used for a burglar-alarm system, for example. The switch of the control circuit may be installed so that the opening of a door or window in a room causes the switch to close. Immediately, the alarm bell starts ringing. This bell may be in the room or, if the wires be extended enough, in the office of a protective agency.

The relay illustrated in Figure 16-12A is known as an *open-circuit relay*—that is, when no current flows through the coil of the electro-

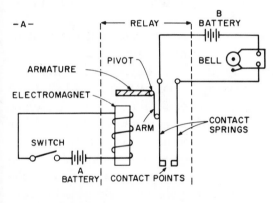

Fig. 16-12.

A. Open-circuit relay.
B. Commercial relay.

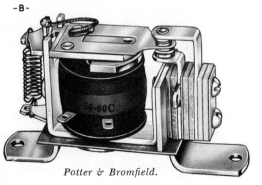

Potter & Bromfield.

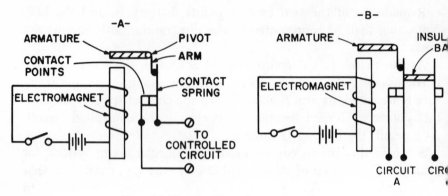

Fig. 16-13. **A**. Closed-current relay.
B. Multi-circuit relay.

magnet the contact points are separated and the controlled circuit is open. We also have *closed-circuit relays* where, with no current flowing through the electromagnet, the contact points touch and the controlled circuit is closed. (See Figure 16-13A.) When current flows through the coil, the armature is attracted and the contact points are separated, opening the controlled circuit.

It is possible to construct relays that can perform several different functions simultaneously. For example, look at Figure 16-13B. Here are two sets of contact points, each set controlling a separate circuit. The two inner springs are connected by means of an insulated bar so that they move together. As the electromagnet is activated, the first set of contact points separate, thus opening circuit **A**. At the same time, the second set of contact points touch, thus closing circuit **B**. Of course, more sets of contact points may be added to control more circuits.

By winding the coil of the electromagnet with many turns of fine wire, the relay can be made very sensitive. That is, it will operate with very little current.

For example, telegraph wires are strung over long distances. Because of the resistance of these wires, the current flowing in them may not be large enough to actuate the telegraph sounder which must operate strongly to produce an audible click. Accordingly, we connect a sensitive open-circuit relay with its coil in series with the telegraph line. The controlled circuit consists of the relay's contact points, the telegraph sounder, and a strong local battery. As a signal comes over the line, the relay closes the controlled circuit, and the sounder produces an audible click.

As another example, suppose we wish an electric lamp to light when a photoelectric cell is illuminated. The current generated by the cell when illuminated (generally in the order of microamperes) is too little to operate the lamp. Accordingly, we send the generated current through the coil of an extremely sensitive open-circuit relay. The controlled circuit consists of the relay's contact points, the lamp, and the power line, all connected in series. As the contact points touch, the lamp lights up.

The *sucking coil* is a variation of the electromagnet. It consists of a hollow coil of wire (the *solenoid*) and a movable soft-iron core (the *plunger*). When current flows through the solenoid, the magnetic field tends to pull, or suck, the plunger into the center of the coil. When current ceases flowing, a spring pulls the plunger out again. If we attach a lever to the plunger, we may operate some mechanical device, such as a valve, as the plunger is sucked in by the magnetic field or pulled back by the spring. Automatic washing machines often use such sucking coils to control the water valves. (The coil and its plunger sometimes are called a solenoid. Strictly speaking, only the coil is the solenoid.)

The sucking coil can be used as a door chime, as shown in Figure 16-14. The coil and its plunger are mounted vertically so that the plunger can slide down by gravity. The spring prevents it from falling through. As the pushbutton is pressed, the circuit is closed and current flows through the solenoid. The plunger is drawn up into the hollow core of the coil and the wooden hammer strikes the chime bar, producing a musical note. When the pushbutton is released, the circuit is opened and the plunger drops back.

If alternating current is passed through an electromagnet, the polarity of the magnet will, of course, change periodically in step with the alternations of the current. Also, once each alternation the current drops to zero. However, in most applications it makes no difference whether it is a north or south pole that is doing the attracting. If a 60-cycle current is used, there are 120 alternations each second and, hence, the interruptions of the magnetic field are of such short duration as to be negligible for most purposes. Accordingly, it is possible to operate electromagnets on alternating currents.

There is one precaution, however. The core of the electromagnet finds itself in the magnetic field of the coil. If a steady direct current flows through the coil, no current will be induced in the core since both the core and field are stationary. But if an alternating current flows through the coil, the changing magnetic field will cause a current to be induced in the core. This is called the *eddy current*.

The eddy current is undesirable on two counts. The flow of current through the core represents a power loss which must come from the source. Also, the flow of current may cause the core to get quite hot. To reduce the eddy current, the core is not built solid but, rather, is made up of many thin slices, called *laminations*. Each lamination is insulated from its neighbor by a coat of varnish or some similar material. This offers considerable resistance and, as a result, the eddy currents are cut down. In sucking coils operating on alternating current, too, the plunger is built up of laminations.

Keep in mind that the coil of an electromagnet will offer a greater opposition to the flow of alternating current than to the flow of direct current. This is because, in addition to the ohmic resistance of

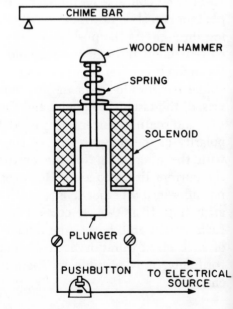

Fig. 16-14.

Electric door chime.

the coil, which is present for both types of current, with alternating current there is the inductive reactance. Hence, if a coil designed to operate on alternating current at a certain voltage should be connected to a source of direct current at the same voltage, the flow of current may be great enough to burn out the winding.

B.   *The transformer*

Suppose we send an alternating current through a coil of wire. As the current goes through its first alternation, it starts from zero, reaches its positive maximum, and drops to zero again. During its next alternation the current drops from zero to its negative maximum and goes back to zero. Then the entire cycle is repeated.

As the current flows, the magnetic field around the coil expands from zero to its maximum value in one direction, and collapses to zero again. Then the field reverses itself, expands to its maximum value in the other direction, and collapses to zero. This completes one cycle. Thus the coil is surrounded by a constantly changing magnetic field.

Suppose, now, we place a second coil near the first. As the changing magnetic field around the first coil cuts across the turns of the second, a voltage is induced in this latter coil. If a circuit is connected to the second coil, the induced voltage will cause a current to flow through that circuit. Here, then, is a method for transferring electrical energy from one circuit to another without any electrical connection. We say that the two coils are *magnetically coupled.*

We call such a combination of two coils a *transformer.* The first coil is called the *primary winding* and the second coil is the *secondary winding.* Generally, the two coils are wound over each other so that the magnetic field of the primary winding can readily cut the turns of the secondary.

The transfer of energy from the primary to the secondary winding of the transformer depends upon the magnetic lines of force around the primary winding cutting across, or *linking,* with the turns of the secondary winding. In an ideal transformer, all these lines of force would link up with the turns of the secondary winding, achieving 100 per cent (or unity) coupling. This is impossible to obtain in practice. A certain amount of the magnetic lines of force leak off into the air. We call this *leakage flux,* and its effect is termed *leakage reactance.*

To reduce this leakage flux, the primary and secondary windings may be wound on a core of iron or other magnetic substance. This tends to concentrate the lines of force and to keep them from leaking off. If this core is in the form of a straight bar, we have what is called an *open-core* transformer.

More frequently, this core is in the form of a closed ring or square. Thus, a closed magnetic circuit is furnished, and the leakage flux is reduced further. We call this type a *closed-core* transformer (Figure 16-15). A variation that is greatly used is the *shell-core* type illustrated in Figure 16-15B. The primary and secondary windings are placed one over the other on the center arm of the core. The shell-core transformer can be designed to produce a coupling that closely approaches unity, or 100 per cent.

The symbol for the transformer is ⧙⧙ . The vertical lines between the two coils represent the iron core. If the transformer has no iron core, that is, if it is an air-core type, the vertical lines are omitted from the symbol.

In addition to the losses due to imperfect coupling, we may have *copper* and *iron* losses in a transformer. The copper loss is due to the resistance of the wire making up the turns of the windings. The iron loss may be divided into two parts.

Since the core is in the magnetic field, it is magnetized. But the alternating current causes the iron core to change the polarity of its

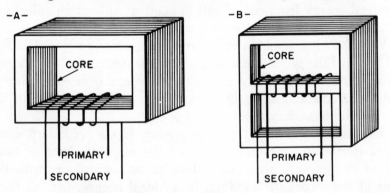

Fig. 16-15. Closed-core transformers.
A. Simple type.
B. Shell-core type.

poles in step with the frequency of the current. A certain amount of energy is required to make this change. This energy comes from the electrical source and, therefore, is a loss. We call this loss *hysteresis loss*. It may be partially reduced by using cores of silicon steel or of certain other alloys that are much more permeable than iron—that is, are easier to magnetize and demagnetize.

The other iron loss is due to the electric current that is induced in the iron core by the changing magnetic fields of the coils wound upon it. This induced current is the *eddy current*. Since the eddy current must come from the electrical source, it, too, is a loss. To reduce eddy-current losses, these cores are not made of solid metal, but are built up of very thin laminations. Each lamination is coated with an insulation of oxide or varnish so that the eddy currents cannot circulate through the core.

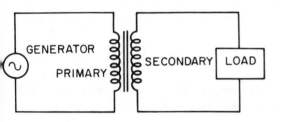

Fig. 16-16.

Transformer circuit.

Let us examine the circuit of the transformer as illustrated in Figure 16-16. The primary winding is connected to an electrical source, such as an a-c generator. The secondary winding is connected to some electrical device which furnishes a load on this secondary circuit. Suppose we start with the secondary circuit open and drawing no current. In the primary circuit, current flows from the generator, through the primary coil, and back to the generator.

Only a small current flows through the primary circuit. This is because the magnetic field, constantly cutting across the turns of the primary coil, induces in it a counter electromotive force that is nearly equal to the applied voltage. What power is consumed is used mainly to magnetize the core.

Suppose, now, that we complete the secondary circuit, permitting current to flow through the secondary winding and load. As current flows through this winding, a magnetic field is set up around it which, according to Lenz's law, tends to neutralize a certain amount of the magnetic field around the primary winding. This reduces the counter electromotive force induced in the primary and, as a result, more current flows through that coil from the source.

If the load is increased (that is, its impedance is reduced), more current flows through the secondary circuit. As a result, the counter electromotive force of the primary is further reduced and more current is drawn from the source through the primary circuit. If the load is reduced and less current flows through the secondary circuit, less current flows through the primary circuit. Thus the transformer automatically adjusts itself to changes in load. However, if the load be made too great, enough current may flow through the primary circuit to burn out its winding.

In addition to transferring electrical energy from one circuit to another, the transformer may perform another function. Assume that the generator furnishes 100 volts and the primary winding has 100 turns. Assume, too, that the transformer is an ideal type—that is, it has no losses.

In such a transformer the primary circuit draws no power from the source except upon demand from the load in the secondary circuit. Electrical energy is changed to magnetic energy and back again. The counter electromotive force produced by the primary winding is equal to the voltage of the source, 100 volts. Hence, as the magnetic field cuts across this 100-turn winding, each turn has one volt induced in it. But the same magnetic field is cutting across the turns of the secondary winding as well. Hence each turn of this winding, too, has one volt induced in it. If the secondary winding also has 100 turns, the induced voltage across the secondary is 100 volts.

Suppose, however, we construct our transformer with only 10 turns in the secondary. Since one volt is induced in each turn, the secondary voltage will be 10 volts. This is called a *step-down* transformer. If we construct the transformer with 1,000 turns in the secondary, the secondary voltage will be 1,000 volts. This is a *step-up* transformer. Thus the transformer can be used to step up or step down alternating voltage.

From the above, we can see that the ratio between the voltage across the primary winding and that across the secondary winding is equal to the ratio between the number of turns of the primary winding and the number of turns of the secondary winding. This relationship may be expressed in a formula as follows:

$$\frac{E_p}{E_s} = \frac{N_p}{N_s}$$

where E_p is the voltage across the primary winding, E_s is the voltage across the secondary winding, N_p is the number of turns in the primary winding, and N_s is the number of turns of the secondary winding.

Example. A transformer is required to deliver a 360-volt alternating current across the secondary winding. Assume a primary winding of 1,000 turns connected across the 120-volt a-c line. How many turns must we have in the secondary winding?

$$\frac{E_p}{E_s} = \frac{N_p}{N_s}, \text{ or } \frac{120}{360} = \frac{1000}{N_s}$$

$$N_s = \frac{1000 \times 360}{120} = 3{,}000 \text{ turns.} \quad \textit{Ans.}$$

In our ideal transformer, we assume no losses. Thus, the power $(E \times I)$ of the secondary circuit is equal to the power of the primary circuit. If, as in the above example, the voltage across the secondary winding has been stepped up three times, the current set flowing in the secondary winding will be reduced to one-third that of the primary. From this, we may obtain the following formula:

$$\frac{I_p}{I_s} = \frac{N_s}{N_p}$$

where I_p is the current flowing in the primary winding, I_s is the current flowing in the secondary winding, N_s is the number of turns in the secondary winding, and N_p is the number of turns of the primary winding. Thus, the transformer can be used as well to step up or step down alternating current. Of course, if the voltage is stepped up, the current is stepped down, and vice versa.

The ability to step up or step down alternating voltage and current makes the transformer an extremely useful instrument. Step-down transformers are used to step down the line voltage for low-voltage circuits. For example, look at the bell-ringing circuit illus-

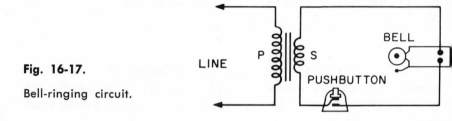

Fig. 16-17.

Bell-ringing circuit.

trated in Figure 16-17. The secondary voltage is about 6 volts. Note that the primary winding is permanently connected to the line. When the pushbutton is open—that is, when the secondary circuit is drawing no current—very little power is consumed in the primary circuit. Since the secondary voltage is only about 6 volts, there is very little sparking across the contact points of the pushbutton. If the pushbutton were in the primary circuit, there would be a good deal more sparking every time it was operated.

Step-down transformers are also used to obtain the high currents needed for welding. With a large number of turns in the primary and a single turn of heavy wire in the secondary, the voltage step-down ratio is very great and, accordingly, secondary current is very large.

Step-up transformers are employed to step up the voltage for use in high-voltage circuits. For example, let us consider the problem of transmission of electrical power from a source, such as the hydro-electric plant at Hoover Dam, to Los Angeles, several hundred miles away. At the plant, the generators produce the power at about 12,000 volts. This voltage is about the maximum that can be produced because of the necessity for heavy insulation of the wires of the fields and armatures of the generators. At higher voltages, the insulation would become so bulky as to render the generators impractical.

Since the power ($E \times I$) that must be transmitted is tremendous, if it were sent at 12,000 volts, the current would be enormous. As the current flows through the wires, it heats them because of the resistance encountered. The loss of energy owing to the heating effect (I^2R) would, accordingly, become so large as to render the transmission of power impractical, except for comparatively short distances. And even then, the wire would have to be of very large diameter in order to have low resistance.

It is here that the transformer comes to the rescue. After the power is generated at 12,000 volts, it is sent into transformers that step up the voltage 25 times to 300,000 volts (see Figure 16-18). Because the voltage has been multiplied 25 times, we obtain the same power with $\frac{1}{25}$ the current. The power is transmitted at 300,000 volts and, since the current is only $\frac{1}{25}$ of its original value, the loss due to heat is much smaller.

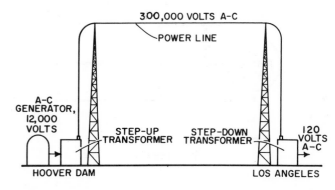

Fig. 16-18. How transformers are used to transmit electrical power over long distances.

At Los Angeles, the voltage is stepped down by other transformers to the 120 volts that is supplied at the house mains. There is no power loss (except for the slight amount in the transformers) because the current is stepped up in equal degree.

While on the subject of transmission of power, it may be pointed out that most power generated and distributed today is of the three-phase a-c type discussed in Chapter 11, Subdivision A, 3. The generator, you will recall, contains three armature coils, each wound 120° from its neighbor. It thus produces three output voltages, each having a phase difference of 120° from the others. (See Figure 11-5C.) The armature coils are joined at the generator in a Y or delta connection (see Figure 11-7) and hence current may be transmitted over three lines, one for each phase.

Note that the three-phase line is different from the three-wire line discussed in Chapter 14, Subdivision F. In the latter system,

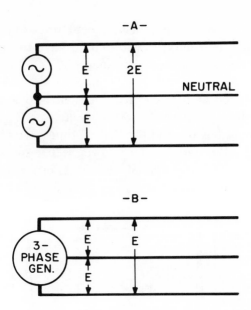

Fig. 16-19. A. Three-wire line.
B. Three-phase line.

two in-phase sources are connected in series, with the neutral line going to the junction. (See Figure 16-19A.) The voltage between one of the outside lines and the center is equal to that between the other outside line and the center. The voltage between the two outside lines is twice as great. But all three voltages are in phase. Hence we are dealing with single-phase current.

In the three-phase system (Figure 16-19B) all three voltages are equal (assuming a balanced system, which is normal) but 120° apart in phase from each other. Where three-phase current is required, all three wires are used. Where single-phase current is needed, only two wires are used.

In three-phase circuits, a separate transformer is used for each phase. Thus, in the power transmission circuit illustrated in Figure 16-20, for example, the transformers are used in sets of three. The transmission line consists of three wires.

Transformers may be constructed with more than one secondary. For example, in certain types of radio receivers, one secondary may be used to step up the line voltage to the high value required by the plates of the tubes. Another secondary may be used to step down the line voltage to the low value required by the heaters. Sometimes even more step-up or step-down windings may be employed. (See Figure 16-21.)

Transformers may be constructed with more than one primary

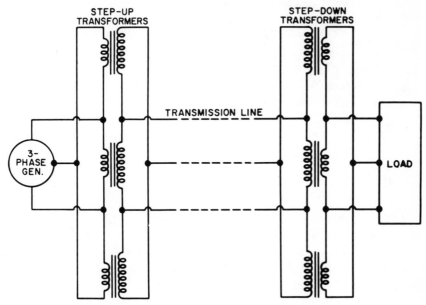

STEP-UP
TRANSFORMERS

STEP-DOWN
TRANSFORMERS

TRANSMISSION LINE

3-
PHASE
GEN.

LOAD

Fig. 16-20. Three-phase transmission system.

as well. For example, where line voltages of either 120 volts or 240 volts are available, the transformer may have two primary windings, each suited for one of the two line voltages. Thus, to obtain the same secondary voltage, the 240-volt primary winding would have twice the number of turns of the 120-volt winding.

There is still another function the transformer can perform—that of matching the impedance of the source to that of the load. It can be shown that the maximum transfer of power takes place when the impedances of the source and load are matched.

Examine Figure 16-22. The source is a generator producing a voltage which we may call E_{gen} and causing a current (I) to flow. For the sake of simplicity, we will consider all impedances to be simple resistors. The impedance of the generator is represented by R_1, which is in series with the load (R_2).

Fig. 16-21.

Transformer containing several secondary windings.

United Transformer Corp.

The voltage drop across the load ($I \times R_2$) is represented by E_{R2}. Let us assume E_{gen} to be equal to 100 volts, R_1 to be equal to 10 ohms, and R_2 to be equal to 1 ohm. The total resistance of the circuit ($R_1 + R_2$) is equal to 11 ohms. From Ohm's law, we can determine the current (I) flowing through the circuit.

$$I = \frac{E_{gen}}{R_{total}} = \frac{100}{11} = 9.09 \text{ amperes.}$$

The voltage drop (E_{R2}) across the load resistor can be determined as follows:

$$E_{R2} = I \times R_2 = 9.09 \times 1 = 9.09 \text{ volts.}$$

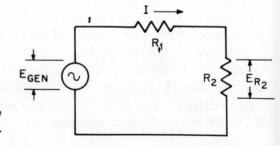

Fig. 16-22.

Diagram illustrating the transfer of electrical power.

If we assume different values for the load resistance, we can draw up the following table:

E_{gen} (Volts)	R_1 (Ohms)	R_2 (Ohms)	I (Amperes)	E_{R2} (Volts)	P_{R2} (Watts)
100	10	1	9.09	9.09	82.62
100	10	5	6.66	33.30	221.77
100	10	10	5.00	50.00	250.00
100	10	20	3.33	66.60	221.77
100	10	100	0.90	90.00	81.00

Note that the voltage of the generator was kept at 100 volts under all conditions of load. From this table, we can see that when the resistance (or impedance) of the load (R_2) is equal to the resistance (or impedance) of the source (R_1), the maximum transfer of power from the source to the load occurs. This rule applies to any circuit where electric energy is transferred from one circuit to another.

At times, a maximum transfer of power is desired even though the impedance of the load does not match that of the source. Under such circumstances, we may employ the transformer as an impedance-matching device. If the impedance of the primary winding matches that of the source and the impedance of the secondary winding matches that of the load, an impedance match is effected between the source and load (Figure 16-23). Impedance-matching transformers, called *output transformers,* often are used to match the high-impedance plate circuit of the power-output stage of a radio receiver (the source) to the low-impedance voice-coil circuit of the loudspeaker (the load).

A variation of the two-winding transformer is the *autotransformer,* which employs a single tapped coil. The circuits for both types are shown in Figure 16-24. In Figure 16-24A we have the

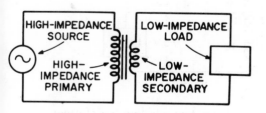

Fig. 16-23.

How the transformer is used to match a high-impedance source to a low-impedance load.

circuit of the ordinary two-winding transformer. Assume that the voltage of the source is 100 volts and that a current of 3 amperes is flowing through the primary in a direction, at that particular instant, as indicated by the arrow.

Further assume that the transformer is a step-down type, producing a voltage of 75 volts across the secondary. That is, the secondary winding will have three-quarters of the number of turns of the primary. If we assume no losses, the secondary current will be stepped up to the same degree as the voltage is stepped down. Hence, a current of 4 amperes will flow through the secondary circuit. Since the direction of current flow in the secondary circuit is opposite to the current flow in the primary, the 4 amperes will flow as indicated by the arrow.

In Figure 16-24B you see the circuit of an equivalent autotransformer. The entire winding from points A to C forms the primary. Again the source supplies a current of 3 amperes at 100 volts. One-quarter of the way down the winding from point A, a tap is taken off the coil at point B. Hence three-quarters of the turns of the en-

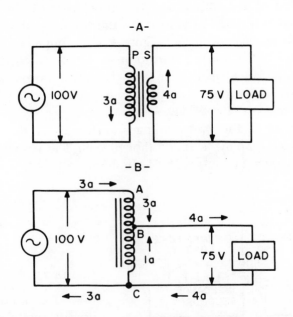

Fig. 16-24. A. Circuit of step-down, two-winding transformer.
B. Circuit of equivalent autotransformer.

tire winding lie between points B and C. If we consider this portion of the coil as the secondary, you see that we have here the same relationship between primary and secondary as in the two-winding transformer above. Hence, 75 volts appear between points B and C, and 4 amperes flow through the load.

Assume that the direction of current flow through the primary circuit at a particular instant is as indicated by the arrows. Three amperes of current flow from the source through the primary winding and back to the source. As a result, a 4-ampere current is set flowing through the secondary circuit. However, the current flow in the secondary circuit is opposite in direction to that in the primary circuit. Hence 3 amperes flow from points B to C and 4 amperes flow through the same portion of the winding from C to B. Since these currents are in opposition, the net result is a flow of one ampere.

Here, then, is one advantage for the autotransformer. Only one ampere flows through the secondary winding instead of 4 amperes for the two-winding transformer. This results in a lower I^2R loss in the secondary of the autotransformer. Another advantage results from the fact that the portion of the winding between points B and C serves the double purpose of secondary and a portion of the primary. Hence less wire is required, producing a cheaper and lighter transformer.

The autotransformer may also be used for step-up purposes. (See Figure 16-25.) Again assume that the coil is tapped one-quarter the way down at point B. This time the portion of the winding between points B and C is the primary. Assume once more that the source furnishes a current of 3 amperes at 100 volts. The entire winding

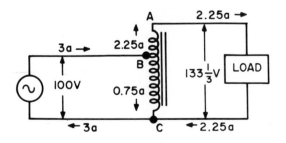

Fig. 16-25. Circuit of step-up autotransformer.

now becomes the secondary. Hence the secondary voltage is 133⅓ volts (⁴⁄₃ × 100 volts) and the secondary current is 2.25 amperes (¾ × 3 amperes). Current flows as indicated by the arrows and only 0.75 ampere (3 − 2.25 amperes) flows through the winding between points B and C.

Note that the advantages of the autotransformer become greatest as the primary and secondary approach a one-to-one turn ratio, that is, as the primary and secondary windings tend to coincide. The greater the step-up or step-down ratio between the windings, the less they coincide and, hence, the less the advantages of the transformer. Accordingly, the autotransformer usually is employed where only a small rise or fall in the source voltage is desired. For example, the voltage at the end of a long power line may drop somewhat because of the IR loss in the wires. To compensate for this small drop, a step-up autotransformer may be inserted at the far end of the line to raise the voltage to its initial value.

As is true of all other machines, the efficiency of a transformer can be determined from the following formula:

$$\text{Per cent efficiency} = \frac{\text{power output}}{\text{power input}} \times 100.$$

The power input is the power consumed by the primary circuit. The power output is that of the secondary circuit. The true power of each circuit may be obtained by using a wattmeter or by multiplying each value of apparent power (volts × amperes) by its power factor. Transformers can be designed to have very high efficiencies.

Example. The true power in the primary circuit of a transformer was found to be 1,000 watts and that of the secondary circuit 960 watts. What is the efficiency of the transformer?

$$\text{Per cent efficiency} = \frac{\text{power output}}{\text{power input}} \times 100 = \frac{960}{1,000} \times 100$$
$$= 96\%. \quad \textit{Ans.}$$

[The power output of a transformer usually is rated in *voltamperes* (or *kilovolt-amperes*) instead of watts (or kilowatts). This is because the inductance and capacitance of the load affect the phase relationships between the output voltage and current and, hence, the power. You will recall that the output power rating of the a-c generator is in the same units for the same reason.]

The copper and iron losses show up as heat in the transformer. Small transformers generally are cooled by natural radiation to the surrounding air. Large transformers, however, may be cooled by blowing air over them or by immersing them in tanks of oil which carry off the heat.

Since the iron losses increase with the frequency of the current flowing through the windings, the laminated iron-core transformer can only be used with currents of relatively low frequencies (15,000 cycles per second and lower). At higher frequencies, such as those encountered in radio, air-core transformers must be used.

In air-core transformers, only a small portion of the magnetic field cuts across the primary and secondary windings. Thus, the voltage and current ratios described for the ideal transformer do not hold true. In recent years, a high-frequency transformer has been developed which uses a special core of powdered iron. Although this type does not achieve the coupling that is possible with laminated cores of silicon steel, it provides much better coupling than does the air core.

C. Induction and ignition coils

The transformer is an alternating-current device since it utilizes a changing magnetic field to induce the voltages in the windings. Suppose the primary winding were connected to a steady direct-current source. At the moment the primary circuit is completed, current flows, a magnetic field expands around the coils, and a voltage is induced in the secondary winding. Then, as the current in the primary circuit reaches its steady value, the magnetic field, too, becomes steady and the induced voltage in the secondary winding drops to zero. When the primary circuit is broken, the magnetic field collapses and, again, an induced voltage appears momentarily in the secondary winding, though now in the opposite direction.

Thus, you see, a voltage is induced in the secondary winding every time the primary circuit is completed or broken. If we periodically interrupt the direct current flowing in the primary circuit, an alternating voltage will be induced in the secondary winding.

This is how the *induction coil* (Figure 16-26) operates. The core

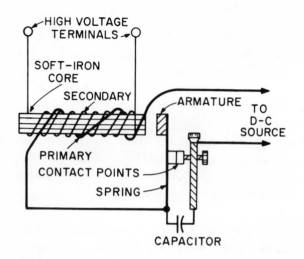

Fig. 16-26.

Induction coil.

consists of a bundle of soft-iron wires. A primary winding of few turns and a secondary winding of many turns are wound over this core. An *interrupter,* somewhat similar to the mechanism of the electric bell, is connected in series in the primary circuit to interrupt periodically the flow of direct current through that circuit.

A soft-iron armature is mounted on a flat spring and is placed near the end of the core. A contact point, also mounted on the flat spring, normally touches another fixed contact point. The primary current then flows from the source (which may consist of several dry cells connected in series), through the contact points, through the primary winding, and back to the source.

As it does so, the primary winding and core become an electromagnet, attracting the armature and spring. This causes the contact points to separate, opening the primary circuit. The electromagnet loses its magnetism and the spring pulls back the armature, causing the contact points to touch once more. The primary circuit is completed again and the entire cycle is repeated.

Each time the contact points separate, the self-induction of the primary winding will cause a spark to arc across the points. This, in time, will pit and burn these contact points. A capacitor is connected across the points to cut down the arcing. Now, as the contact points are separated, the electrical energy between them is utilized to charge up the capacitor, rather than to produce a spark.

Before the use of alternating current became so widespread, the induction coil was employed to step up a relatively low-voltage direct current to the high alternating voltage needed to operate devices such as X-ray tubes. It also was employed in early radio transmitters to produce sparks across its high-voltage terminals. Hence the induction coil is sometimes called a *spark coil*.

Today, we use a variation of the induction coil in the automobile to produce the high-voltage spark needed to explode the gasoline-and-air mixture in the cylinders of the engine. (Look at Figure 16-27.) The primary and secondary windings and the soft-iron core are housed in a plastic insulating case. The interrupter in the primary circuit is a portion of the distributor. It consists of a rotating cam that, as it turns, periodically raises and lowers the breaker arm that causes the contact points to separate and touch. The voltage source is the storage battery of the automobile. The primary circuit is completed through the metal frame of the automobile, as indicated by the symbol ⏚ (ground).

Each time the contact points touch and separate, a high voltage is induced in the secondary winding. However, the shape of the cam is such that the separation of the points is much quicker than the touching. Since the induced voltage is a function of the speed with which the points separate or touch, a much higher voltage is induced when the points separate. It is this higher voltage that is sufficient to fire the mixture in the cylinders.

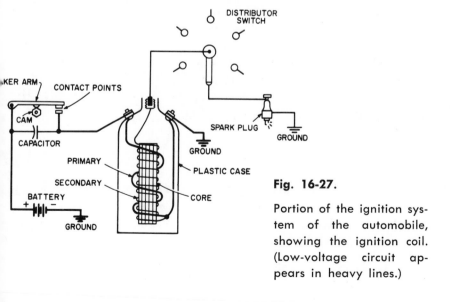

Fig. 16-27.

Portion of the ignition system of the automobile, showing the ignition coil. (Low-voltage circuit appears in heavy lines.)

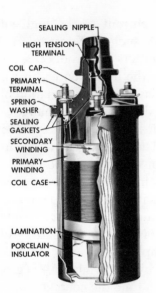

Fig. 16-28.

Cross-sectional view of an automobile ignition coil.

General Motors Corp.

The high-voltage secondary circuit consists of the secondary winding, the distributor switch, and the spark plug. This circuit, too, is completed through the frame of the automobile. The distributor switch consists of a rotating arm and a series of contact points, each connected to one of the spark plugs. It is so constructed that it is rotated by the engine in step with the cam. Switch and cam are so adjusted that, as the contact points are separated and a high voltage is induced in the secondary, the rotating arm is touching one of its contact points and a high-voltage surge is sent to its respective spark plug. A spark is produced and the mixture in the corresponding cylinder is fired.

QUESTIONS

Wherever possible, diagrams should be used to clarify the answers to these questions. These diagrams need not be elaborate, but they should be drawn neatly with the significant portions clearly labeled.

1. **Referring to the illustration in Figure 16-2, explain the operation of the electric bell.**

2. Draw a simple circuit of a two-way telegraph system. Label the important parts and explain the function of each.
3. Explain the action of a carbon-granule microphone.
4. Explain the action of the telephone receiver.
5. Explain how sound can be recorded on magnetic tape. How can this tape be used to reproduce sound?
6. Explain the action of the overload circuit breaker illustrated in Figure 16-10.
7. Explain the operation of the relay whose circuit is illustrated in Figure 16-12A.
8. What changes must be made in a d-c electromagnet if we wish it to operate on alternating current?
9. Describe the construction of an iron-core transformer. Explain the function of each of its parts.
10. What is meant by the *leakage flux* of a transformer? How may it be reduced? Explain.
11. What are the *copper* and *iron* losses of a transformer due to? What can be done to reduce these losses? Explain.
12. Explain what is meant by *a*) a *step-up transformer;* *b*) a *step-down transformer.*
13. A transformer has a primary winding of 500 turns and a secondary winding of 5,000 turns. If the primary winding be connected across a 120-volt a-c line, what will be the voltage across the secondary winding?
14. Explain how transformers are used to transmit electric power over long distances. Why are the transformers needed?
15. State three functions of the transformer. Explain.
16. Explain the operation of a *step-up autotransformer,* using a simple diagram. How may this transformer be used as a *step-down* type?
17. The true power in the primary circuit of a transformer was found to be 100 watts and that of the secondary circuit 87 watts. What is the efficiency of the transformer?
18. Explain the operation of the automobile ignition system whose circuit is illustrated in Figure 16-27.

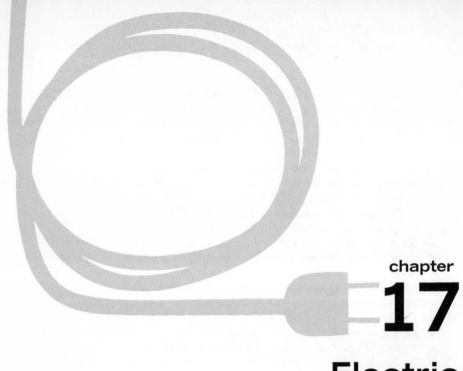

chapter

17

Electric
Motors

In Chapter 16 we discussed some applications depending upon the magnetic effects of electricity. The electric motor, which we will consider in this chapter, is another such application.

You will recall in our discussion of the generator (Chapter 11) we found that as a conductor is moved through a magnetic field, a current is induced in that conductor. It was soon discovered that if a conductor is placed in a magnetic field and current passed through it, the conductor is caused to move. Let us see why.

Assume a conductor is placed in the magnetic field existing between the poles of a magnet, as in Figure 17-1A. Since we are looking at a cross-section of this conductor, it appears as a circle. The magnetic field of the magnet is indicated by the dotted lines going from the north pole to the south pole.

Now assume that a current is sent through the conductor in such a direction that the current is flowing into the page. (The X appearing in the center of the conductor represents the tail feather of an arrow that indicates the direction of current flow.) If we apply the left-hand rule illustrated in Figure 5-14 of Chapter 5, Subdivision

D, 2, we find that the conductor is surrounded by a counterclock-wise magnetic field. (This rule, you may remember, states that if the conductor be grasped by the left hand with the thumb out-stretched and pointing in the direction of current flow, the curved fingers will point in the direction of the magnetic field around the conductor.)

Note that the magnetic field around the conductor aids the magnet's field above the conductor, but opposes the field below it. The effect, then, is to distort the magnet's field, as indicated in Figure 17-1B. Since the magnetic lines of force act somewhat as stretched rubber bands, the effect of the distorted field is to push the conductor downward.

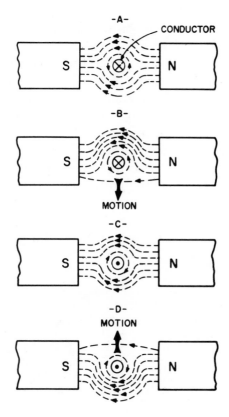

Fig. 17-1. Why a current-carrying conductor in a magnetic field is caused to move. The direction of movement is indicated.

If, as in Figure 17-1C, we reverse the current flow through the conductor (as shown by the dot in the center of the conductor which represents the tip of an arrow indicating the direction of current flow), the magnetic field around the conductor aids the magnet's field below the conductor, but opposes the field above it. The effect, then, is to distort the magnet's field, as indicated in Figure 17-1D. As a result, the conductor is pushed upward.

We can formulate a *motor rule* to find the direction of motion imparted to a current-carrying conductor in a magnetic field. Extend the thumb, forefinger, and middle finger of the right hand so that they are at right angles to each other. Let the forefinger point in the direction of the magnetic field (from north to south pole). Let the middle finger point in the direction of current flow in the conductor. The thumb then points in the direction of motion imparted to the conductor.

The force acting upon a current-carrying conductor in a magnetic field depends upon the strength of the field, the length of the conductor in that field, and the amount of current flowing through the conductor. The greater any of these components becomes, the greater is the force exerted on the conductor.

Suppose we were to mount a single loop of wire between the poles of a magnet so that it was free to rotate on its horizontal axis. Now let us send a current through this loop as indicated in Figure 17-2. (The two sides of the loop are seen in cross-section and therefore appear as the two circles between the poles of the magnet. The current flows in one direction in one side and in the other direction

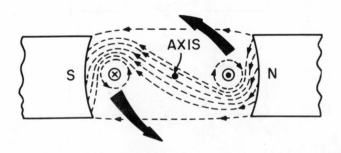

Fig. 17-2. How the magnetic field is distorted to give the loop a rotating motion.

in the other side.) One side of the loop is moved down and the other up. As a result, the loop tends to rotate in a counterclockwise direction around its axis. The rotating effect produced by the re-action between the magnetic field of the magnet and the magnetic fields around the conductors of the loop is known as *torque*.

A. *Direct-current motors*

If, as in Figure 17-2, a direct current is passed through the loop, the reaction between the magnetic fields tends to push the left-hand side of the loop down in a counterclockwise direction. However, when the conductor reaches the bottom of its sweep, it encounters an equal and opposite push. Hence it becomes stationary. Simul-taneously, the right-hand side of the loop becomes stationary at the top of its sweep. The result, then, is that the loop remains fixed in its vertical position. Since there is no rotating effect and, hence, no torque, we call this the *zero-torque* position of the loop.

However, if we had some way of reversing the direction of cur-rent flow in the loop every time it reached the zero-torque position, the loop would continue to rotate counterclockwise. This is accom-plished by the *commutator*, which we have discussed in the chapter on generators (Chapter 11, Subdivision B, 1).

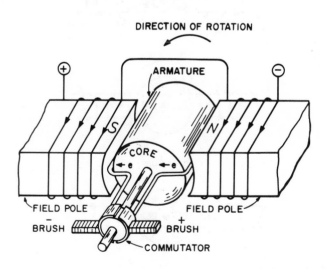

Fig. 17-3. Simplified version of the d-c motor.

This, then, is how the direct-current motor operates. The loop, or *armature*, rotates in a magnetic field, This *field* may be set up by permanent magnets or, more commonly, by electromagnets. The *commutator* periodically reverses the direction of current flow through the armature.

A simplified version of such a motor is shown in Figure 17-3. The soft-iron armature core upon which the armature loop is wound is used to concentrate the magnetic field. Note the resemblance between the d-c motor and the d-c generator. As a matter of fact, in 1873, Zénobe T. Gramme, a Belgian engineer, had two identical d-c generators standing side by side. One of these generators was being rotated by a steam engine. When the current output of this generator was accidentally fed into the second generator, the latter started to rotate as a motor.

There is another way of looking at the motor. Look at Figure 17-4A. Note that, as current flows as indicated through the arma-

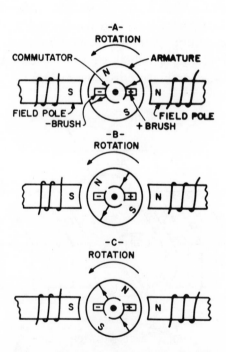

Fig. 17-4. D-c motor rotates because of attraction between unlike magnetic poles and the repulsion between like poles.

ture winding, the iron core becomes a magnet with its north pole at the top and its south pole at the bottom. Since unlike poles attract, the north pole of the core is attracted to the south field pole and the south pole of the core to the north field pole. As a result of this attraction, the armature rotates in a counterclockwise direction until the opposing poles line up (Figure 17-4B).

However, as the armature rotates, so does the commutator. Thus, as the opposing poles come in line, the commutator causes the current to reverse its direction through the armature winding. This, in turn, causes a reversal of the polarity of the core (Figure 17-4C). The south field pole finds itself facing the south pole of the core and the north field pole the north pole of the core. Since like poles repel, the armature is forced to rotate in a counterclockwise direction. Since the polarity of the core is reversed every half-revolution, the armature continues to rotate.

If, as in Figure 17-4, the armature contains a single winding, the rotary motion would be jerky since the attraction between opposite poles becomes greater the nearer these poles approach each other. Accordingly, if, instead of one, a number of windings be employed, each with its set of two commutator bars, the rotary action becomes smoother. This produces a multicoil armature similar to the type employed in the d-c generator (Chapter 11, Subdivision B, 2).

Look at Figure 17-5. Note that, as current flows as indicated through the armature windings, the iron core becomes a magnet with its north pole at the top and its south pole at the bottom. Thus

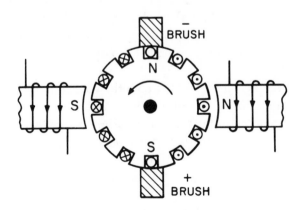

Fig. 17-5. D-c motor using a drum-type multicoil armature.

the armature's magnetic field is at right angles to the field between the field poles. Since unlike poles attract, the core rotates counterclockwise. However, so does the commutator which controls the current flow to the windings. As a result of its action, the magnetic field of the core is always maintained at right angles to the field between the field poles. The armature thus continues to rotate as unlike poles seek to line up.

Modern motors have their windings placed in slots along the surface of the armature core in a manner similar to that employed by the drum-type armature used in d-c generators (see Figure 11-17). The slot winding presents a number of advantages over a surface-wound armature. For one, since the wires lie in slots where there is very little of the field flux, very little force is exerted on them. Hence there is less danger of damage to their insulation. The main force is exerted on the teeth-like portions of the iron core between the wires where most of the flux is found. Secondly, the air space between the armature and the field poles can be made much smaller, thus reducing the reluctance of the magnetic path through the motor.

Like the d-c generator, practical d-c motors may have two, four, or more field poles. For each set of poles there is a set of brushes, and all brushes of the same polarity are connected together.

The motor does indeed resemble a generator. In fact, it is a generator. Current is sent into the windings from the line, causing the armature to rotate. But as the armature rotates, its windings cut across the magnetic field set up by the field poles. As a result, an induced voltage is generated in the armature windings just as in the generator. However, by Lenz's law, this induced voltage opposes the line voltage. Hence it is called a *counter electromotive force* (counter emf).

We may see the effect of this counter electromotive force if we connect an ammeter in the line to the motor. As the line switch is closed, the ammeter indicates that a large current is flowing to the motor. Since the armature is at rest, no counter emf is generated. Hence the full line voltage is applied and the current is determined mainly by the resistance of the armature, which generally is quite low.

As the motor starts to speed up, a counter emf is generated in the armature winding. Since this counter voltage opposes the line voltage, the *net* voltage applied to the motor is reduced. Since the armature resistance remains constant and the applied voltage is reduced, the line current starts to fall. When the motor reaches full speed, the counter emf reaches its maximum and, hence, the net applied voltage its minimum. Accordingly, the line current, too, reaches its minimum value.

From our discussion of induced voltage (Chapter 7, Subdivision A) we learned that the induced voltage depends upon the strength of the magnetic field, the number of conductors cutting that field, and the speed at which they cut it. Accordingly, in the motor,

$$\text{Counter emf} = \text{strength of field} \times \text{speed of rotation} \times K$$

where K represents the number of conductors and certain other factors that are constant for any given motor. From this we can say that the counter emf is directly proportional to the speed of rotation and to the strength of the magnetic field between the field poles. Keep in mind, however, that the line voltage is always somewhat larger than the counter emf since a certain amount of current must always be made to flow into the armature if the motor is to rotate.

From the above equation we may evolve the following:

$$\text{Speed of rotation} = \frac{\text{counter emf}}{\text{strength of field} \times K}.$$

Thus the speed of rotation is *inversely* proportional to the strength of the field. Increasing the field strength decreases the speed.

Since the motor acts as a generator, it also suffers from *armature reaction*. This, you will recall (see Chapter 11, Subdivision B, 1), is the result of the interaction between the magnetic field around the armature and that produced by the field coils. The effect is to shift the neutral running plane of the generator slightly forward in the direction of rotation (see Figure 11-12). In the motor, however, armature reaction shifts the neutral running plane slightly backwards. If the brushes are placed in this neutral running plane, sparking will be reduced.

However, since the load on a motor rarely is constant, the armature current and, hence, the armature reaction, varies widely. This requires constant shifting of the brushes if excessive sparking is to be avoided. To avoid this nuisance, *commutating poles,* or *interpoles,* are employed as in the d-c generator (see Figure 11-14).

General Electric Company.

Fig. 17-6. A. D-c motor, showing commutator and brushes.
B. Stator, showing interpoles between regular field poles.

However, in the motor these commutating poles are wound so that their polarities are the same as those of the field poles they *follow* in the direction of rotation.

1. TYPES OF DIRECT-CURRENT MOTORS

When looking at the characteristics of a motor, there are two main questions that we seek to answer. How does the torque of the motor behave under variations of load? How does the speed behave under such variations? The behavior of the motor determines whether a particular motor is suitable for a particular job.

To aid us in finding an answer to these questions, keep in mind the following relationships:

1. The torque is directly proportional to the current flowing through the armature and to the strength of the magnetic field in which the armature rotates.

2. The speed is inversely proportional to the strength of the magnetic field.

3. The counter emf is directly proportional to the speed and the strength of the magnetic field.

4. In any motor, an increase in load tends to slow it down. A decrease in load tends to speed it up.

As is true for d-c generators, d-c motors can be placed into three general classes, depending upon the manner in which their field windings are connected into the circuit. These are the *series field motors, shunt field motors,* and *compound field motors.*

a. Series field motors

In this motor the field coil is connected in series with the armature winding, as illustrated in Figure 17-7. Because they are in series, the armature current also flows through the field coil. The coil, therefore, is made of heavy wire to safely carry the heavy armature current, and it has relatively few turns so as not to introduce too much resistance. Since the current flowing through it is high, the coil, in spite of its few turns, can set up a powerful magnetic field.

When a series motor is started, because there is no counter emf, a large current flows through the armature and field windings. This produces a large starting torque. As the motor speeds up, however, the counter emf developed cuts down the armature and field current. As a result, the torque drops somewhat.

Should the load be increased while the motor is running, the

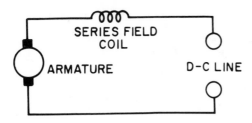

Fig. 17-7. Circuit of series field motor.

tendency is to slow down the motor. Since the counter emf depends upon the speed of rotation, it, too, drops. As a result, the armature and field current increases and the torque rises. Should the load be lessened, the motor tends to speed up, the counter emf increases, the armature and field current decreases, and the torque drops.

Should the load be removed from the series motor while it is running, a dangerous situation arises. The removal of the load causes the motor to speed up. The counter emf rises sharply and the armature and field current drops to a very low value. Because of the small current flowing through the field coil, the strength of the field drops sharply. But we have seen that the speed of a motor is inversely proportional to the strength of the field. Hence, as the field strength drops, the motor speeds up. This process is cumulative and may cause the armature to rotate at speeds high enough to make it fly apart by centrifugal force.

It is for this reason that the series motor must always be connected directly to the load. Belts and other connecting devices that may slip or break are not used. This danger is not so great for very small series motors where friction and other losses may slow the motor down before it can damage itself.

The high starting torque of the series motor makes it valuable in applications where the inertia of a heavy load must be overcome. Such applications include streetcars, electric locomotives, cranes, and the like.

b. Shunt field motors

In the shunt field motor the field coil is connected in parallel, or shunt, with the armature winding, as illustrated in Figure 17-8. In order that as much of the line current as possible should flow

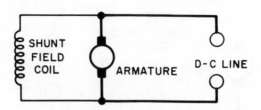

Fig. 17-8. Circuit of shunt field motor. Heavy lines indicate the path of armature current.

through the armature, the shunt field has a fairly high resistance. Accordingly, it is wound with many turns of relatively fine wire. Although little current flows through it, the proper field strength is maintained because of the many turns of the coil.

When a shunt motor is started, because of the lack of counter emf, a heavy line current flows through the armature, just as in the series motor. However, since the shunt field has a high resistance, comparatively little line current flows through it. Hence the starting torque of a shunt motor is less than that of a comparable series motor.

Since comparatively little of the line current passes through the shunt coil, the current flowing through this coil varies but slightly with variations in the line current. Hence the strength of the field remains fairly constant under all conditions of load. As the load is increased, the motor tends to slow down. The counter emf is thus reduced and a greater current flows through the armature, increasing the torque and raising the speed to normal. If the load is decreased, the motor tends to speed up, the counter emf is increased, the armature current is decreased, and the torque is reduced, causing the speed to drop back to normal. Thus the speed of rotation tends to remain constant under all conditions of load.

If the load is removed from a series motor, it tends to run away with itself. In the shunt motor, however, since the field remains fairly constant, the faster the armature rotates, the greater is the counter emf developed. Hence the motor will speed up until the counter emf becomes equal to the line voltage. At that point, since the two cancel out, the armature current drops to practically zero and the motor cannot speed up any more. The speed of the motor at this point is only slightly greater than its normal running speed.

Should the field winding of a shunt motor become open, the field, and hence the counter emf, would drop to zero. As a result, the armature current and speed would rise sharply, and the motor might be damaged. As a precautionary measure, therefore, devices such as overload circuit breaker and fuses usually are connected in the line to open when the current becomes excessive.

Shunt motors have fair starting and operating torques. Their chief advantage is a fairly constant speed under varying conditions of load. Hence they are used to operate machine tools, blowers, and the like, where a constant speed is desired.

c. Compound field motors

In this motor two field coils are employed. One is wound with few turns of heavy wire and is in series with the armature winding. The other is wound with many turns of fine wire and is in shunt with the armature winding. (See Figure 17-9.)

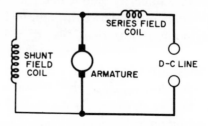

Fig. 17-9. Circuit of compound field motor.

Like the compound generator discussed in Chapter 11, Subdivision B, 3, b, (3), the compound motor has both the series and shunt coils wound upon the same field poles. These windings may be such as to aid each other (*cumulative compound*) or they may be wound to oppose each other (*differential compound*), as illustrated in Figure 11-26.

Cumulative compound motor. This motor acts very much like a series motor. Since the two fields aid each other, it has a very large starting torque. However, since it has a shunt field coil, it cannot run away if the load is reduced. This represents a great improvement over the series motor and, as a result, the cumulative compound motor is used where loads may vary suddenly from no-load to heavy overload. Such conditions occur, for example, in punch presses, rolling mills, and elevators.

Differential compound motor. This motor acts very much like a shunt motor. Since the two fields oppose each other, the resultant field is less than if only the series field were present. Hence the starting torque of this motor is considerably less than that of a comparable series motor. However, because of the opposition of the two fields, the resultant field is decreased as load is applied to the motor. Because of this decreased field, the motor is speeded up. As a result, the differential compound motor produces a very constant speed under varying conditions of load. Nevertheless, because this motor offers very little advantage over the simpler shunt motor, it is little used.

B. *Alternating-current motors*

1. THE UNIVERSAL MOTOR

What would happen if alternating current were to be applied to the motors we have previously discussed? Theoretically, they should run, since the poles of the field coil and the armature would reverse in step as the current reverses its flow. Two south poles repel each other just as effectively as two north poles.

However, we would have difficulty with the shunt-wound motor. In this type of motor, the field coil consists of many turns of wire and the armature coil of relatively few turns. Consequently, the self-inductance of each of these coils is quite different. This produces a difference in the counter emf of each and, as a result, the currents flowing through these windings are retarded in different degrees. Thus, the currents flowing through them get "out of step" and the motor action soon ceases.

In the series-wound motor, however, both the field and the armature windings are in series and the same current flows through each. Thus the change of polarity in the field and the change in the armature windings are "in step." This type of motor will run on either direct or alternating current and it is called a *universal* motor.

In such a motor, all iron portions are laminated to reduce eddy currents and less turns are used in the windings so that their impedances will be low enough for the flow of sufficient current. The motor tends to run faster on direct current than on alternating current because the inductive reactance, which is present when alternating current is applied, reduces the line current.

One drawback is the considerable sparking that takes place between the brushes and commutator when this motor is used on alternating current. When we discussed the commutator in the section on d-c generators, you may recall learning that the brushes were set at the neutral plane. At this plane the brushes made contact with the commutator bars connected to the ends of the armature coil that, at the moment, was not cutting across the magnetic field. In effect, the brushes were short-circuiting this coil, but since there was no induced voltage in the coil at the moment there was no current and hence no sparking.

When the motor is used on alternating current, however, there are changing magnetic fields around every coil carrying a current. The short-circuited coil now finds itself in the fluctuating fields set up by the other windings of the motor. As a result, a heavy induced current flows through the short-circuited coil, producing considerable sparking at the brushes.

This is one of the reasons why the ordinary universal motor is not used for heavy-duty purposes where large currents are involved. It is widely used, however, for certain light-duty purposes such as operating vacuum cleaners, fans, and the like.

2. THE INDUCTION MOTOR

There are a number of types of motors that are designed expressly for alternating-current use. In general, these fall into two classes: the *induction motor,* and the *synchronous motor.*

Most common, perhaps, is the induction motor. Imagine a transformer with the primary winding stationary, but with the secondary winding wound upon a separate core that is free to rotate between a set of bearings. Further, consider the primary wound on two opposite poles of an iron ring, as shown in Figure 17-10. Here the secondary winding consists of a single closed loop wound on a spherical iron core that is pivoted between the two poles. Let us call the

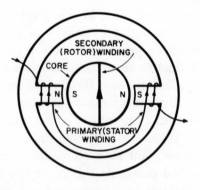

Fig. 17-10. Simplified version of induction motor.

fixed iron ring, the poles, and the ring's primary winding, the *stator;* and the iron core and its secondary winding, the *rotor.*

As current flows through the primary winding (as indicated in the illustration) north and south poles appear at opposite poles of the stator and a magnetic field is produced between them. The closed loop of the secondary winding cuts across the magnetic field and, as a result, current is induced in the loop. From Lenz's law you know that the direction of current induced in the loop is such that magnetic poles opposite to those of the stator will appear in the rotor core. That is, a *south* pole will appear at the portion of rotor that is opposite to the *north* pole of the stator, and vice versa. As a result, the poles of the rotor will be attracted to the poles of the stator.

As the alternating current flows through the stator winding, its poles will alternate in step with the alternations of the current. But the poles of the rotor will change too, and will continue to be attracted to the poles of the stator. How, then, can we make the rotor rotate? If we could make the stator poles rotate, or, what amounts to the same thing, if we could make the magnetic field rotate, then the rotor would rotate with it. The problem, of course, is to obtain the rotating magnetic field.

a. Polyphase induction motors

Assume that we have two identical a-c generators, one starting up a quarter-revolution (90°) behind the other. The graph showing the current output from each generator appears in Figure 17-11. We call currents that bear this relationship to each other, *two-phase*

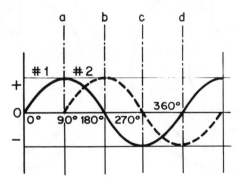

Fig. 17-11. Graph showing what is meant by a two-phase alternating current.

alternating current. (You will recall that we may obtain such two-phase output from a single two-phase generator, as discussed in Chapter 11, Subdivision A, 3. For the sake of simplicity, however, we shall consider the current as being obtained from two generators, as described above.)

Now, suppose that we have four poles set in a stator ring, as in

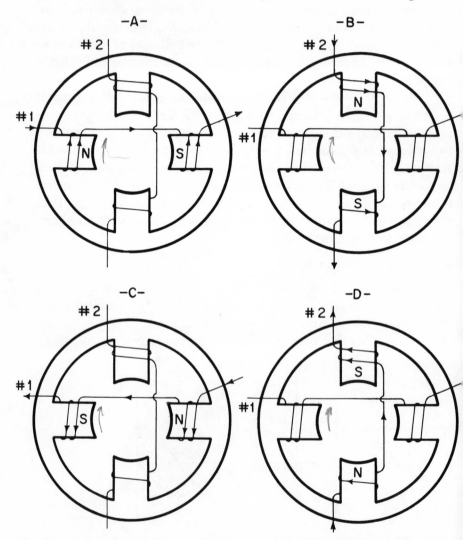

Fig. 17-12. Diagram showing how a two-phase alternating current is used to obtain a rotating magnetic field.

Figure 17-12. Assume that one winding, which is connected to the first generator (#1), is wound on two opposite poles, as shown. Another winding, which is connected to the second generator (#2), is wound on the other two poles.

At Point a on the graph in Figure 17-11, the output from generator #1 is at its positive maximum. The current flowing through winding #1 produces N and S poles, as indicated in Figure 17-12A. At that instant, there is no current from generator #2 and, consequently, there are no magnetic poles for winding #2.

At Point b of the graph (90° later), the current from generator #1 has fallen to zero and there are no magnetic poles for winding #1 (Figure 17-12B). However, the current output from generator #2 has risen to its positive maximum and winding #2 now has N and S poles as indicated.

At Point c of the graph, current #2 has fallen to zero and current #1 is at its negative maximum. Accordingly, winding #2 has no magnetic poles (Figure 17-12C) and winding #1 has N and S poles again. However, because the current is flowing in the opposite direction now, the poles are in reverse position from those in Figure 17-12A.

At Point d of the graph, current #1 has fallen to zero and current #2 is at its negative maximum. Winding #1 now has no magnetic poles (Figure 17-12D), and the poles of winding #2 are reversed from Figure 17-12B.

Look closely at the four illustrations in Figure 17-12. You will note that the north and south poles have, in effect, revolved in a clockwise direction. Or, what is the same thing, *the magnetic field has revolved as the currents have proceeded through their alternations.*

This, then, is how we obtain a revolving magnetic field. We wind the stator as illustrated in Figure 17-12 and connect its windings to a source of two-phase alternating current. As the magnetic field of the stator revolves, so does the rotor.

Note, in Figure 17-12, there are four stator poles. However, at any instant only two of these are active. Actually, when we talk about the number of poles of such a motor we mean the *number of poles per phase*. Since we are dealing here with two-phase current, the four poles represent two poles per phase and, hence, we have a *two-pole* motor.

The speed of rotation (revolutions per minute) depends upon the number of current reversals per minute divided by the number of poles. If we are using 60-cycle alternating current there are 120 current reversals per second and 7,200 per minute. If, as in our illustration, there are two poles, the field will rotate at 7200÷2, or 3,600 revolutions per minute.

The rotor then should also rotate at 3,600 revolutions per minute. But if the rotor were to turn at the same rate of rotation as the magnetic field, it would not cut across any lines of force and, accordingly, no current would be induced in it. This condition is approached when there is no load on the motor.

But as the motor is loaded, the rotor tends to lag behind the rotating field. Now it cuts across lines of force and a current is induced in it. This current produces stronger north and south poles on the rotor and thus there is a greater turning effect, or torque. Therefore, the greater the load on the motor, the more the rotor lags behind the rotating field. More current is induced in the rotor and the torque of the motor is increased. In a motor running at full load, the rotor rotates at a speed of about 5 to 20 per cent slower than the magnetic field, depending upon the design of the individual motor. The difference between the rotor speed and the field speed is called *slip*.

In most commercial installations, *three-phase alternating current* is used. The effect is the same as if three generators were employed, operating 120° apart. Accordingly, the motor must be three-phase, the rotating field being obtained by three stator windings wound on three sets of poles, 120° apart. These windings usually are placed in slots along the inner surface of the stator frame. Thus the effect of "poles" is obtained without the use of protruding pole pieces. The result is a more compact motor with a reduced air gap between the stator and rotor.

The simplest rotor employed in induction motors is the *squirrel-cage* type. Its core consists of a laminated iron cylinder. Instead of wires, copper bars are inserted into slots in the surface of the core. The ends of these bars are joined together, thus forming a series of closed loops arranged in a sort of squirrel cage; hence its name. The magnetic field set up by the stator cuts across these closed loops and large currents are induced in them. As a result of these induced currents, the rotor becomes a magnet which is rotated by the rotating magnetic field of the stator.

In the *wound rotor*, a drum-type laminated iron core, very much like the one illustrated in Figure 11-17, is employed. The wire windings are placed in the slots on the surface of the core and are grouped to form a Y-connected or delta-connected three-phase winding (see Figure 11-7A). The three ends of the winding are connected to three slip rings. These slip rings are for the sole purpose of permitting the

General Electric Company.

Fig. 17-13. A. Squirrel-cage polyphase induction motor.
  B. Stator.
  C. Squirrel-cage rotor. Note cooling fins.

insertion of resistance into the rotor winding for starting. When the rotor reaches its operating speed, an automatic switch cuts out the resistance and short-circuits the slip rings. The rotor then runs as a squirrel-cage type.

We can determine the speed of an induction motor from the following formula:

$$\text{Speed} = \frac{f \times 120}{\text{number of poles}}$$

where the speed is in revolutions per minute and f is the frequency of the line current in cycles per second. The characteristics of the squirrel-cage induction motor are very much like those of the shunt field d-c motor. It has a fair starting torque and a fairly constant speed with variations in load. In the wound-rotor type of induction motor, the starting torque can be improved by inserting resistance into the rotor windings at the start.

b. Single-phase induction motors

We have seen how the polyphase current produces a rotating field in the polyphase induction motor. Hence such a motor is self-starting. Most industrial installations use polyphase current and, therefore, there is no starting problem. But house current usually is of the single-phase type which cannot produce a rotating field. How, then, do motors operating from the single-phase line start?

If a single-phase alternating current is sent through the stator windings, the polarity of the field will change in step with the alternations of the current. So will the polarity of the rotor. If we once get the rotor of a motor such as illustrated in Figure 17-10 rotating at approximately the same rate as the changes in the field, the rotor will continue rotating even though single-phase current is flowing through the stator windings. As a matter of fact, if one leg of a three-phase line is opened, the remaining legs furnish a single-phase current. It has been found that if a three-phase motor is brought up to speed and one leg of the line should open, the motor will continue running on the resulting single-phase line.

One method of starting the single-phase motor, then, is to convert the single-phase current to a polyphase type for starting purposes. After the motor has been brought to proper speed, it continues to rotate, drawing current from the single-phase line.

We have two ways of converting single-phase current to poly-phase current, or of *splitting the phase,* as this procedure is called. One method consists of dividing the single-phase current by causing it to flow through two parallel paths. Each path contains an inductor, but the inductance of one is much greater than that of the other. The effect of inductance, you will recall, is to cause a current lag in the line (Chapter 9, Subdivision B, 2). However, the path with the greater inductance will have a greater current lag. Hence a phase difference will exist between the currents flowing in both paths. This, in effect, produces a two-phase current.

The other method is to place an inductor in one path and a capacitor in the other. The effect of capacitance is to cause a current lead in the line (Chapter 9, Subdivision C, 3). Hence we have a current lead in one path and a lag in the other. Again we have a phase difference between the two currents and thus the effect of a two-phase current.

Look at Figure 17-14 where the circuit of a *split-phase induction motor* is illustrated. The rotor is of the squirrel-cage type. There are two field coils. One, the *main,* or *running,* coil, is wound with many turns of relatively heavy wire. The other, the *starting,* or *auxiliary,* coil, is wound with fewer turns of finer wire. These coils are wound in slots in the stator and the two windings are placed 90 electrical degrees apart so that the poles of the starting winding lie between the poles of the main winding.

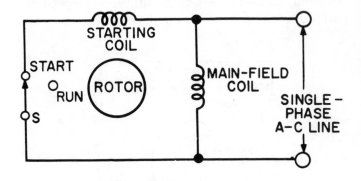

Fig. 17-14. Circuit of split-phase induction motor.

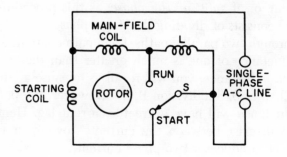

Fig. 17-15. Circuit of inductance-start, split-phase motor.

At the start, the two coils are connected in parallel across the single-phase a-c line. Because the main winding has many turns of heavy wire, it contains inductance which causes the current flowing through the coil to lag the voltage by an amount approaching 90°.

The starting winding, on the other hand, composed of fewer turns of finer wire, has very little inductance. Hence it produces very little current lag. The voltage across both windings is the same, since they are connected in parallel. Thus a phase difference appears between the currents flowing in the coils. The effect, then, is that of a two-phase current. A rotating field is produced and the rotor starts to turn.

Because the starting winding is wound with fine wire, it is not designed for continuous operation. Accordingly, when the rotor reaches about three-quarters of its full running speed, a centrifugal switch (S), mounted on the rotor shaft, is thrown to the RUN posi-

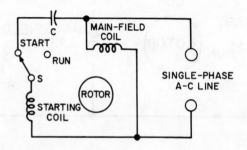

Fig. 17-16. Circuit of capacitor-start, split-phase motor.

Westinghouse Electric Corp.

Fig. 17-17. Cutaway view of single-phase, capacitor-start induction motor. Note the centrifugal switch mounted on the rotor shaft.

tion, thus cutting the starting winding out of the circuit. The motor then continues to run as a single-phase induction motor.

The direction of rotation is from a starting pole to a main pole having the same magnetic polarity. Thus, to reverse the direction of rotation, we must reverse the starting winding or the main winding, not both.

Sometimes an inductor (L in Figure 17-15) is inserted in series with the main winding to increase the phase difference between the two currents. The greater this phase difference, the greater will be the starting torque of the motor. When the rotor reaches about three-quarters of its full running speed, the centrifugal switch (S) cuts both the starting coil and the inductor out of the circuit. Such a motor is known as an *inductance-start, split-phase induction motor.*

In the *capacitor-start, split-phase motor* (see Figure 17-16) a capacitor (C) is placed in series with the starting coil when the motor is started. The result is to make the current in that path lead the current in the main-field path. Again we have the effect of a two-phase current and the rotor starts rotating. When it reaches about three-quarters of its maximum speed, the centrifugal switch (S) opens the starting-coil path. The motor then operates as a single-phase induction motor.

As is true of all induction motors, the split-phase type operates at a fairly constant speed under variations in load. But the split-phase method does not produce a true two-phase relationship between currents in the two windings; it merely approximates the

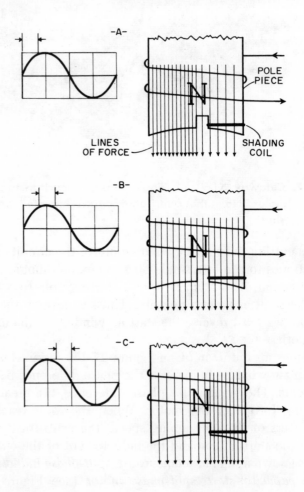

Fig. 17-18. Diagram illustrating the action of the shading coil.

two-phase relationship. Accordingly, the starting torque of the split-phase motor is not as great as for a comparable two-phase squirrel-cage induction motor. Split-phase motors are used for such devices as fans, oil burners, small power tools, and light machinery.

Another method of starting an induction motor on a single-phase line is employed by the *repulsion-start, induction-run motor*. The stator of this motor resembles that of the ordinary induction motor. The rotor resembles the armature of a d-c motor—drum-type core and winding, commutator, and brushes. However, the brushes do not connect to the line; they are connected to each other.

As current flows through the stator windings, a current is induced in the rotor winding. Accordingly, magnetic poles are set up on the rotor, very much as poles are set up on the rotor of the induction motor. By adjusting the positions of the brushes on the commutator, the magnetic poles of the rotor may be set up slightly out of line with similar poles of the stator. The repulsion between like poles, then, starts the rotor rotating.

When the rotor reaches about three-quarters of its full running speed, a centrifugal device mounted on the rotor shaft completely short-circuits the commutator. The rotor then resembles the squirrel-cage type and the motor continues to run as a straight induction type. In some motors the centrifugal device also lifts the brushes from the commutator to reduce wear. Motors of this type have fairly good starting torques.

Perhaps the simplest method of starting the induction motor on a single-phase line is by means of the device whose principle of operation is illustrated in Figure 17-18. The rotor is the ordinary squirrel-cage type. The stator, however, is similar to the field structure of the d-c motor. A slit is cut in the face of each stator pole, making it two-pronged. A single closed loop of wire, called a *shading coil,* is placed over one of these prongs.

Now assume that the current flows through the stator winding in such a way that the pole of our illustration becomes a north pole. We have indicated the magnetic strength of this pole by means of the lines of force. Where these lines of force are numerous, the magnetic pole is strong. Where they are few, the pole is weak.

Start with the portion of the alternating-current cycle indicated between the arrows in Figure 17-18A. The current is ascending rapidly and the strength of the magnetic pole consequently is increasing. A current is induced in the shading coil, and, because of this current, the coil is surrounded by a magnetic field. However, according to Lenz's law, this field will oppose the field that creates it. It tends to weaken the magnetic field of the portion of the stator pole that is enclosed by the shading coil. The effect, then, is that the strongest portion of the magnetic field appears at the left side of the stator pole.

In Figure 17-18B, we advance to the portion of the a-c cycle indicated by the arrows. Now the rate of current change is slow. The induced current in the shading coil is low and so is the strength of its opposing magnetic field. Accordingly, the magnetic field is distributed more uniformly over the entire stator pole.

In Figure 17-18C, we consider the next portion of the cycle, as indicated by the arrows. Now the current is decreasing rapidly, and the magnetic field around the stator pole is decreasing likewise. However, the induced current in the shading coil opposes the collapse of the original current. The effect, then, of the current flow in the shading coil is to create a strong north pole in the portion of the stator pole enclosed by the coil. The strongest portion of the magnetic field now appears at the right side of the stator pole.

If you examine the three parts of Figure 17-18, you will notice that the over-all effect is as if the north pole had moved from left to right across the face of the stator pole. A similar action in the opposite direction takes place at the south pole of the stator. Hence, we have created a rotating magnetic field that can be used to start our motor.

Motors that start in this way are called *shaded-pole motors*. Because the current and force in the shading poles are small, single-phase induction motors of this type are used only where the load on the motor is light, as in small fans and similar devices.

3. THE SYNCHRONOUS MOTOR

We have seen how a polyphase alternating current can produce a rotating field in the stator of a motor. The speed of rotation of this field depends upon the number of poles and the frequency of the current. In the induction motor the current necessary to produce torque is induced in the rotor only when it rotates at a speed slower than that of the rotating magnetic field and hence cuts across lines of force. The rotor therefore must revolve more slowly than the field, especially when the motor is heavily loaded.

But if we made the rotor an electromagnet by a means other than the induced current, as, for example, by connecting it to a direct-current source, there would be no need for the rotor to slip behind the rotating field. If the rotor then were brought up to the same speed as that of the rotating field by some external means, its poles would lock in step with this rotating field, and the rotor would rotate at the same speed, regardless of its load. We say that the rotor is then *synchronized* (that is, *in time*) with the rotating field, hence the name *synchronous motor*.

The alternating-current generator, shown in simplified form in Figure 11-3, can be modified to form such a synchronous motor. The stator is rewound and connected to a source of polyphase alternating current to produce a rotating magnetic field. The rotor is made an electromagnet by connecting it to a d-c source supplied through the slip rings. An induction motor may be attached to the rotor to bring it up to the required speed for starting.

Modern synchronous motors, however, do not need external starting motors. Instead, the rotor is constructed as a combination squirrel-cage and wound type with definite poles. At the start, the direct current is not applied to the rotor. When the polyphase alternating current is applied to the stator, the motor starts running as an ordinary squirrel-cage induction motor. When the speed of the rotor reaches about 95 per cent of the speed of rotation of the stator field, the direct current is applied to the wound portion of the rotor through the slip rings, thus setting up north and south poles. These poles lock in with the poles of the rotating field and, hence, the rotor revolves at the same speed as the field, that is, in synchronization.

Because the bars of the squirrel-cage portion of the rotor now rotate at the same speed as the rotating stator field, these bars do not cut any lines of force and, therefore, have no induced current in them. Hence the squirrel-cage portion of the rotor is, in effect, removed from the operation of the motor.

The speed of rotation of the synchronous motor is determined by the number of poles and the frequency of the alternating current applied to the stator, according to the following formula:

Speed (revolutions per minute) $= \dfrac{120 \times \text{frequency of current}}{\text{number of poles}}$.

Motors come in sizes ranging from four poles (1,800 rpm) to 100 poles (72 rpm).

The starting characteristics of the synchronous motor using the squirrel-cage rotor for starting are the same, of course, as those of a comparable squirrel-cage induction motor. The chief advantage of the synchronous motor is its constant speed under varying conditions of load. Its constant-speed characteristics make it suitable for operating blowers, air compressors, centrifugal pumps, and so forth, and for turning d-c generators.

There is another use for the synchronous motor. In our discussion of power factor (Chapter 8, Subdivision C) you learned that if there is a phase difference between the current and voltage in a line, the true power is less than the apparent power and the power factor is less than 1. Also, if the current lags behind the voltage, the power factor is a *lagging* one. If the current leads the voltage, the power factor is *leading*. Thus, inserting an inductance in the line produces a lagging power factor. A capacitor in the line produces a leading power factor.

If we connect an induction motor to the a-c line and measure the voltage and current by suitable meters, we obtain the apparent power consumed by the motor. But if we use a wattmeter, we find that the true power is less than the apparent power. Thus the motor has introduced a component that reduces the power factor. This is called the *reactive component* and, in the case of the induction motor, it produces a lagging power factor.

The presence of this reactive component requires the power company to maintain over-size generators, transformers, and transmission lines. Accordingly, a penalty is charged the consumer who operates equipment that reduces the power factor and, the greater the reduction, the greater is the penalty. Obviously, it is to the advantage of the consumer to keep the power factor of his line as close to unity as possible.

It is here that the synchronous motor comes to the rescue. You will recall that the rotor field is excited by the use of direct current. Increasing this field strength has no effect upon the speed of the rotor, but it does change the phase angle between the voltage and current of the applied alternating current. At a certain field current,

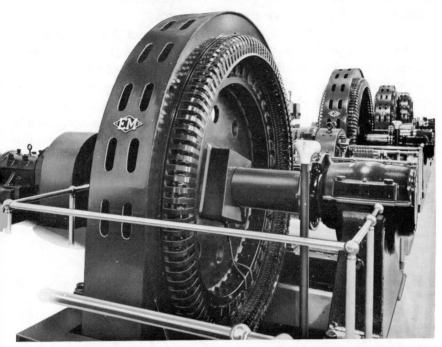

Electric Machinery Mfg. Co.

Fig. 17-19. Synchronous motor, 700 horsepower, 180 rpm, 0.8 power factor.

the voltage and current are in phase and the power factor is at unity. This is called the *normal* field current. Below the normal field current (the motor is said to be *underexcited*) the power factor is less than unity and lagging. Above the normal field current (the motor is *overexcited*) the power factor is less than unity and leading.

So you see that by operating an overexcited synchronous motor on a line whose power factor is lagging, we can compensate for the lag. The field current is adjusted until the leading power factor produced by the overexcited motor is about equal to the lagging power factor of the line. The power factor then approaches unity.

In some installations where a number of induction motors are employed or where the lagging power factor of the line is caused for other reasons, an overexcited synchronous motor that carries no load is used merely for the purpose of correcting the power factor.

Such a motor then is called a *synchronous capacitor* since it has the same effect on the line as a capacitor would.

Since the speed of a given synchronous motor is determined by the frequency of the alternating current applied to it, and since most power companies carefully maintain their current at a constant frequency, you can see that the synchronous motor can be used to operate an electric clock. The synchronous motor, you will recall, requires an external source of direct current for its rotor. Such a source is not available in the average home. But if the load upon the motor is very small, we may use a permanent magnet for the rotor, instead of an electromagnet, thereby eliminating the necessity for a direct-current source.

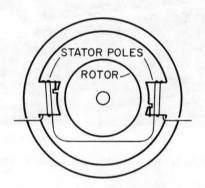

Fig. 17-20. Electric clock motor.

The rotor of the clock motor may consist of a steel disk mounted between two field poles (Figure 17-20). The magnetic field between the poles magnetizes the disk and, if the rotor is started rotating at a speed approximating the alternations of the magnetic poles of the stator, the poles of the rotor will lock in with the poles of the stator and the rotor will continue to rotate in step with the stator's alternations. Since synchronous motors, like induction motors, are not self-starting on a single-phase line, some electric clocks are fitted with an extension of the rotor shaft, which may be spun by hand to bring the rotor to the required speed. Most electric clocks, however, are made self-starting by use of the shaded-pole device.

The motor turns a gear wheel, which, in turn, engages a train of gears similar to that of an ordinary spring-motor clock. However, because the speed of the motor is constant, we need neither balance wheel nor escapement movement. Hence, the electric clock is much simpler than its spring-motor counterpart.

C. Motor control

There are a number of factors to be considered when discussing motor control. First of all, we must consider the starting and stopping of the motor. We must consider, too, certain protective devices that safeguard the motor from damage while it is operating. In some applications reversal of the direction of rotation is necessary. Finally, speed control generally is desirable.

1. D-C MOTOR CONTROL

a. Series field motor

When the motor is first started, the armature is at rest. Hence there is no counter emf developed and the full line voltage is applied. In very small motors the field and armature windings have fairly high resistances. The current, then, is low and thus a simple switch may be employed to start such motors.

In larger motors, however, the resistances of the armature and of the series field are quite small. A very heavy current will flow through them, therefore, which may be sufficient to burn out these windings. Accordingly we need some protective device, such as a series resistor, to drop the voltage at the start to a safe level. After the motor has gotten up speed and a sufficient counter emf is being generated, the resistor is cut out.

There are a number of different types of starting devices. Simplest is the *manual starter box* illustrated in Figure 17-21. This resembles the starter shown in Figure 16-11. To start the motor, the line switch is closed and the arm of the starter is moved to contact #1. This places the entire resistance of the box in series with the armature and field windings of the motor and thus the starting current is held to a safe value. As the motor speeds up, the arm is moved progressively to the other contacts. Thus resistance is cut out gradually as the motor gains speed. When it has reached its full running speed, the arm is moved to contact #5 and now all the resistance is

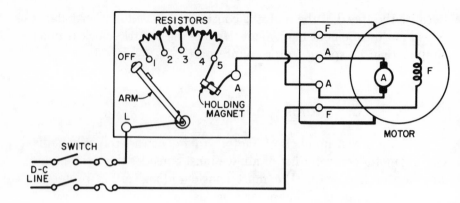

Fig. 17-21. Starter box for series motor.

removed from the circuit. The holding magnet, which is in series in the line, holds the arm in place. To stop the motor, the line switch is opened, the holding magnet loses its magnetism, and the spring snaps the arm back to its OFF position.

The spring and holding magnet act to prevent the motor from being started without the series resistor. Otherwise, the arm might be left to contact #5 (resistance all cut out) when the line switch was opened and the motor came to rest. Then, as the switch was closed again, the full voltage would be applied to the windings of the motor, without the protection of the series resistor.

When moving the arm over contacts #1 to #4, care should be taken to hold it at each contact only long enough to permit the motor to gather up sufficient speed. Otherwise, the heavy current flowing through the resistors might damage them. On the other hand, the arm should not be moved from point to point so rapidly that a sufficient counter emf cannot be developed. Generally, a pause of about 20 seconds at each contact is sufficient.

The holding magnet, as illustrated here, is known as a *no-voltage release*, since it releases the arm if the line voltage is removed (as, for example, the line switch is opened or one of the line fuses "blows"). Some starter boxes may also be equipped with an *overload release*. This is a relay whose coil is in series with the line and whose contact points connect to the two ends of the coil of the holding magnet. The relay is *normally open;* that is, if a normal current is flowing in the line, the contact points are separated. Should the line current rise sharply (for example, as the result of a short-circuit in the motor), the contact points close, shorting out the holding magnet. The arm of the starter box flies back, opening the line.

There is another protective device that may be used with all kinds of motors. This is the *thermostatic cutout,* which is a heat-operated switch that is mounted inside the motor. (See Chapter 13, Subdivision A.) When the motor overheats—because, for example, of a sustained overload—this switch opens the line. Essentially the cutout consists of a bimetallic strip that bends and operates the switch when the heat becomes excessive. After the motor has cooled off, the thermostatic switch may be reset by pressing a pushbutton set in the motor frame.

A d-c motor rotates primarily because of the repulsion between the poles of the field and the similar poles of the armature. It makes no difference whether it be two south poles or two north poles that are repelling each other. Accordingly, if we reverse the polarity of *both* the field and armature, it would make no difference and the motor would continue to rotate in the same direction. In order to reverse the direction of rotation we must reverse the polarity of the field *or* the armature. Generally, the armature's polarity is reversed.

Note, in Figure 17-21, that the armature and field windings are not connected within the motor. Instead, the ends of each winding are brought out to a terminal strip at the side of the motor and connections are made there. This makes it easy to reverse the polarity of the windings. A simple double-pole, double-throw switch, wired as in Figure 17-22, may be used.

The speed of the series motor may be controlled by means of a variable resistor (*rheostat*) placed in series with it. (See Figure

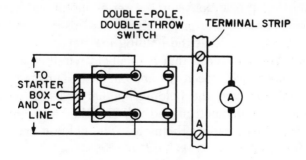

Fig. 17-22. Reversing circuit for d-c motor.

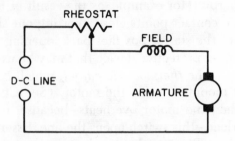

Fig. 17-23. Speed-control circuit for series motor.

17-23.) Increasing the resistance decreases the armature current and the strength of the field. Hence the torque and speed of rotation are reduced. Decreasing the resistance increases the speed. After being adjusted, the speed remains constant as long as the load, too, is kept constant. Increasing the load reduces the speed. The rheostat then must be adjusted to decrease its resistance if the speed is to be restored to normal. If the load is decreased, the motor speeds up. The rheostat then is adjusted to increase its resistance to bring the speed back. (But remember, the load must never be removed completely from a d-c series motor!)

The rheostat used for this purpose is a heavy-duty type wound with heavy resistance wire. This is because it must be able to carry the full motor current continually. In contrast, the wire need not be so heavy in the resistors of the starter box, since they carry the motor current for only short periods of time.

b. Shunt field motor

The starting precautions for the series motor apply equally for the shunt motor. The starter-box circuit for this type motor is shown in figure 17-24. Note that the holding magnet is in series with the shunt field. You will recall that if this field winding should become open, the motor will speed up and may be damaged. Before this can happen, however, the holding magnet in series with the field winding loses its magnetism and releases the starter arm, opening the line, and thus stopping the motor. The holding magnet, as illustrated here, is known as a *no-field release.*

Note that when the starter arm is at the full-running position (contact # 5) the entire resistance of the starter box is in series

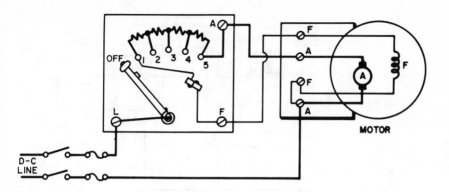

Fig. 17-24. Three-point starter box for shunt motor.

with the holding magnet and shunt field. Since the resistance of the field is high and that of the starter-box relatively low, it makes very little difference so far as field excitation is concerned. Since comparatively little current flows through the field winding (usually only about 5 per cent of the total motor current), there is no danger of the resistors burning up.

The starter box illustrated in Figure 17-24 is also known as a *3-point starter box* because it contains three terminals—one to the armature winding, one to the field winding, and one to the line. Reversing the shunt motor is the same as reversing the series motor. Either the polarity of the armature winding or the polarity of the field winding is reversed; generally, it is the armature winding. The windings of the motor are brought to a terminal strip to facilitate the connections.

The speed of the shunt motor usually is controlled by means of a rheostat placed in series with the field, as shown in Figure 17-25. Increasing the resistance of the rheostat decreases the current flow-

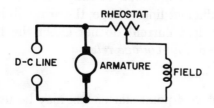

Fig. 17-25. Speed-control circuit for shunt motor.

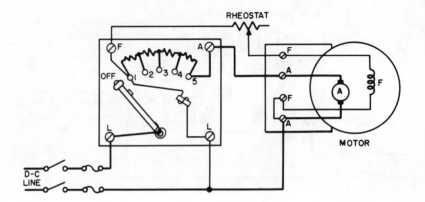

Fig. 17-26. Four-point starter box for shunt motor permitting the use of a field rheostat for speed control.

ing through the field winding, thus decreasing the strength of its magnetic field. Decreasing the strength of the field, you will recall, increases the speed of the motor. If the resistance of the rheostat is decreased, the strength of the field is increased, and the speed of the motor is cut down. The rheostat used here need not be as heavy as the one used to control the speed of the series motor (Figure 17-23) since it carries only the field current which is a small portion of the full motor current.

If the speed-control rheostat is used with the 3-point starter box of Figure 17-24, it must be connected in series with the holding magnet and the field winding. Thus, if its resistance is increased to speed up the motor, the field current may be reduced to the point where the holding magnet no longer can hold the arm. As a result, the arm flies back to its OFF position and the motor stops.

Accordingly, the *4-point* starter box illustrated in Figure 17-26 is employed. Here the holding magnet is no longer in series with the field winding, but is connected directly across the line. Thus, as long as there is sufficient line voltage, the arm will be held in place. Variations in the field current do not affect the holding magnet, which is now called a *no-voltage release.*

c. Compound field motor

Either a 3-point or 4-point starter box may be used for the compound motor. The 3-point box is illustrated in Figure 17-27. Connections are made to the terminal strip of the motor. Note that by

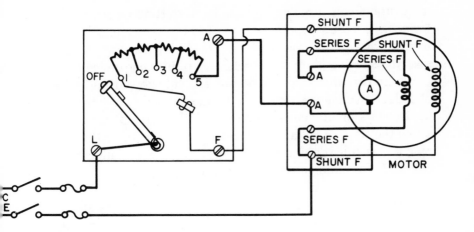

Fig. 17-27. Three-point starter box for compound motor.

reversing the polarity of the series field winding it is possible to operate this motor as either a cumulative or a differential compound type.

To control the speed of the compound motor, a rheostat may be inserted in series with the shunt field, just as in the shunt motor. In such a case, the 4-point starter box should be employed. Such adjustment of the shunt field current is not too satisfactory since, as the shunt field strength is reduced, the effectiveness of the series field is increased, thus partly offsetting the change in the shunt field.

A rheostat may be inserted in series with the armature and series field, just as in the series motor. However, this requires a heavy-duty rheostat. Some compound motors are constructed so that both series and shunt fields are used for starting. After the motor has reached its full running speed, a centrifugal device mounted on the motor shaft cuts out the series field. The motor then continues to run as a shunt motor and its speed may be controlled as such.

2. A-C MOTOR CONTROL

When the squirrel-cage induction motor is at rest it is similar to a transformer whose secondary winding is short-circuited. Accordingly, when such a motor is started, a large current flows through the stator winding. Modern motors are designed to take this current surge with their stator windings specially braced to withstand the magnetic effects produced by the large starting currents. As a matter of fact, most a-c motors are started by connecting them directly to the power line, except where the line is not heavy enough to pass the starting current and where certain other difficulties exist.

Where conditions do not permit full-voltage starting, some form of reduced-voltage starter is used. One method is to introduce similar resistors or inductors into each of the three-phase lines to cut down the starting voltage to the stator of the motor. After the motor reaches its full running speed, these resistors or inductors are cut out and the motor continues to run at full line voltage. Another method is to use an autotransformer in each line that reduces the line voltage at the start. When the running speed is attained, the autotransformers are adjusted to produce the full line voltage.

Still another method is to use a switching system that changes

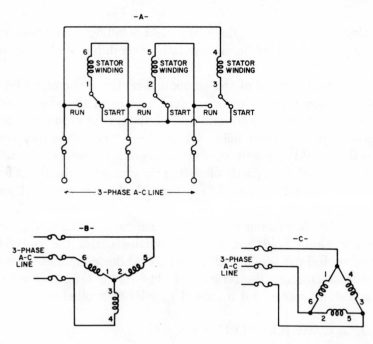

Fig. 17-28. **A.** Switching arrangement for changing the three-phase stator winding from a Y connection to a delta connection.
B. Y connection formed when switches are thrown to START position.
C. Delta connection when switches are thrown to RUN position.

the three-phase stator winding from a Y-connection for starting purposes to a delta-connection after the running speed is reached. In our discussion of three-phase generators (Chapter 11, Subdivision A, 3) we learned that if the armature coils are connected in Y formation, the voltage between any two of the lines is equal to 1.73 times the voltage across each armature coil. Conversely, if three windings are Y-connected across a three-phase line, the voltage across each winding is equal to the voltage between any two of the lines divided by 1.73. In other words, the voltage across the winding would be about 58 per cent of the line voltage.

On the other hand, the voltage across the windings in a delta connection is equal to the full line voltage. Hence, by connecting the windings of the stator of the motor in a Y formation at the start, only 58 per cent of the line voltage is applied to the motor. When the motor reaches its running speed the stator windings are switched to a delta connection and the full line voltage now is applied.

Figure 17-28A shows the switching arrangement. When the three-pole switch is thrown to its START position, the stator windings are Y-connected (Figure 17-28B). With the switch thrown to its RUN position, they are delta-connected (Figure 17-28C).

In the wound-rotor induction motor, you will recall, the ends of the rotor windings terminate in slip rings, by means of which, resistances can be introduced for starting purposes. How this is done is illustrated in Figure 17-29. A triple rheostat is employed. The

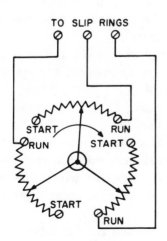

Fig. 17-29.

Triple rheostat used for starting wound-rotor induction motor.

slider arms of the three sections are connected together electrically and joined so that they move in unison. One end (marked RUN) of each resistor goes to one of the three slip rings of the rotor. With the slider arms at the START position, the entire resistance of each section is inserted into the winding to which it is connected. As the motor starts rotating, the sliders are slowly moved clockwise, thus reducing the resistances. When the sliders reach the RUN position all the resistances are cut out and the slip rings are short-circuited. The motor then runs as a squirrel-cage type.

Because single-phase induction motors generally are small, they are operated directly from the line. Synchronous motors that start as squirrel-cage induction motors have the same types of starting controls, of course.

It is quite simple to reverse the direction of rotation of a three-phase motor. All we need do is to interchange any two of the three line wires going to the motor. This reverses the direction of rotation of the rotor. To reverse a split-phase induction motor we must reverse the connections to either the main-field coil or the starting coil.

To reverse the repulsion-start, induction-run motor, the brushes must be shifted far enough to reverse the magnetic poles of the rotor. To reverse the shaded-pole motor, the rotor and shaft must be removed and reinserted after having been turned end for end.

Since a-c motors are essentially constant-speed devices, the disadvantage of such a motor is the lack of adequate speed control. Where variable-speed control is essential, the general practice is to change the alternating current to direct current to be used to operate d-c motors that permit such control.

Nevertheless, some speed control of the a-c motor is possible. We have seen that, for a given line frequency, the speed of the motor depends upon the number of poles. Accordingly, some motors have their stators so wound that, by suitable switching, the number of poles are halved. This doubles the speed of the motor.

To a limited extent the speed of a wound-rotor induction motor can be controlled by inserting resistances into the rotor windings. This can be done through the slip rings to which the windings are connected. Increasing these resistances decreases the speed of rotation.

Since speed control is not too feasible for a-c motors, variable-speed transmission systems are often employed. These generally consist of gear trains, belts with stepped pulleys, and so forth.

3. AUTOMATIC MOTOR CONTROL

The various types of motor controls we have discussed are manual types. When using d-c starter boxes the operator must judge the proper time to move the arm from one contact point to the next. When starting a-c motors the operator must judge the proper time to cut the various starting devices in or out of the circuit.

Modern practice, especially where large motors are involved, tends to the use of automatic control devices. Thus, at the pushing of a button, relays and timing devices cut the necessary resistors, inductors, or whatever, into or out of the circuits at the proper times. Let us consider a simple example. You will recall that when we start a d-c motor, we cut in a resistor to limit the current flow through the armature until the counter electromotive force has had a chance to build up. We may do this manually by means of the starter box.

The illustration in Figure 17-30 shows an automatic method for doing the same thing merely by pressing the START button. This causes the line current to flow through the coil of relay #1 and, hence, contacts #1 and #2 touch. As a result, the line current flows through the series field of the motor (L), the armature (A), and

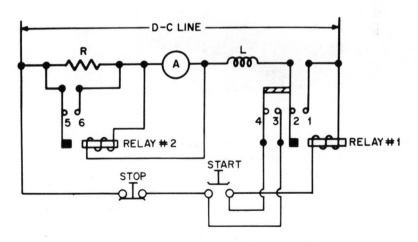

Fig. 17-30. Automatic d-c motor control circuit.

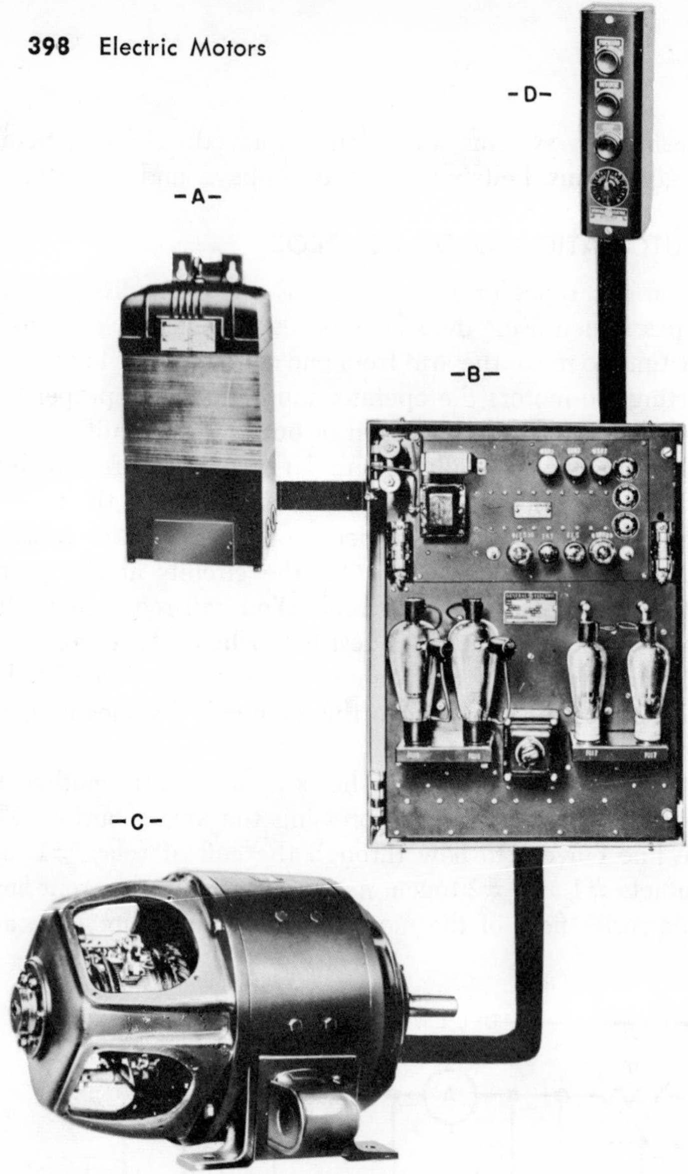

General Electric Company.

Fig. 17-31. Electronic motor-control system.
   A. Power transformer supplying power to the electron control panel (B) at correct voltage.
   B. Electron control panel. Electron tubes convert the alternating current to direct current for the field and armature of the d-c motor (C).
   C. Shunt-wound d-c motor.
   D. Control station.

the starting resistor (R). The motor starts to rotate. At the same time that contacts #1 and #2 of relay #1 close, contacts #3 and #4 close as well. This shorts out the START pushbutton so that the motor continues to run even after the button is released.

The coil of relay #2 is connected across the armature. Because its resistance is much greater than that of the armature, very little line current flows through the coil. Also, at the start of the operation the counter electromotive force developed in the armature is quite low. Hence relay #2 remains unenergized. However, as the motor reaches its proper speed of rotation, the counter electromotive force reaches a point where the relay becomes energized. Contacts #5 and #6 close, shorting out the starting resistor, and the motor continues to run normally. To stop it, all we need do is press the STOP pushbutton. This de-energizes relay #1, opening the line circuit.

There are many variations of such automatic controls, some of them considerably more complicated and performing other duties as well. Frequently, automatic controls are tailored to suit a particular installation and perform highly specialized tasks.

The most recent development in this field is the use of electronic control devices that change the alternating current of the line to direct current which is fed to d-c motors. Then, by controlling the voltages of the current fed to the stators and rotors of these motors, the speed of rotation is controlled. This makes for a very flexible speed-control system. For example, the motor may be set to rotate at a predetermined speed. Any variations from that speed would cause corresponding variations in the currents fed to the motor and thus it would be brought back to its original speed. Also, the motor could be speeded up or slowed down automatically to suit the specific needs of the load. Of course, these electronic devices also perform all the other functions of automatic controls (starting, protection, and so forth.)

D. Rating and efficiency of motors

Motors are rated by the amount of torque they can produce. This rating is in *horsepower*. (One horsepower = 550 foot-pounds per second. That is, 1 horsepower is the amount of power required to lift 550 pounds 1 foot per second, 1 pound 550 feet per second, or any combination that gives 550 foot-pounds per second.) Small motors that may be used in the home generally have an output less than 1 horsepower. On the other hand, the synchronous motors used to operate the pumps at the Grand-Coulee installation are rated at 65,000 horsepower each.

Horsepower output of a motor can be measured by a brake test whereby a brake is applied to the armature shaft of a running motor and the force in pounds exerted on the brake by the shaft is measured. Horsepower input to the motor can be determined by measuring the power (in watts) consumed by the motor running with a specified load. Then, since 746 watts are equivalent to 1 horsepower, we can calculate the horsepower input to the motor.

Example. A motor operating under full load draws 20 amperes at 240 volts. What is the horsepower input to the motor?

$$P = E \times I = 240 \times 20 = 4800 \text{ watts}$$

$$\cdot \text{Horsepower} = \frac{\text{watts}}{746} = \frac{4800}{746} = 6.4 \text{ horsepower.} \quad Ans.$$

Power is always lost in a motor (as in every other type of machine). These losses fall into several categories.

Copper losses. This is the I^2R loss in the windings of the field and armature.

Hysteresis loss. This is due to the rapid magnetization and demagnetization of iron portions of the motor that find themselves in a changing magnetic field. This loss can be kept down by constructing such iron portions (armature core, and so forth) of soft iron or annealed steel.

Eddy current loss. Since these iron portions are conductors, eddy currents are induced in them by the changing magnetic field. Lamination is used to keep this loss down.

Mechanical losses. This is due to friction and includes the friction between brushes and commutator or slip rings, bearing friction, and air friction produced by rotating portions of the motor.

The power lost in the motor is transformed to heat. Accordingly, where it is feasible, the frame is left open to permit the free circulation of air. Also, fan blades usually are mounted on the rotor shaft to blow air through the motor.

As is true of all other types of machines, the efficiency of a motor is the ratio between the power output and the power input. To obtain this efficiency in per cent we may use the following formula:

$$\text{Efficiency (in per cent)} = \frac{\text{power output}}{\text{power input}} \times 100.$$

Example. A motor rated at 5 horsepower, operating under full load, was found to draw 25 amperes at 240 volts. What is its efficiency?

Power output = 5 horsepower × 746 = 3730 watts

Power input = 25 amperes × 240 volts = 6000 watts

$$\text{Per cent efficiency} = \frac{\text{power output}}{\text{power input}} = \frac{3730}{6000} \times 100 = 61.6\%.$$

Ans.

The efficiency of very small motors may be less than 50 per cent. On the other hand, the efficiency of large motors may be over 90 per cent.

QUESTIONS

Wherever possible, diagrams should be used to clarify the answers to these questions. These diagrams need not be elaborate, but they should be drawn neatly with the significant portions clearly labeled.

1. Explain how a current-carrying conductor in a magnetic field is made to move. Explain the right-hand motor rule for determining the direction of motion of the conductor.
2. What are the four main parts of a d-c motor? Explain the function of each part.
3. Explain the operation of the d-c motor.
4. Explain why a motor draws more current at its start than when it is running.
5. Explain the use of commutating poles in the d-c motor. How do they differ from the commutating poles of the d-c generator?

6. Complete the following sentences:
   a) The torque of a d-c motor is _____ proportional to the current flowing through the armature.
   b) The torque of the d-c motor is _____ proportional to the strength of the magnetic field in which the armature rotates.
   c) The speed of a d-c motor is _____ proportional to the strength of the magnetic field.
   d) The counter emf of a d-c motor is _____ proportional to the speed of rotation.
   e) The counter emf of a d-c motor is _____ proportional to the strength of the magnetic field.
7. Draw the schematic circuit of a series field d-c motor. Label all important parts.
8. Explain the starting characteristics of the series field d-c motor.
9. Explain why the load should never be removed from a running series field d-c motor.
10. Draw the schematic circuit of a shunt field d-c motor. Label all important parts.
11. Compare and explain the difference in starting characteristics of the series field and shunt field d-c motors.
12. What is the chief advantage of the shunt field motor over the series field motor? Give two examples where shunt field motors may be used.
13. What is the chief advantage of the series field motor over the shunt field motor? Give two examples where series field motors may be used.
14. Draw the schematic circuit of a compound field d-c motor. Label all important parts.
15. Explain the advantages of the cumulative-wound compound field d-c motor. Give two examples where such a motor may be used.
16. Explain why a *universal motor* may be used on either direct or alternating current. Give two examples where such a motor may be used.
17. List the two main parts of an induction motor. Explain its principle of operation.
18. Using the diagrams in Figures 17-11 and 17-12, explain how the rotating magnetic field is obtained.
19. What are the starting and running characteristics of the squirrel-cage induction motor?
20. An induction motor operating from a 60-cycle, three-phase line has 12 stator poles. What is the speed of rotation of the stator field?

21. Explain how the inductance-start, split-phase induction motor operates.
22. Explain how the capacitor-start, split-phase induction motor operates.
23. Explain how the repulsion-start, induction-run motor operates.
24. Explain how the shaded-pole motor operates.
25. Explain the principle of the synchronous motor.
26. Explain how a synchronous motor can be used to correct the power factor of the a-c line.
27. Explain the use of a three-point starter box for starting a shunt field d-c motor.
28. Explain how the speed of a series field d-c motor may be controlled. How would you control the speed of a shunt field d-c motor?
29. A motor operating under full load draws 40 amperes at 600 volts. What is the horsepower input to the motor?
30. List four types of power losses in a motor. Explan how these losses are reduced.
31. A motor rated at 30 horsepower, operating under full load, was found to draw 60 amperes at 600 volts. What is its efficiency?

Electronics

The
Electron
Tube

A. Introduction

Electronics is the science that deals with the electron. In a broad sense, this science includes the whole field of electricity, since we consider the electric current to consist of a stream of electrons. But in a narrower sense, we may consider electronics to be that branch of science that relates to the conduction of electricity through gases or in a vacuum. (Because devices that rely upon the passage of electrons through a *semiconductor* act like electron tubes, we will include a discussion of such devices in this section. This will be done in the next chapter.)

Obviously, since we are dealing with the movement of electrons through a vacuum or a gas, this flow must take place in a sealed tube. This tube may be made of glass or metal, or of a combination of the two. Also, we must have at least two electrodes sealed into this tube. One electrode is the source of electrons and is called the *emitter,* or *cathode.* The electrode at the other end of the tube attracts the electrons and is called the *plate,* or *anode.* In order to attract the negative electrons, the plate must have a positive charge.

There are a number of ways in which the emitter may be made to give out electrons. Most common is the use of heat to produce *thermonic emission.* (See Chapter 4, Subdivision D.) Another method makes use of a high positive charge on the plate to pull the negative electrons free from the cathode. Because there is no need for heat, this method is called *cold-cathode emission.* Certain types of X-ray tubes, for example, utilize this method.

Still another method makes use of the fact that when light (visible, ultraviolet, or infrared) falls upon certain substances, such as sodium, potassium, or cesium, the light energy causes electrons to be emitted from these substances. This is the *photoelectric effect* (discussed in Chapter 4, Subdivision D, and in Chapter 12, Subdivision D).

When the electrons flow through a conductor, such as copper wire, they are confined within the boundaries of the conductor and, therefore, control over them is limited. But when electrons move through a vacuum or a gas, they are much freer and can be more easily controlled by external means. For example, as electrons flow from the cathode to the plate, they may be made to pass between the openings of a metal grid inserted in their path. If a positive charge is placed upon this grid, the electrons will be speeded up by the added attraction of the charge. Since speeding up the electron flow means more electrons passing a given point in a given time, the effect, then, is to increase the current flow through the tube. If the grid is charged negatively, the repulsion between the two like charges will slow down the electrons and less current will flow through the tube. Since the flow of electrons constitutes an electric current and, as such, is surrounded by a magnetic field, the interaction between its own magnetic field and another external magnetic field may be used to control the flow of electrons.

The tube, together with the cathode, plate, and any grids that may be placed in the path of the electrons, is called an *electron tube.*

B.   *The diode*

Simplest of the electron tubes is the one containing only a *cathode* that emits electrons and a *plate* that attracts them. Because such a tube contains only two electrodes, it is called a *diode* (*di* meaning two, and *ode* from electrode). For use in circuit diagrams, the symbol for the cathode is Γ , and that for the plate is $\perp$. The symbol for the glass or metal bulb, or *envelope,* into which these electrodes are sealed, is $\bigcirc$. The symbol for a diode is $\ominus$. If, instead of containing a vacuum, the tube is gas-filled, a dot is added, thus $\ominus$.

There are several types of cathodes employed that emit electrons by thermionic emission. Simplest is a filament, generally made of tungsten, which is heated to a low incandescence as a current is passed through it. The filament resembles that of an incandescent lamp and may be formed of wire or ribbon. The filament, therefore, is part of two distinct circuits. One is the *filament circuit* that supplies the current to heat the filament. The other is the *plate circuit,* of which the flow of electrons from filament to plate is but a link. The symbol for the filament is $\cap$.

Another type is the *indirect-heater cathode.* Here, the cathode is a metal tube, generally coated with certain chemicals, such as the oxides of barium and strontium, which are exceptionally good emitters of electrons. The cathode is heated by a tungsten filament coiled inside of it. The filament has no electrical connection to the cathode and is insulated from it by a tube of some heat-resisting material (Figure 18-1). The filament here is called a *heater* and its only function is to heat the cathode until it is hot enough to emit a suf-

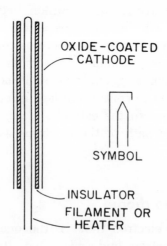

OXIDE-COATED
CATHODE

SYMBOL

INSULATOR
FILAMENT OR
HEATER

Fig. 18-1. Indirect-heater cathode.

ficient quantity of electrons. Note that now the cathode is only in the plate circuit.

A third type of cathode, which is employed for industrial purposes where an extremely heavy emission of electrons is required, consists of a pool of mercury. The mercury is heated by an electric arc formed between a special electrode—called the *ignitor*—and the mercury. Diodes of this type will be discussed in a later chapter.

The anode is a positively charged plate that attracts the electrons emitted by the cathode. It is also known as the *plate;* and the flow of electrons through the tube and its associated circuit is called the *plate current.* The greater the positive charge on the plate, the greater will be the flow of electrons to it. The plate current is limited, of course, by the ability of the cathode to emit electrons.

As the electrons strike the plate, the force of impact creates heat. Therefore, the plate must be made of some material capable of withstanding heat. The materials generally employed are nickel, tungsten, graphite, molybdenum, and tantalum. The size and the shape of the plate are determined by the amount of heat that must be dissipated. In some of the larger tubes that pass relatively large quantities of current, cooling by forced-air or water is employed.

In some tubes, the plate is merely a metallic button near the emitter, as in Figure 18-2A. In other tubes it may be constructed as a cylindrical or rectangular can surrounding the emitter (Figure 18-2B). Connections are made to the various electrodes of the tube by means of wires sealed into the bulb or envelope. These wires may terminate in any number of different types of contacts. Special sockets usually are provided into which these contacts fit. In this way, the tube may be removed from its socket without the necessity for unsoldering or unscrewing connections.

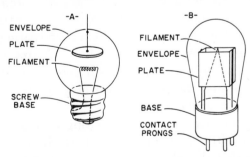

Fig. 18-2. Diodes, showing two types of plates.

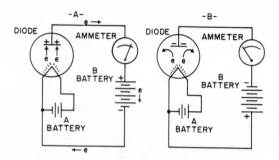

Fig. 18-3. Diode circuit, showing electron flow.
A. With positive charge on plate.
B. With negative charge on plate.

Now let us study the action of the diode. Assume that we connect a hot-filament, vacuum-type diode in the circuit illustrated in Figure 18-3. The filament is heated by a filament battery, which is also known as the A *battery*. Thus the filament circuit consists of the A battery and the filament.

A large positive charge is placed on the plate of the tube (Figure 18-3A) by *plate*, or *B, battery*. The plate circuit, then, consists of the B battery, the filament, the stream of electrons from the hot filament to the plate, the plate, and the ammeter. The ammeter is placed in the circuit to indicate the flow of current.

When the B battery is placed so that its positive electrode is connected to the plate (as in Figure 18-3A), the positive charge on the plate attracts the electrons emitted by the filament, and current flows through the plate circuit as indicated by the arrows. But if the B battery is reversed (as in Figure 18-3B), the plate becomes negatively charged. Now the electrons emitted by the filament are repelled, and no current flows through the plate circuit.

Here, then, is a kind of switch with which to control the flow of current. If the B battery is replaced by an alternating-current generator, the plate will have a positive charge during one half-cycle and a negative charge during the next half-cycle. Current will flow through the tube and the plate circuit only during the half-cycles when the plate is positive.

The relationship between the alternating current applied to the plate and the resulting plate current is shown by the graphs of Figure 18-4. Note that the plate current is a pulsating direct current.

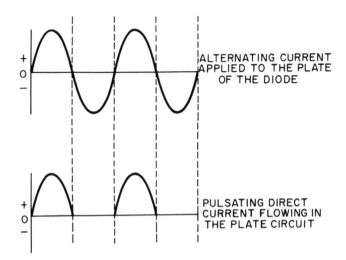

ALTERNATING CURRENT
APPLIED TO THE PLATE
OF THE DIODE

PULSATING DIRECT
CURRENT FLOWING IN
THE PLATE CIRCUIT

Fig. 18-4. Graphs illustrating half-wave rectification.

The conversion of alternating current to direct current is called *rectification* and the device that performs it (in this case, the diode) is called a *rectifier*. (You will recall we encountered similar rectification when discussing a-c measuring instruments in Chapter 10, Subdivision B, 1.)

So you see, if a diode is placed in series with an a-c generator and some device, which we may call a *load,* a pulsating direct current will be supplied to the load (Figure 18-5). From the graph of Figure 18-4, you will see that direct current flows to the load only during half the a-c cycle. Such a rectifier is called a *half-wave rectifier.*

We may supply direct current to the load during each half of the

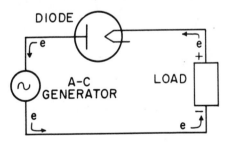

Fig. 18-5. How the diode is connected as a half-wave rectifier. The filament circuit is omitted for simplicity.

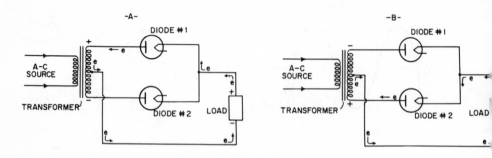

Fig. 18-6. Full-wave rectifier circuit.
  A. Current flow during one half-cycle.
  B. Current flow during the next half-cycle.

cycle by using two diodes and a transformer whose secondary winding is center-tapped. Look at Figure 18-6A. Assume a half-cycle when the top of the secondary winding is positive and the bottom is negative. Only diode #1 will pass current since its plate is positive. The plate of diode #2 is negative and no current flows through it. The current flow in the circuit is indicated by the arrows.

During the next half-cycle, the polarity of the transformer is reversed (Figure 18-6B). Now diode #2 is operative and no current flows through diode #1. Again the arrows indicate the direction of the current flow in the circuit. Note that in both instances the direct

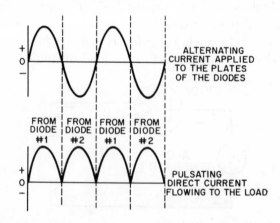

Fig. 18-7. Graphs illustrating full-wave rectification.

current flowing to the load is in the same direction. We call this a *full-wave rectifier circuit.*

The graphs of Figure 18-7 will help make this clear. Because both halves of the cycle are utilized, full-wave rectification is more efficient than the half-wave type. Sometimes both diodes are placed in the same envelope to form a *full-wave rectifier tube,* or *duodiode.* Where a steady direct current instead of a pulsating direct current is required by the load, a filter, similar to the one illustrated in Figure 11-21, is inserted between the output of the diodes and the load.

We have seen how the electrons emitted by the cathode form a flow of current through the tube as they are attracted to the positively charged plate. These electrons "boil off" from the heated cathode in a sort of cloud. Because all the electrons bear the same negative charge, they tend to repel each other and also to repel the electrons that are about to come out of the cathode. The effect of this cloud of electrons is to deter the flow of current through the tube. We call this the *space-charge effect.*

Because of the space-charge effect, the positive charge on the plate must be relatively high in order to pull over more electrons, and even so, the current flow through the tube is limited. Were it not for this space-charge effect, a small positive charge on the plate would attract all the electrons that the cathode is capable of emitting.

Therefore, where a relatively large current is required to flow through the tube, a small amount of some gas, such as neon, argon, or mercury vapor, is introduced into the envelope. The atoms of gas are large, compared with the electrons. As the electrons rush out

3 3/8"

Fig. 18-8.

Duodiode, type 5Y3-GT, for use in full-wave rectifying circuit.

Radio Corporation of America.

of the cathode, they collide with the gas atoms. As a result, electrons are knocked off the atoms, forming positive ions.

The new electrons join the rush toward the plate, but the positive ions, being heavier, move more slowly toward the negative cathode. As they do so, they neutralize the negative space charge set up by ·the cloud of electrons. Because the space-charge effect is reduced, a greater flow of electrons through the tube is produced.

The vacuum diode is used for the rectification of alternating current where a high voltage and a small current output are required. It is used to supply the direct current required by radio receivers and small transmitters when they are operated from the a-c mains. It also supplies the high-voltage direct current used in the dust-collecting apparatus and the electrostatic manufacture of sandpaper described in Chapter 2, Subdivision C.

Where moderate amounts of direct current are required—as, for example, for charging storage batteries—the gas-filled diode is used

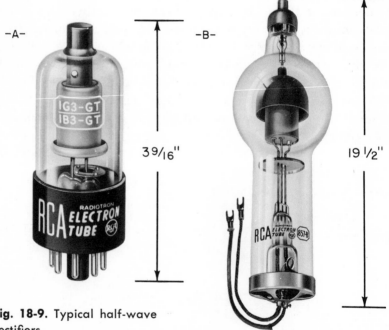

Fig. 18-9. Typical half-wave rectifiers.

A. Vacuum-type 1G3-GT.
B. Gas-filled type 857-B.

Radio Corporation of America.

to rectify the alternating current from the mains. Where very large amounts of direct current are needed—as, for example, for welding —a gas-filled diode using a mercury-pool cathode is employed.

There are a number of other diodes in addition to those we have described above. The fluorescent lamp (Chapter 14, Subdivision D) is, in reality, a diode. So, too, is the phototube (Chapter 12, Subdivision D).

C. The triode

In 1904, J. Ambrose Fleming, an English scientist, invented the diode. In this tube, electrons, emitted by the cathode, flow in a one-way path through a vacuum to a positively charged plate. Within the electron-emitting limits of the cathode, the more positive the plate, the more electrons will be attracted to it.

In 1907, an American inventor, Lee De Forest, inserted a metal grid in the path of the electrons flowing from the cathode to the plate. As long as the grid has no charge on it, most of the electrons will flow unimpeded through its openings. But if a negative charge is placed on the grid, it will have a repelling effect on the electron stream passing through its openings. In this way, it will tend to reduce the number of electrons passing through. The greater the negative charge, the fewer the number of electrons passing through the grid. If the grid is made negative enough, no electrons will pass through (see Figure 18-10A).

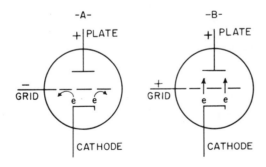

Fig. 18-10. Effect of the grid in a triode.
    A. Negative charge on the grid.
    B. Positive charge on the grid.

If, however, a positive charge is placed on the grid, it will attract the electrons. The greater the positive charge, the more the electrons will be attracted. Of course, some of the electrons will strike the wires of the grid. But since most of the grid consists of open space, most of the accelerated electrons will flow through to strike the plate (Figure 18-10B). Consequently, the effect of the positive charge on the grid is to increase or speed up the flow of electrons to the plate.

Here, then, is a valve to control the current flowing through the tube. Suitable voltages being applied to the grid, more or less plate current can be made to flow at will. The symbol for the *grid* is ——···· , and the three-element tube is called a *triode*. Its symbol is ——⊕ . (Where an indirect-heater cathode is used the symbol for the heater or filament may be omitted.)

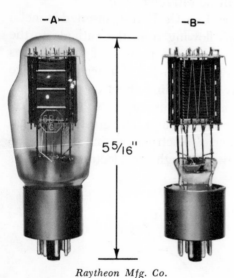

−A−   −B−

5⁵⁄₁₆″

Raytheon Mfg. Co.

Fig. 18-11.

A. Triode, glass envelope, type 6B4-G.

B. Cutaway view showing internal structure.

Of course, we can make more or less plate current flow by making the plate more or less positive. But, since the grid is closer to the source of electrons, a smaller variation in the charge on the grid will have the same effect on the plate current as a larger variation in the charge on the plate. A small change in the grid voltage will produce a large change in the plate current. We call this *amplification* and it is as an amplifier that the triode is most widely employed.

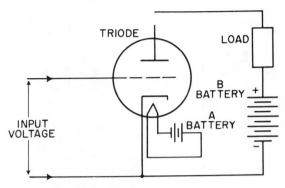

Fig. 18-12. Basic triode circuit.

The triode has three distinct circuits (Figure 18-12). One is the *filament circuit* consisting of the heater and A battery (or other source of heating current). Another is the *output,* or *plate, circuit,* consisting of the cathode, the electron flow from cathode to plate within the tube, the plate, the load, and the B battery. The third is the *input,* or *grid, circuit* consisting of the cathode and grid, and the source of input voltage.

Assume a small varying voltage is applied to the grid circuit of the triode. As the charge on the grid varies with the applied voltage, it will cause the plate current flowing through the tube to vary in step. This, in turn, will cause similar variations in the current flowing through the load. If the resistance of this load is high, the resulting voltage drop ($I \times R$) across it, too, will be high and will vary in step with the variations in the input voltage. Thus a small varying voltage applied to the input circuit of the triode produces a large similarly varying voltage in the output circuit.

Another important use of the triode is as a generator of the high-frequency alternating currents used in radio and in the inductive and capacitive heating devices discussed in Chapter 13, Subdivision F. Assume that an inductor and capacitor are connected in a circuit as illustrated in Figure 18-14, and that a current is started flowing through the circuit. As the current flows through the inductor, a magnetic field is created around it. As a result of this magnetic field, a counter emf is generated in the inductor that sends current in the opposite direction through this circuit.

The new flow of current piles up a charge on the plates of the capacitor and, as a result, a second counter emf is created that sends

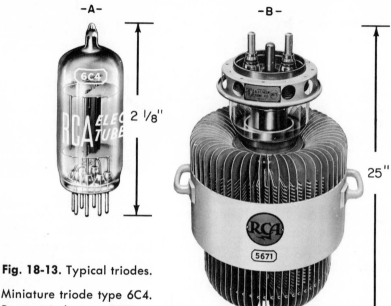

Fig. 18-13. Typical triodes.

A. Miniature triode type 6C4.
B. Power triode type 5671.

Radio Corporation of America.

the current flowing back through the circuit. The entire process is repeated and current continues to flow through the circuit, first in one direction, and then in the other. We say that the current *oscillates* in the circuit and, accordingly, we call it an *oscillating circuit*.

Here, then, is a method for generating an alternating current. The current will oscillate at its *resonant frequency* (see Chapter 9, Subdivision D, 4, b) and this frequency will be determined by the values of the inductor and capacitor. If proper values are selected,

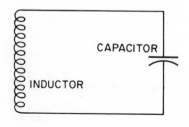

Fig. 18-14.

How inductor and capacitor are connected to form an oscillating circuit.

currents with frequencies of millions, even billions, of cycles per second may be generated.

Example. If, in Figure 18-14, the value of the inductor is 20 microhenrys (0.000,02 henry) and that of the capacitor 80 micromicrofarads (0.000,000,000,08 farad), what will be the frequency of the oscillating current?

$$f_r = \frac{1}{2\pi\sqrt{L \times C}}$$

$$f_r = \frac{1}{6.28\sqrt{0.000,02 \times 0.000,000,000,08}}$$

$$= \frac{1}{0.000,000,2512} = 3,980,891 \text{ cycles per second.} \quad Ans.$$

However, as the current flows through this circuit, it encounters a certain amount of resistance that dissipates the electrical energy, and the oscillations quickly stop. Energy is taken away from the oscillating circuit, too, when we apply an external load. If, however, we were able to supply new energy to the circuit to compensate for these losses, the current would continue to oscillate.

It is here that the amplifying ability of the triode comes to the rescue. The oscillating circuit is connected to the input circuit of the tube (Figure 18-15). Thus, an alternating voltage is placed on the grid of the triode. Since the resulting plate current is sufficient to supply the needs of the load and still have enough left over to feed back to the oscillating circuit to compensate for its losses, it remains in oscillation.

Feedback is accomplished by passing the plate current through another coil (called the *feedback coil*) that is inductively coupled to the

Fig. 18-15.

Basic oscillator circuit.

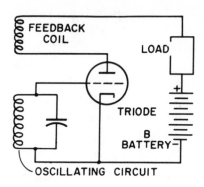

inductor of the oscillating circuit. Hence, we have a transformer with the feedback coil as a primary and the inductor of the oscillating circuit as the secondary.

We call a tube used in this way, with its accompanying components, an *oscillator*. At this point, you may be troubled with a problem. Where does the power to compensate for the losses in the oscillating circuit come from? The answer is that it comes from the B battery in the plate circuit of the tube.

A variation of the three-element tube is the gas-filled triode called a *thyratron*. Assume that we have such a triode with a positive charge on the plate and with the grid negative enough to cut off entirely the flow of electrons from the cathode to the plate. Assume, further, that we start reducing the negative charge on the grid (that is, the grid becomes more positive). No electrons will flow through the grid until a critical point is reached when the negative charge on the grid is small enough to permit electrons to flow through it. This flow of electrons will cause the gas in the tube to ionize. Some of the positive ions are attracted to the negative grid. There they form a sheath around the grid which prevents the grid from having any further effect on the flow of electrons through the tube.

Since the grid has lost its control, the only way to stop the flow of current through the tube is to remove the positive charge of the plate. Therefore, the grid acts as a trigger to start the flow of current through the tube. Once the flow is started, however, the grid is unable to stop the current. The tube, consequently, acts as a relay by means of which a small amount of power applied to the grid can control relatively large currents.

Assume that an alternating voltage is applied to the plate of the thyratron. During the half-cycle when the plate is negative, no current will flow through the tube, of course. During the positive half-cycle there is a possibility that current may flow, but only if the grid is not more negative than the cathode by a definite amount which is dependent upon the plate voltage.

Within the thyratron, the electrons are subjected to a sort of tug-of-war between the attracting force of the positive plate and the repelling effect of the negative grid. Thus, for every positive value of plate voltage there is a negative value of grid voltage sufficient to restrict the flow of electrons to the point where the gas within the tube cannot ionize.

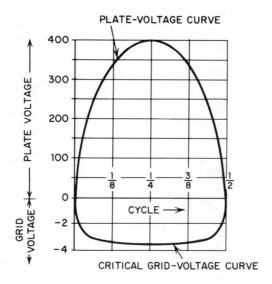

PLATE-VOLTAGE CURVE

CRITICAL GRID-VOLTAGE CURVE

Fig. 18-16. Graph showing plate-voltage and critical grid-voltage curves for a typical thyratron.

This can be seen from the graph illustrated in Figure 18-16 where is plotted the positive half-cycle of the alternating voltage applied to the plate and the *critical grid-voltage curve* indicating the grid voltages required to keep the gas from ionizing at all voltage values of the half-cycle.

Thus, at 100 plate volts the critical grid voltage is −2.5 volts; at 200 plate volts, −3.0 volts; at 300 plate volts, −3.25 volts; and at the peak, 400 plate volts, −3.5 volts. If, at any time during the half-cycle, the grid should become less negative (or, what is the same thing, more positive) than the critical voltage indicated for the plate voltage at that point, the gas will ionize, the grid will lose control, and plate current will flow for the rest of that half-cycle. At the next (negative) half-cycle, the plate current will be cut off.

You can see, therefore, that the thyratron acts as a rectifier. Further, by controlling the grid voltage we may determine the portion of the positive half-cycle during which plate current will flow. Since the average output of the tube depends upon the length of time the current flows, we may in this way control the output. A rectifier of this type is called a *controlled rectifier* and, as you will see later, is widely used in industry.

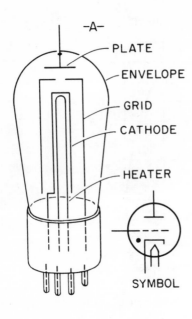

-A-
PLATE
ENVELOPE
GRID
CATHODE
HEATER
SYMBOL

-B-
10 3/32"

5563-A

Radio Corporation of America.

Fig. 18-17. A. Thyratron.
B. Commercial thyratron, type 5563-A.

The grid of the thyratron generally consists of a metal can completely surrounding the cathode, with one or more holes in the top through which the electrons may pass (see Figure 18-17). The envelope generally is of glass for the low-power types and may be of metal for the high-power types. Its cathode may be a filament or of the indirect-heater type. The plate usually is a block of nickel or graphite.

D. Multielectrode and multiunit tubes

We have seen how the grid controls the flow of electrons from the cathode to the plate. Many electron tubes, generally of the high-vacuum type, have two or more grids inserted in the path of the electrons. For example, the *tetrode* (whose symbol is ⟨symbol⟩) has two such grids.

One grid, known as the *control grid,* controls the flow of electrons, as we have previously discussed. The other, called the *screen grid,* is charged positively. The function of this positively charged grid is to help neutralize the space-charge effect and, in this way, to speed up the flow of electrons to the plate.

The speeding up of electrons, however, is a mixed blessing. Because of their higher speed, the electrons strike the plate with greater force and, as a result of this impact, electrons are knocked off the plate. This phenomenon is called *secondary emission*. Many of the electrons so liberated are attracted to the positive screen grid and are lost to the plate circuit.

To offset the loss due to secondary emission, a negatively charged third grid, called the *suppressor grid*, is inserted between the screen grid and the plate. The electrons freed by secondary emission are repelled from the suppressor grid back to the plate. Hence, they add

2 5/8"

Fig. 18-18.

Metal, octal-base pentode, type 6SJ7.

Radio Corporation of America.

to the plate current. A tube having three grids (plus cathode and plate) is called a *pentode*. Its symbol is ⊣⊞⊢ .

The basic circuit of a pentode amplifier is shown in Figure 18-19. As in the triode, the input voltage is applied between the control grid and the cathode. The screen grid is made slightly less positive than the plate by connecting it to a tap on the B battery. The suppressor grid connects to the cathode. Since the cathode is negative with respect to the plate, the suppressor grid, too, is negative with respect to the plate. The gain of a pentode amplifier is considerably greater than that of an equivalent triode amplifier.

Many tubes have even more grids. They are used for special purposes. There is the *hexode* with six electrodes (four grids, a cathode

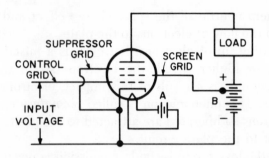

Fig. 18-19. Basic circuit of pentode amplifier.

and a plate); the *heptode* with seven electrodes (five grids); and the *octode* with eight electrodes (six grids). These tubes are called *multielectrode* tubes. The electron stream flows from the cathode, through the various grids, to the plate.

In addition, there are *multiunit* tubes—two or more tubes enclosed in the same envelope. Each section of the tube has its own cathode, grids (if any), and plate. Thus each section of the multiunit tube may be a diode, triode, tetrode, and so forth.

E. The cathode-ray tube

One of the most ingenious devices invented by man is the *cathode-ray tube* used in television and radar receivers and in the cathode-ray oscilloscope. Its operation depends on the fact that if a phosphor (usually zinc oxide or silicate) is struck by an electron beam, the phosphor will *fluoresce,* or glow.

In the cathode-ray tube, the electron beam is produced by an *electron gun,* illustrated in Figure 18-20. The *heater* heats the *cathode,* causing it to emit electrons. The *control grid* is a metal tube having a small opening in one end and enclosing the cathode. This grid is negative with respect to the cathode and thus tends to repel the electrons that are emitted by the cathode. As a result, the electrons stream through the hole in the end, in the form of a narrow beam. The effect of the grid, then, is to control the amount of emission from the cathode and to concentrate these electrons into a beam somewhat as a lens concentrates light.

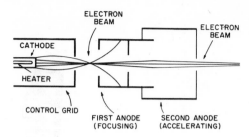

Fig. 18-20. Electron gun.

After leaving the aperture of the grid, the electrons, which repel one another, tend to spread out. The electrons are made to pass, therefore, through the first anode, called the *focusing anode*, whose positive charge speeds them up. Thus, the spreading effect is reduced and the electrons form a narrow beam once more.

The electrons pass through a second anode which has a still higher positive charge. They are greatly accelerated and come out of this anode (called the *accelerating anode*) with a very great velocity and in the form of a very narrow beam which strikes a screen at the far end of the cathode-ray tube. This screen is covered with a thin coat of phosphor, and where the beam strikes the screen, a pinpoint of light appears.

Before the beam reaches the screen, however, it must pass between two sets of metal *deflecting plates*. Each set consists of two parallel plates and each set is at right angles to the other, one set being horizontal and the other vertical (Figure 18-21).

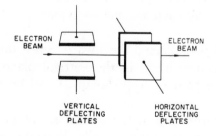

Fig. 18-21.

Relative positions of vertical and horizontal deflecting plates in cathode-ray tube.

Since the electrons of the beam carry a negative charge, they will be attracted to a positively charged plate and repelled from a negatively charged one. Thus, if the upper plate of the first set of deflecting plates is charged positive and the bottom one is charged negative, the electron beam will be deflected upward. If the charges

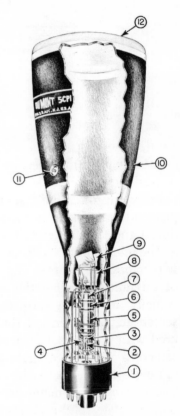

1. Base
2. Heater
3. Cathode
4. Control grid
5. Preaccelerating electrode
6. Focusing electrode
7. Accelerating electrode
8. Deflection plates
9. Deflection plates
10. Internal coating (Aquadag)
11. High-voltage contact
12. Fluorescent screen

Allen B. Du Mont Laboratories, Inc.

Fig. 18-22. Cutaway view of cathode-ray tube, showing the structure of the electron gun and deflecting plates.

are reversed, the beam will be deflected downward. Since this first set of plates moves the electron beam in the vertical plane, it is called the *vertical deflecting plates* (even though the plates themselves are horizontal).

Similarly, if the plate nearest you in the second set of plates is charged positive and the one furthest from you is charged negative, the beam will be deflected toward you. If the charges are reversed, the beam will be deflected away from you. These plates are called *horizontal deflecting plates.*

Now let us turn our attention to the spot of light produced as the electron beam strikes the screen. Assume that there is no charge on any of the deflecting plates. The electron stream will be focused to a pinpoint of light appearing in the center of the screen (Figure 18-23A).

If a voltage is placed on the vertical deflecting plates so that the upper plate is positive and the lower is negative, the point of light appears above the center of the screen (Figure 18-23B). The distance that the point of light is displaced above the center of the screen depends upon the voltage on the vertical deflecting plates. You can see that we may use the cathode-ray tube as a voltmeter merely by measuring the amount of deflection produced by a voltage on the deflecting plates.

If the charges of the plates are reversed so that the lower vertical deflection plate is positive, the spot moves below the center of the screen (Figure 18-23C). If an alternating voltage is placed on the plates, the spot of light will move up and down in step with the alternations of voltage.

If the frequency of the alternating voltage is low enough, we actually can see the spot move up and down. But if the frequency

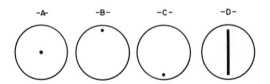

Fig. 18-23. View of the broad end of cathode-ray tube, showing the positions of the spot of light.

is too high for our eye to follow, say, 60 cycles or more per second, the moving spot will appear as a continuous vertical line (Figure 18-23D).

Of course, a corresponding effect can be had by using the horizontal deflecting plates. Our spot then moves from left to right or vice versa.

Assume that we have placed a 60-cycle alternating voltage on the vertical plates. In $\frac{1}{60}$ second, the spot will have moved from the center of the screen, up to the top of its path, down to the bottom of its path, and up again to the center. You know, of course, that this sequence represents one complete cycle. Assume that at the same time a constantly increasing voltage is placed on the horizontal plates, which tends to drive the spot from the extreme left of the screen to the extreme right in $\frac{1}{60}$ second. As a result of the two voltages, the spot describes a sine curve (Figure 18·24). The picture appearing on the screen is called a *trace*.

If, at the instant the spot reaches the extreme right of the screen, the voltage on the horizontal deflecting plates drops instantly to its original value and then gradually increases again, another sine curve is traced over the original one. This continues, and the effect is as if the curve stood still, enabling us to inspect it.

The horizontal component of the movement of the spot of light is a continuous, even, left-to-right motion until the extreme right of the screen is reached. At that instant, the spot is returned to its original position at the extreme left of the screen. This motion is known as the *linear sweep* of the cathode-ray tube. The voltage waveform that must be placed on the horizontal deflecting plates to accomplish this sweep is shown in Figure 18-25. Because of the shape of the waveform, the device that produces it is called a *saw-*

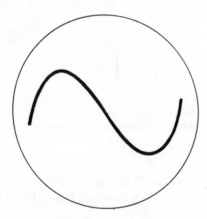

Fig. 18-24.

Trace produced by sinusoidal alternating voltage.

tooth oscillator. Another name for it is the *sweep oscillator*. (This oscillator will be discussed in a later chapter.)

We can see, therefore, how the cathode-ray tube permits us to make *visual* observations of variations in currents and voltages. The electron beam is extremely light and, therefore, may be moved with great rapidity without running into problems of inertia. It is this property of the tube that permits its use in television receivers. The picture being transmitted is converted into voltage variations at the transmitting station and at the receiver these variations cause the electron beam of the tube to reproduce the picture in light on the screen.

The complete cathode-ray tube is shown in Figure 18-26. The tube is a high-vacuum type. The phosphor is deposited on the inside surface of the wide end of the envelope. The *aquadag coating* is a deposit of graphite, also on the inside of the envelope. This coating carries a positive voltage and is used to attract any secondary electrons that are emitted as a result of electronic bombardment of

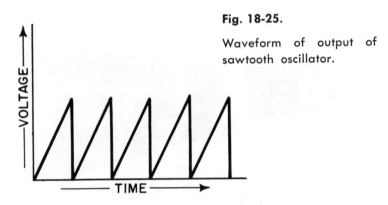

Fig. 18-25.

Waveform of output of sawtooth oscillator.

the screen. If this coating were omitted, such secondary electrons might collect on the screen, causing interference.

The cathode-ray tube described above is known as the *electrostatic-deflection* type because deflection of the electron beam is accomplished by means of electrostatic charges on the deflection plates. Another kind of cathode-ray tube is known as the *electromagnetic-deflection* type. In this type tube, deflection of the beam is accomplished by means of external electromagnets. Since the electron beam constitutes a flow of current, it is surrounded by a magnetic field, which reacts with the fields produced by the external electromagnets to produce deflection of the beam. Tubes of this type are used in most television receivers.

How electromagnetic deflection is accomplished is illustrated in Figure 18-27. Here you see a cross-sectional view of the neck of the tube. In the center is the electron beam flowing out of the page toward you. This electron beam is surrounded by a magnetic field, as represented by the circle of dotted lines around the beam. The

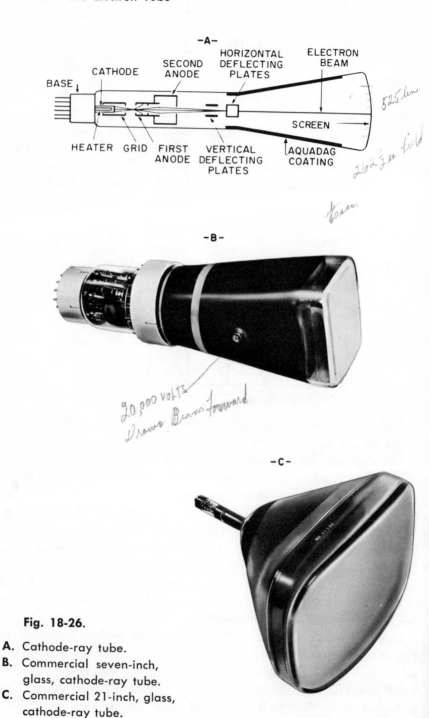

Fig. 18-26.

A. Cathode-ray tube.
B. Commercial seven-inch, glass, cathode-ray tube.
C. Commercial 21-inch, glass, cathode-ray tube.

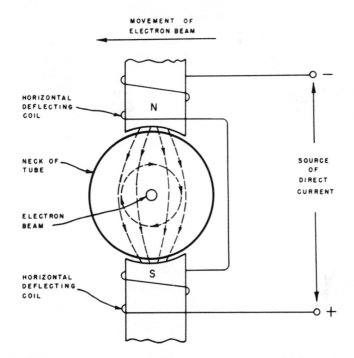

Fig. 18-27. How electromagnetic deflection coils can deflect the electron beam.

arrows on these dotted lines indicate the direction of these magnetic lines of force.

Two electromagnets are placed above and below the neck of the tube. The coils of these electromagnets are connected in series and their windings so arranged that as a direct current flows through them, as indicated, a north pole appears above the tube and a south pole below it. The magnetic field between the two poles is indicated by the dotted lines connecting them, and the direction of the magnetic lines of force is indicated by the arrows on the dotted lines.

Note that to the right of the electron beam the two magnetic fields augment each other, as indicated by the arrows all in the same direction. At the left side of the beam the opposing arrows show that the two fields oppose and weaken each other. Because the resulting field is stronger on the right than on the left, the electron beam is deflected to the left. (Note the similarity to the motor action described in Chapter 17.)

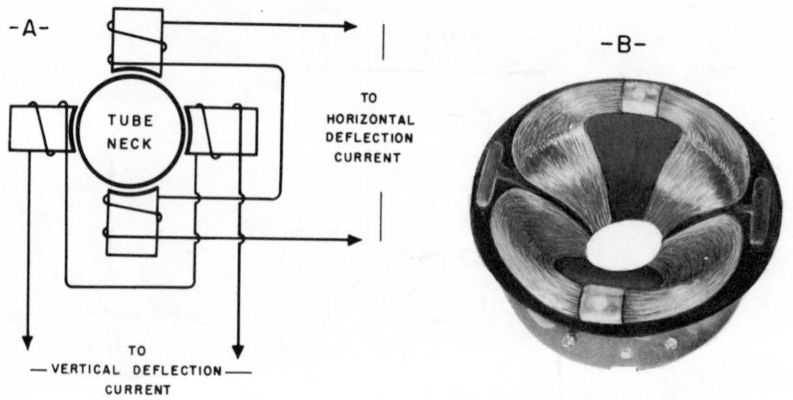

Fig. 18-28. A. How the horizontal and vertical deflection coils are placed around the neck of the tube.
    B. A deflection yoke.

The greater the current flowing through the coils, the stronger their magnetic fields will be, and the more the electron beam is deflected. By reversing the current flow through the coils, the direction of their magnetic fields is reversed, and so is the direction of deflection of the beam. These coils are the *horizontal deflection coils*.

A similar set of two coils, placed to the left and right of the neck of the tube, causes the electron beam to be deflected up and down; they are called the *vertical deflection coils* (see Figure 18-28A). In practice, both the horizontal and vertical deflection coils are enclosed in a common form, called the *yoke*, which fits over the neck of the tube. By properly positioning the yoke on the neck of the tube and controlling the amount of current flowing through each set of coils, the electron beam can be deflected to strike any desired spot on the screen.

QUESTIONS

Wherever possible, diagrams should be used to clarify the answers to these questions. These diagrams need not be elaborate, but they should be drawn neatly with the significant portions clearly labeled.

    1. In reference to the electron tube, what is meant by *a*) thermionic emission; *b*) cold-cathode emission; *c*) photoelectric emission?

2. Draw the basic circuit of the diode used as a half-wave rectifier. Explain its action.

3. Draw and explain the basic circuit of two diodes used in a full-wave rectifier circuit.

4. Explain why a certain amount of gas is introduced into the envelope of some diodes.

5. Describe and explain the structure of the triode.

6. Draw and explain the basic circuit of the triode used as an amplifier.

7. Draw and explain the basic circuit of the triode used as an oscillator.

8. Explain the action of the thyratron.

9. Describe and explain the structure of the tetrode.

10. Describe and explain the structure of the pentode.

11. Describe and explain the structure of the cathode-ray tube.

12. Explain how the deflection system of the cathode-ray tube forms a trace on the screen of the tube.

19

Semiconductors

Conductors, we learned in Chapter 1, Subdivision B, 2, are substances made up of atoms whose outer-orbit electrons are loosely held. At ordinary room temperature enough heat energy is applied to the atoms to permit large numbers of these electrons to be liberated (*free electrons*) and to drift aimlessly about from atom to atom. If an electrical pressure (*voltage*) is applied to the ends of the conductor, the free electrons will stream to the positive side as other electrons flow in from the negative side. It is in this way that we visualize a current flowing through a conductor. We may consider the moving electrons as *carriers* of electricity from the negative to the positive side of the conductor.

In an *insulator*, on the other hand, the outer-orbit electrons are tightly held and there are very few free electrons. As a result, if a voltage is applied to the ends of the insulator, very little current will flow. (Of course, if we apply a high enough voltage, the electrical pressure may become great enough to rupture the insulator and the current may arc through.)

Between these two extremes we have a number of substances whose outer-orbit electrons are not as loosely held as in conductors or as tightly held as in insulators. We call such substances *semiconductors*, examples of which are *germanium* and *silicon*. If a voltage is applied across a semiconductor, current will flow, but not as readily as in a conductor. As an example, at ordinary room temperature a cubic centimeter of pure copper will offer a resistance to current flow of about 0.000,0017 ohm. A cubic centimeter of slate (an insulator) has a resistance of about 100,000,000 ohms. A cubic centimeter of pure germanium has a resistance of about 60 ohms.

The germanium atom is pictured as having a nucleus that contains 32 protons. This nucleus is surrounded by 32 planetary electrons arranged in four concentric shells or orbits. The three shells closest to the nucleus are completely filled by 28 of these electrons. The outermost shell contains the remaining 4 electrons. The electrons of the outer shell are called the *valence* electrons and determine the chemical and electrical properties of the atom.

Since the outermost electrons are loosely held to the nucleus, at ordinary room temperature a number of such electrons usually escape and wander around as free electrons. Where an electron escapes from its atom, a gap or "hole" is left in its place. The loss of the electron (and the appearance of the hole) converts the neutral atom to a positive ion. Thus we may consider the hole as carrying a positive charge that is equal and opposite to the negative charge carried by the electron.

Where a hole appears in an atom, an electron from a neighboring atom may move in to fill the gap, leaving a hole in its place. The hole, then, has moved from the first atom to its neighbor. So you see that holes may travel from atom to atom just as the free electrons; only, in this case, they carry positive charges.

The movement of electrons is increased by increases in temperature or by the presence of an electric field which applies electrical pressure, forcing the free negative electrons to move toward the positive pole of the field. As the electrons move toward the positive pole of the field, the holes move toward its negative pole.

In a crystal of pure germanium, the atoms arrange themselves in a geometric pattern, each atom being a relatively great distance away from its neighbor. The atoms are held in place as one valence electron of one atom combines with a valence electron of its neigh-

.7V depletion layer. Silicon
.3V depletion layer

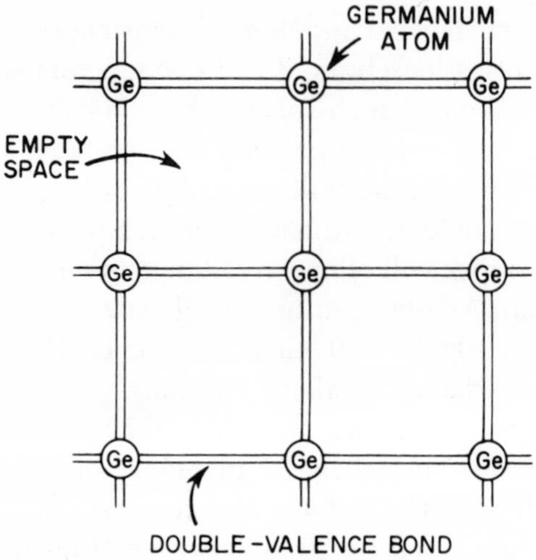

Fig. 19-1.

Structure of germanium crystal. Each germanium atom is attached to its neighbor by double-valence bonds.

bor to form a *double-valence bond.* The crystal is a three-dimensional structure, but in Figure 19-1 we show a theoretical two-dimensional view of it. The two parallel lines linking each germanium atom ((Ge)) to its neighbor represent the double-valence bond made up of one valence electron from each atom. Note that each germanium atom is linked to four others, thus accounting for its four valence electrons. Where an electron escapes, it is from one of the double-valence bonds, leaving a single-valence bond and a hole.

The number of free electrons in a germanium crystal can be increased by adding a very small amount of some impurity, such as *arsenic,* which has five valence electrons in its outermost orbit. The arsenic atom replaces one of the germanium atoms in the crystal, combining with its four neighbors and leaving one of its electrons free, as shown in Figure 19-2A. Such a germanium crystal is called an *n-* (for *negative*) type.

As you know, the neutral atom contains an equal number of positive and negative charges (see Chapter 1, Subdivision B, 1). Hence the n-type crystal is neutral. For every free electron (negative charge) there is a corresponding hole (positive charge) and for every excess electron introduced by the five-valence atom there is an excess positive charge on the nucleus of the parent atom.

Similarly, the number of holes in a germanium crystal can be increased by adding a very small amount of some impurity, such as *boron,* which has three valence electrons in its outermost orbit. The boron atom replaces one of the germanium atoms in the crystal.

However, the boron atom can form double-valence bonds with only three of its germanium neighbors. With the fourth it can form only a single-valence bond, leaving a hole for the missing electron, as shown in Figure 19-2B. Such a germanium crystal is called a *p*- (for *positive*) type.

The p-type crystal, too, is neutral. For every hole introduced by the three-valence atom there is left a free electron from its neighboring four-valence germanium atom.

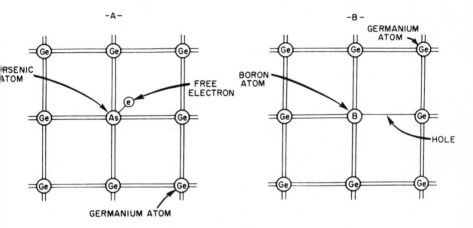

Fig. 19-2. **A.** Structure of n-type crystal.
         B. Structure of p-type crystal.

A. The junction diode

Suppose a p-type crystal is joined to an n-type crystal, as shown in Figure 19-3A. The minus (−) signs indicate free or excess electrons. The plus (+) signs indicate holes. Some of the free electrons from the n-crystal move into the p-crystal and some of the holes move from the p-crystal to the n-crystal. The crystals are no longer neutral. The p-crystal now has more electrons than before and the n-crystal has fewer. Hence the p-crystal has a net negative charge and the n-crystal has a net positive charge.

(In practice, two separate crystals are not used. Instead, an *n-region* and a *p-region* are created side by side in the same crystal. Hence the n-region has a net positive charge and the p-region a net negative charge.)

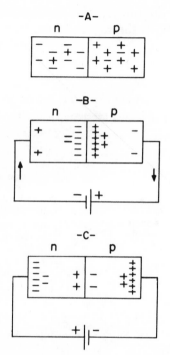

Fig. 19-3.

A. Distribution of free electrons and holes in a p-n junction crystal.

B. Distribution of free electrons and holes when voltage is applied in forward direction.

C. Distribution of free electrons and holes when voltage is applied in reverse, or nonconducting, direction.

Because of these opposite charges, an electric field (that is, a voltage), called the *potential barrier*, exists at the junction of the two regions. This is a permanent feature of a p-n junction. When the two regions were first joined, the flow of electrons from the n-region to the p-region and holes from the p-region to the n-region stopped when the resulting potential barrier became high enough to prevent further flow and a condition of equilibrium was established.

If an external voltage is applied to the crystal as indicated in Figure 19-3B, the free electrons in the n-region tend to move toward the junction, as do the holes in the p-region. Also, the positive charge of the n-region is reduced by the negative voltage of the external source and the negative charge of the p-region is reduced by the positive voltage of the source.

As a result of the reduction in the charges of the regions, the electric field at the junction and, hence, the potential barrier is lowered. Accordingly, additional electrons from the n-region are able to move into the p-region and more holes from the p-region can move into the n-region. The net result, then, is a flow of electrons through the crystal from the n-region to the p-region, the external voltage source supplying additional electrons to the n-region and removing them from the p-region.

Thus the crystal is conductive (that is, its resistance is low). When an external voltage is applied in this manner, we say it is in the *forward* direction.

If an external voltage is applied to the crystal as indicated in Figure 19-3C, the free electrons in the n-region tend to move away from the junction, as do the holes in the p-region. The scarcity of electrons and holes from the vicinity of the junction creates a *depletion zone* there.

Also, the positive charge of the n-region is increased by the positive voltage of the source and the negative charge of the p-region is increased by the negative voltage of the source. This results in an increase of the electric field at the junction and, hence, the potential barrier is raised.

Because of the increase in the potential barrier and the presence of the depletion zone, very little current flows through the crystal (that is, its resistance is high). When the external voltage is applied in this manner, we say it is in the *reverse* direction.

If a source of alternating voltage be applied to the crystals connected in series with a load, the voltage for one half-cycle will be in the forward direction (Figure 19-4A) and current will flow through the circuit. During the next half-cycle the voltage will be

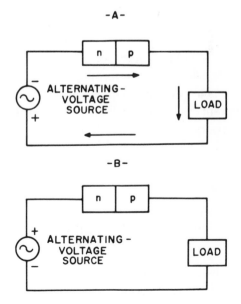

Fig. 19-4. The junction diode as a rectifier.

A. Voltage applied in forward direction. Arrows indicate current flow.

B. Voltage applied in reverse direction. There is no current flow.

Fig. 19-5. The junction diode.
    A. Low-power type.
    B. High-power type.

applied in the reverse direction (Figure 19-4B) and very little current will flow. You see, then, that the action of the crystals is to *rectify* the alternating voltage in a manner similar to the rectification produced by the copper-oxide rectifier discussed in Chapter 10, Subdivision B, 1, and the electron-tube diode discussed in Chapter 18, Subdivision B. We call the p-n rectifier *a junction diode.*

The symbol for the junction diode is ――◄――. The arrowhead represents the p-region and indicates the direction *opposite* to the flow of current through the diode in the forward direction. The heavy vertical bar of the symbol represents the n-region and, by analogy to the electron-tube diode, sometimes is called the *cathode.*

The low-power junction diode generally is enclosed in glass, ceramic, or plastic and is quite small, a quarter-inch or so in length. Those employed for higher power generally are enclosed in metal so that the heat generated may be radiated away.

B. *The point-contact diode*

There is another type of crystal rectifier in common use today. If a very fine wire of platinum or tungsten (called a *catwhisker*) makes contact with an n-type crystal, it produces a rectifier. Current flows through this rectifier if the crystal is negative with respect to the catwhisker. This is the forward direction. (See Figure 19-6.) If the crystal becomes positive with respect to the catwhisker

Fig. 19-6.

Rectifier circuit using a point-contact diode. Voltage during this half-cycle is in forward direction and arrows here indicate current flow.

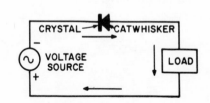

(during the next half-cycle), the voltage is in the reverse direction and very little current flows through the circuit.

A rectifier of this type is known as a *point-contact diode*, and is illustrated in Figure 19-7. It is believed that a p-region is formed in the area where the catwhisker touches the crystal and thus we obtain the equivalent of a p-n junction crystal. The symbol for this diode is the same as for the junction diode. The heavy vertical bar represents the crystal and the arrowhead represents the catwhisker.

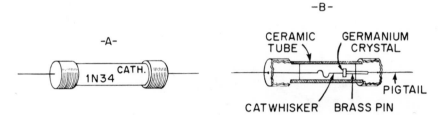

Fig. 19-7. A. Point-contact diode.

       B. Cross-section view, showing how the diode is constructed.

C. *Metallic rectifiers*

The meter rectifier illustrated in Figure 10-6 and discussed in Chapter 10, Subdivision B, 1, is another example of the semiconductor rectifier. A coating of copper oxide, you will recall, is deposited on a copper disk. The copper oxide (a semiconductor) acts somewhat as the p-region of the junction diode. The copper, though not a semiconductor, has many free electrons and thus acts somewhat as an n-region. Hence we have the equivalent of a p-n junction diode.

When voltage is applied in the forward direction (negative to the copper, positive to the copper oxide) the resistance of the rectifier is low. When the voltage is applied in the reverse direction, the resistance is very high. By analogy to the vacuum-tube diode, the copper is the cathode and the copper oxide the anode.

Because the copper-oxide coating is very thin, the peak inverse (reverse) voltage the rectifier cell can safely withstand without breakdown is quite small, about 8 to 10 volts per cell. Where a greater inverse voltage is to be applied, several cells may be connected in series to form a *stack*. (The rectifier illustrated in Figure 10-6 is such a stack.)

A similar type of rectifier is made by depositing a thin coating of selenium (a semiconductor) on an iron plate. This rectifier can withstand a peak inverse voltage of about 26 volts per cell. It, too, may be stacked for a higher voltage rating. (See Figure 19-8.)

Rectifiers such as the copper oxide-copper and selenium-iron types are called *metallic rectifiers*. Their symbols are the same as for the junction diode; the arrowhead represents the anode, the bar the cathode, and the forward direction is from the bar to the arrowhead.

Fig. 19-8.

Stacked selenium rectifier.

D. The transistor

Let us sandwich a thin p-type crystal between two n-type crystals, as shown in Figure 19-9. The lead to the left-hand n-type crystal is called the *emitter* terminal. The lead to the other n-type crystal is called the *collector* terminal. The lead to the p-type crystal is called the *base* terminal. The junction between the left-hand n-type crystal and the p-type crystal is called the *emitter junction*. The junction between the right-hand n-type crystal and the p-type crystal is called the *collector junction*.

The entire sandwich with its leads is called a *junction transistor*. (Actually, the junction transistor usually does not consist of three different crystals but, rather, of a single crystal into which the three distinct regions or layers have been introduced by adding controlled

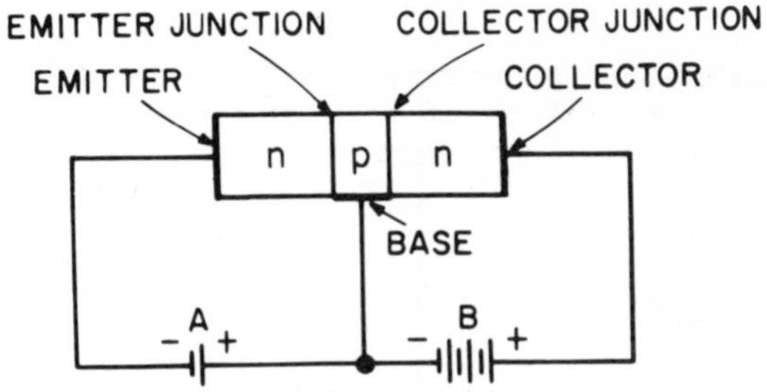

EMITTER JUNCTION   COLLECTOR JUNCTION

EMITTER   COLLECTOR

Fig. 19-9.

Basic transistor circuit.

| n | p | n |

BASE

A   B

amounts of the various impurities. The transistor, then, is a sandwich of these three regions or layers in a single crystal.) The symbol for a transistor is shown below.   EMITTER   COLLECTOR

BASE

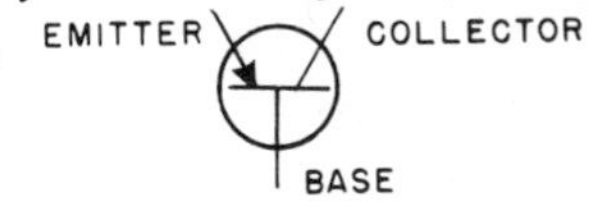

Note that the voltage from battery A is applied in the *forward* direction, as far as the emitter junction is concerned. Hence the impedance of that junction is low. On the other hand, the voltage from battery B is applied in the *reverse* direction, as far as the collector junction is concerned. Hence the impedance of that junction is high.

Electrons will flow readily from the emitter to the base region. Here some of these electrons will combine with the holes in the p-type crystal. But if this crystal be made thin enough, practically all the electrons entering it from the emitter will be attracted to the positive collector terminal and through the external collector circuit to battery B.

Hence, for every electron entering through the emitter of the transistor, approximately one electron will flow from the collector. That is, a flow of current in the emitter circuit will produce approximately a similar flow of current in the collector circuit. However, since the impedance (Z) of the emitter circuit is quite low and that of the collector circuit very high, the power ($I^2 \times Z$) in the collector circuit will be much greater than in the emitter circuit. It is in this way that the junction transistor acts as a power amplifier. An indication of the amount of gain that may be obtained may be seen from the fact that the impedance of the emitter circuit may be as low as about 25 ohms, whereas the impedance of the collector circuit may be several megohms. (A megohm is one million ohms.)

The basic amplifying circuit is shown in Figure 19-10. Assume that the incoming signal is in the form of an alternating voltage. The

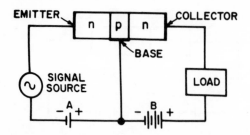

Fig. 19-10.

Basic circuit using an n-p-n junction transistor as an amplifier.

signal source is connected into the emitter circuit. In this way it alternately adds to or subtracts from the voltage of battery A. Hence a larger or smaller current, respectively, flows through the low-impedance emitter circuit. Accordingly, a larger or smaller current flows through the high-impedance collector circuit (which contains the load in series). As explained above, a low power input to the emitter circuit produces a large power output at the load in the collector circuit. Where did the extra power come from? From battery B.

Because of the arrangement of the two types of crystals (or regions) in the transistor we have been discussing, it is called an *n-p-n* junction transistor. It is possible to form a *p-n-p* junction transistor, as illustrated in Figure 19-11. Here the two outside portions are p-type while the center one is an n-type. The action and circuitry for this type of transistor are the same as for the n-p-n type, except that, since the relative positions of the regions have been reversed, the polarity of the batteries, too, must be reversed. And this time, instead of electrons, positive holes will flow from the emitter to the negatively charged collector terminal.

Fig. 19-11.

Basic circuit employing a p-n-p junction transistor as an amplifier.

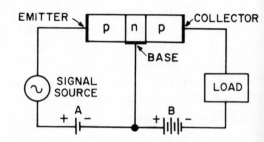

When using the symbol for the transistor, we can differentiate between the n-p-n type and the p-n-p type in the following manner. If the symbol appears as

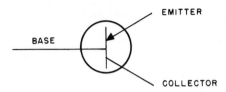

it is a p-n-p type. If the symbol appears as

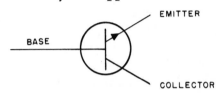

it is an n-p-n type.

There is another type of transistor that closely resembles the point-contact diode, except that *two* catwhiskers are employed, touching the surface of the germanium crystal at points about 0.002 inch apart. (See Figure 19-12.) The crystal generally is of the n-type. Such a transistor is known as an *n-type point-contact transistor.*

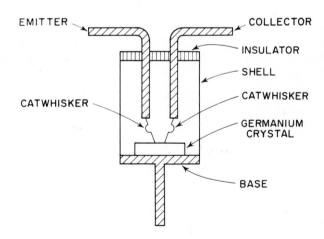

Fig. 19-12. Cross-section of point-contact transistor.

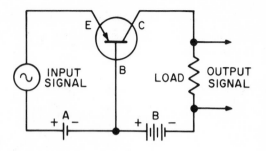

Fig. 19-13.

Basic common-base ampli-
fier circuit.

The basic circuit for this type of transistor is similar to that of a p-n-p junction transistor. One of the catwhiskers becomes the emitter, the other the collector. The action of the point-contact transistor is somewhat similar to that of the junction transistor. Though generally less efficient and suffering from a lower power-handling ability, the point-contact transistor nevertheless can handle currents of higher frequencies more efficiently than can the junction transistor. However, recent technological improvements in the manufacture of the junction-type transistor have greatly reduced the gap between the two and, as a result, very few point-contact transistors are manufactured today.

There are three ways a transistor may be connected in an amplifying circuit. The basic *common-base* (sometimes called the *grounded-base*) circuit is illustrated in Figure 19-13. Note that the base is common to both the emitter and collector circuits. The output signal is taken from across the load.

The basic *common-emitter* (*grounded-emitter*) circuit is illustrated in Figure 19-14. The emitter is common to both the emitter and collector circuits.

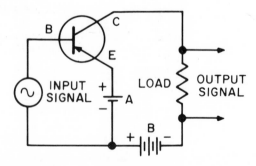

Fig. 19-14. Basic common-emitter amplifier circuit.

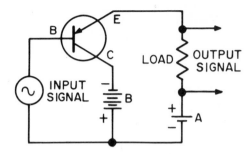

Fig. 19-15. Basic common-collector amplifier circuit.

The basic *common-collector* (*grounded-collector*) circuit is illustrated in Figure 19-14. Here the collector is common to both the emitter and collector circuits.

Each type of circuit has its own characteristics (such as input impedance, output impedance, gain); which type is to be used depends upon the design requirements of the particular amplifier. Note that the symbols indicate the use of a p-n-p transistor in all three illustrations. If an n-p-n transistor is used, the polarities of the batteries must be reversed.

The transistor may also be employed as an oscillator, a typical circuit of which is illustrated in Figure 19-16. The transistor here is connected in a common-emitter circuit. Inductor L_1 and capacitor C form the oscillatory circuit. Feedback to compensate for losses and thus keep the oscillations going comes from the collector circuit through L_2, which is inductively coupled to L_1. The r-f output from

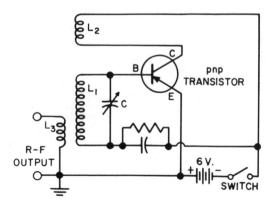

Fig. 19-16. Typical transistor r-f oscillator circuit.

the oscillator is obtained through L_3 which is inductively coupled to L_1. With a transistor such as Raytheon type CK762, this circuit can produce oscillations whose frequencies may be as high as about 25 megacycles.

The transistor has a number of advantages over the electron tube. Its physical structure is much simpler. Hence it is smaller and more rugged. It has no heater, hence it requires no heater power. It is much more efficient, requiring less power and lower voltages for its operation. It has a much longer life than the electron tube and, in the near future, it will be much cheaper to produce.

On the other hand, it is much more vulnerable to excessive heat and moisture than is the electron tube. Furthermore, if the polarities of the voltages applied to the electron tube be reversed accidentally, no harm is done to the tube. The transistor, however, may be permanently damaged by such a mistake.

At the present time, certain types of electron tubes have considerably greater power-handling ability than do transistors. However, when the transistor was first introduced only a few years ago, its power-handling ability was measured in milliwatts. (A milliwatt is $\frac{1}{1000}$ watt.) Today we have transistors that can safely handle 100 watts and there is no reason why this figure should not be increased in the near future.

The same is true of the frequency response of the transistor. When first introduced, the transistor could not handle currents of very high frequencies. Today its frequency response is in the order of hundreds of millions of cycles per second. Of course, the frequency response of the electron tube is still a good deal higher, but it is safe to assume that the transistor will soon catch up.

Sylvania Electric Products, Inc.

Fig. 19-17. Transistors come in different shapes and sizes.

Transistors come in different sizes and shapes. (See Figure 19-17.) Some are smaller than a pea; all are very small compared to comparable electron tubes. They are encased in metal to help radiate away the heat produced. Those handling the larger power frequently are further equipped with cooling fins or flanges. All are hermetically sealed to protect them from moisture and other contamination.

QUESTIONS

Wherever possible, diagrams should be used to clarify the answers to these questions. These diagrams need not be elaborate, but they should be drawn neatly with the significant portions clearly labeled.

1. Draw the theoretical structure of a p-type germanium crystal. Explain.
2. Draw the theoretical structure of an n-type germanium crystal. Explain.
3. In terms of the electron theory, explain the rectifying action of the n-p junction diode.
4. Describe the point-contact diode. Explain what is meant by the *forward direction* of current flow through this diode.
5. Describe the structure of *a*) an n-p-n junction transistor; *b*) a p-n-p junction transistor.
6. Draw the basic circuit of the n-p-n junction transistor as an amplifier. In terms of the electron theory, explain its action.
7. Draw the basic circuit of an n-p-n transistor used as a *grounded-base* amplifier.
8. Draw the basic circuit of an n-p-n transistor used as a *grounded-emitter* amplifier.
9. Draw the basic circuit of an n-p-n transistor used as a *grounded-collector* amplifier.
10. Draw the basic circuit of an n-p-n transistor used as an oscillator. Explain its action.
11. What are the advantages of the transistor over the electron tube? What are its disadvantages?

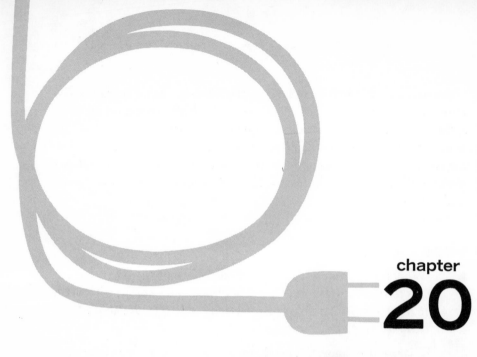

20

Practical Applications of the Electron Tube

A. Radio communication

Man is a restless creature, constantly looking for new horizons. No sooner had he learned how to make an electric current carry intelligence through wires strung around the world, then he began seeking for methods of eliminating the wire.

In 1867, James Maxwell of England announced that he had proved mathematically the possibility of a wave of energy, electrical in nature, that should be able to travel through space with the speed of light (186,000 miles per second). We now know this as the *electromagnetic wave*, which includes radio waves, infrared rays, visible light rays, ultraviolet rays, X-rays, and gamma rays given off by certain types of radioactive materials. These various rays resemble each other, differing only in frequency.

In 1887, Heinrich Rudolph Hertz of Germany succeeded in creating the radio wave. He transmitted this wave across the space of a room and caused it to operate an extremely crude type of receiver. Here was our wireless carrier.

In 1895, Guglielmo Marconi, an Italian, invented a practical system for transmitting and receiving short (dots) and long (dashes) bursts or pulses of the radio wave—in other words, a wireless telegraph system.

In 1900, Reginald A. Fessenden, an American, succeeded in impressing voice signals upon the wireless carrier. Soon, radio waves were carrying messages around the world.

1. THE RADIO WAVE

How the radio wave comes into being is not too well known and the theories and concepts involved are too complex to be discussed in this book. It is enough for us to know, here, that when an alternating current flows through a conductor, energy is radiated from this conductor in the form of radio waves. Although alternating currents of all frequencies send out these radiations, only if the frequencies are high—that is, 15,000 cycles per second or more—can these radio waves be sent out and received readily.

Frequencies that lie within the range that the human ear can hear—that is, up to about 15,000 cycles per second—are called *audio frequencies*. Frequencies beyond the audible range are called *radio frequencies*. At the present time, by law, the standard radio broadcast band covers a spread between 535 and 1,605 kilocycles (per second), but we may have radio waves whose frequencies may run as high as 30,000 megacycles and higher.

The waveform of the radio wave resembles that of the alternating current producing it (see Chapter 7, Subdivision C, 1). If the waveform of the alternating current is sinusoidal and of uniform amplitude and constant frequency, the resulting radio wave will be also

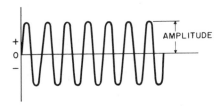

Fig. 20-1. Waveform of radio-frequency carrier wave.

(Figure 20-1). This is the waveform of the basic radio wave used to carry our intelligence and, accordingly, it is called a *carrier wave.* The alternating current that produces this wave is called the *carrier current.*

2. THE RADIO TRANSMITTER

The problem of the radio transmitter is threefold. First of all, it must create the carrier current of suitable strength and frequency. Next, it must impress on this carrier current the intelligence we wish to transmit. Finally, it must convert this carrier current with its intelligence into a radio wave that is broadcast to a distant receiver.

The carrier current is generated by electron tubes operating as *oscillators* (Chapter 18, Subdivision C). The desired frequency is obtained by choosing suitable values for the inductor and capacitor of the oscillating circuit. Electron-tube amplifiers are used to bring the carrier current up to the desired strength.

Intelligence is impressed on the carrier current by a process of *modulation* similar to the method by which the sound wave modulates the steady direct current in the telephone (see Chapter 16, Subdivision A). A *microphone* similar to the telephone transmitter may be used for this purpose. The sound wave, striking the microphone, produces a modulated sound current. The sound current then is mixed with the carrier current produced by the oscillator. The result is a *modulated carrier current.*

This process is illustrated by the graphs of Figure 20-2. Note that the current from the microphone is modulated at *audio* (sound) frequency. The carrier and modulated carrier currents are at *radio* frequency. Note, too, that as a result of mixing the sound current and the carrier current, the modulated carrier current no longer is of a constant amplitude. Its amplitude has been varied to conform with the waveform of the sound current. This can be seen from the dashed line, called the *envelope,* that connects all the peaks of the modulated carrier current. Because the intelligence we wish to transmit causes changes in the *amplitude* of the carrier current, we call this process *amplitude modulation.*

The next step is to convert the modulated radio-frequency carrier current into a radio wave of similar waveform. This is done by per-

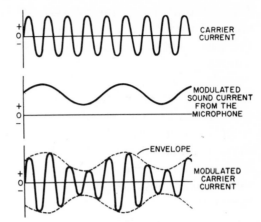

Fig. 20-2.

Graphs showing how the intelligence (sound current) is impressed on the carrier current.

mitting the current to flow through an elevated wire, or network of wires, called an *antenna,* or *aerial.* As the current flows through the antenna, a radio wave is created that radiates in all directions with the speed of light.

A block diagram of the major portions of a radio transmitter is shown in Figure 20-3. As previously stated, this method for impressing intelligence on the carrier wave is called *amplitude modulation (AM)* because it varies the amplitude of the carrier current.

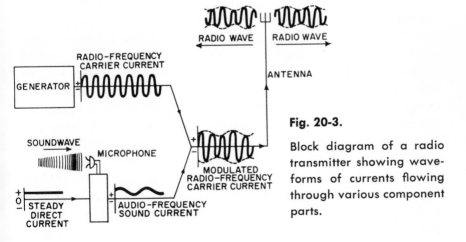

Fig. 20-3.

Block diagram of a radio transmitter showing waveforms of currents flowing through various component parts.

452 Practical Applications of the Electron Tube

We have other means for impressing such intelligence. For example, we may use it to vary the *frequency* of the carrier current. We call this process *frequency modulation (FM)*.

3. THE RADIO RECEIVER

Like the transmitter, the radio receiver, too, has three functions. It must catch the radio wave as it travels through space and reconvert it to a modulated radio-frequency carrier current similar to the one that flowed in the transmitter. However, since there usually is more than one radio transmitter on the air at any given time, the receiver must be able to select the signals from the desired transmitter and reject those from all others. Finally, the receiver must remove the intelligence from the carrier current and change it to sound waves for the ear to hear.

To catch the radio wave, the receiver employs an *antenna* somewhat similar to the one used by the transmitter. As the radio wave cuts across the wire of this antenna, an alternating voltage is induced in the wire. This voltage, in turn, generates an alternating current in the antenna wire. The waveform of the alternating current resembles that of the radio wave and thus we have our modulated radio-frequency carrier current flowing in the antenna of the receiver.

However, every radio wave that strikes the antenna of the receiver will induce an alternating current in that antenna. Thus, if radio waves from a number of transmitters (each operating at a different frequency) were to strike the antenna simultaneously, different alternating currents, each at a different frequency, would flow through the wire. How, then, do we separate the current we want from all the others?

To understand how this is done, refer to our discussion of oscillating circuits (Chapter 18, Subdivision C). If, as in Figure 20-4, a current is set flowing in the oscillating circuit consisting of the inductor and capacitor, it will tend to continue to oscillate back and forth at a frequency that is equal to the natural frequency of the circuit. This natural frequency, in turn, is determined by the values of the inductor and capacitor. The oscillations will continue until their energy is dissipated by the losses within the circuit. If new energy, sufficient to compensate for these losses, is fed to the oscillating circuit, the oscillations will tend to continue.

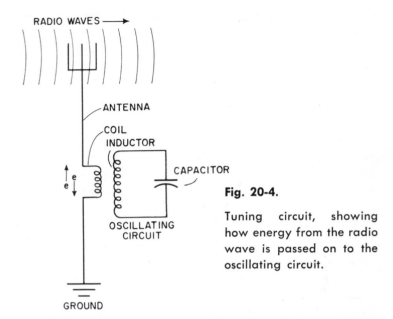

RADIO WAVES ⟶

ANTENNA

COIL
INDUCTOR

CAPACITOR

$\uparrow$ e
e $\downarrow$

OSCILLATING
CIRCUIT

GROUND

Fig. 20-4.

Tuning circuit, showing how energy from the radio wave is passed on to the oscillating circuit.

As the induced currents from the radio waves flow back and forth along the antenna circuit, they are made to pass through a coil inserted in that circuit. This coil is inductively coupled to the inductor of the oscillating circuit; together they form a transformer. In this way electrical energy is fed from the antenna to the oscillating circuit. It is this energy that starts the current flowing in the oscillating circuit and keeps it oscillating by supplying additional energy to compensate for losses.

To do so, however, the frequency of the antenna current must be equal to the natural frequency of the oscillating circuit. If the antenna current is at some other frequency, its energy is fed out of step with the oscillations, the energy is dissipated, and the oscillations die out. By adjusting the natural frequency of the oscillating circuit to the frequency of the transmitter whose signals we wish to hear, we can receive signals of only that frequency and reject all others. This process is called *tuning* and the oscillating circuit used for this purpose is called a *tuning circuit*.

Generally, the transmitter operates at only one frequency, but the receiver is adjustable in order to receive signals from a number of different transmitters at will. Such adjustments are made by varying the natural frequency of the tuning circuit. This can be accomplished by varying the value of the inductor, the capacitor, or both. Usually, the capacitor is variable. It is the value of the capacitor that you change when you turn the tuning knob to receive another station.

Now we have caught the radio wave, converted it to a modulated radio-frequency carrier current that is oscillating in the tuning circuit, and have rejected all unwanted signals. How do we remove the intelligence from the carrier current and convert it to sound waves?

If you re-examine Figure 20-2, you will note that the modulated carrier current contains two components. One is the radio-frequency carrier current and the other is the audio-frequency sound current. Since the modulated carrier current flowing in the tuning circuit of the receiver resembles that flowing in the transmitter, the current in the receiver, too, has the same two components.

You can see that the intelligence is represented by the audio-frequency component. The radio-frequency component merely provides the wireless carrier to convey the intelligence from the transmitting antenna to the receiving antenna. Hence, in the receiver, we must separate the audio-frequency component from the radio-frequency component. This process is called *demodulation,* or *detection.*

The separation of components depends upon the fact that a capacitor offers less impedance to a high-frequency current than to a low-frequency current. A resistor, on the other hand, impedes high-frequency and low-frequency currents equally. (See Chapter 9, Subdivision D, 5.) If a mixture of high-frequency (radio-frequency) current and low-frequency (audio-frequency) current is fed to a filter consisting of a capacitor and resistor in parallel, the high-frequency current tends to flow through the capacitor, which offers it a low-impedance path. The low-frequency current, on the other hand, finding the capacitor a high-impedance path, tends to flow through the resistor. It is in this way that the components are separated.

The circuit of a simple receiver is shown in Figure 20-5A. The radio wave, striking the antenna, produces an induced voltage which, in turn, sets oscillations flowing in the tuning circuit. These oscillations contain both the audio-frequency and radio-frequency components.

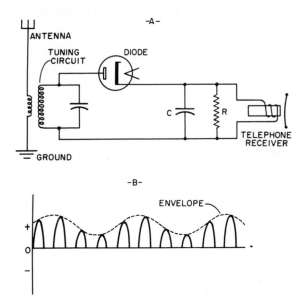

Fig. 20-5. A. Radio receiver showing how the diode is used as a rectifier.

B. Graph showing rectifying action of the diode.

The modulated radio-frequency carrier current flowing in the tuning circuit is fed to a rectifier, in this case, a diode tube. If the current were not rectified, since the negative half-cycles are equal and opposite to the positive half-cycles, cancellation would occur and the net result would be zero. The radio-frequency thus appears as a series of pulses, as shown in Figure 20-5B. The audio-frequency component is indicated by the envelope (dashed line).

The radio-frequency component (the carrier) flows through capacitor C. The audio-frequency component (the sound current containing the intelligence) flows through resistor R. As a result of the current flow through R, a voltage drop appears across it. This voltage bears the same waveform as that of the sound current. When this voltage is applied to a telephone receiver, the sound is reproduced. Since the action of the diode and its associated filter network (C and R) is that of demodulation or detection, we call such a circuit a *detector circuit.*

As the radio wave cuts across the antenna of the receiver, the currents its sets flowing in the wire are extremely small. For this reason, we use electron-tube amplifiers to amplify these currents before detection. Since such currents still contain the radio-frequency component, we call such amplifiers *radio-frequency amplifiers*. We may, also, amplify the sound current after detection. Such amplifiers are called *audio-frequency amplifiers*.

A *loudspeaker* generally is employed instead of the telephone receiver. Such a loudspeaker produces a louder sound by moving a larger quantity of air than does the diaphragm of the telephone receiver (see Figure 20-6). Instead of the coil being wound directly on the permanent magnet, it is wound on a thin form that fits loosely over one end of the magnet. As the sound current flows through the coil (*voice coil*), a magnetic field is set up around it that interacts with the magnetic field of the permanent magnet. As a result of this interaction, the coil moves back and forth on the magnet, in step with the variations of the sound current.

A large *cone*, generally of paper, is attached to the voice coil. As the voice coil moves, the cone moves also, pushing the air next to

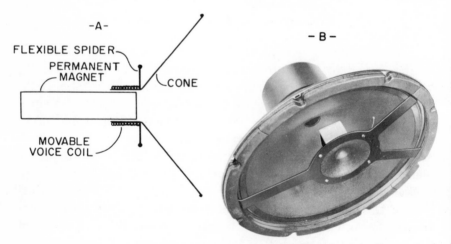

RCA Educational Services.

Fig. 20-6. A. Permanent-magnet loudspeaker.
   B. Commercial loudspeaker. Note that this unit consists of two speakers. The smaller one reproduces sounds of higher frequencies. The larger one reproduces sounds of lower frequencies.

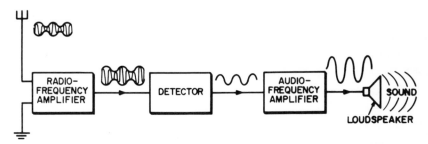

Fig. 20-7. Block diagram of radio receiver showing waveform of the signal at various stages.

it. In this way, a loud sound is produced. A thin, flexible *spider* holds the voice coil and cone in place.

A block diagram of a radio receiver is shown in Figure 20-7. Of course, modern radio receivers are more complicated than the simple one described here. Nevertheless, its basic principles apply to all kinds of receivers, regardless of their complexity.

B. *Television*

The fairy tales of all nations tell of men who could see what was happening at a great distance, far beyond the range of human sight. The twentieth century has seen this dream come true. The invention of television has been one of mankind's greatest achievements. Although the details of television are beyond the scope of this book, the principles are quite simple, and we shall present them briefly here.

The eye sees objects by the light reflected from these objects. If an object did not reflect light, it would be invisible. Assume that we have a spot that is illuminated by a bright light. If this spot is light in color, it will reflect a good deal of the light falling on it. If it is dark, it will reflect but little of the light falling on it.

Further, assume that we have a device, such as a photoelectric cell, that can convert light energy into electrical energy. If the reflected light from the light-colored spot falls upon this device, a relatively large current will be generated. If the reflected light from the dark-colored spot strikes this device, less current will be generated.

A picture can be broken down into spots of light of varying degrees of light and dark shades. If the device that changes light energy into electrical energy (the photoelectric cell) moves from spot to spot successively (we call this *scanning* the picture), the current generated by the photoelectric cell will vary in step with the light and dark spots.

If this varying current is sent, finally, into a device whose action is the reverse of the photoelectric cell—that is, a device whereby electrical energy is changed into light energy—and if this reproducing device moves in step with the photoelectric cell, the picture may be reconstructed on a screen (Figure 20-8).

This explanation covers the basic principles of television. The varying current from the photoelectric cell may be sent over wires or it may be used to modulate a radio wave that carries the variations many miles through space. If the scanning is rapid enough, pictures of moving objects may be shown in rapid succession on the screen of the television receiver, giving the illusion of motion, just as motion pictures do.

These are a number of methods for producing the varying current at the television transmitter. One method employs the cathode ray in a device called the *iconoscope*, invented by an American scientist, Vladimir K. Zworykin.

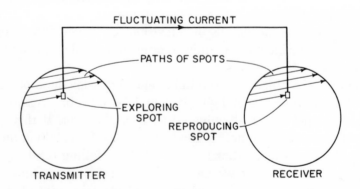

Fig. 20-8. Diagram illustrating basic principle of television. The two spots keep in step with each other.

There are certain materials, such as the metal *cesium,* that have the peculiar property of shooting off electrons when exposed to light. We call such materials *photoelectric* materials. The electrons emitted in this fashion are called *photoelectrons.* The greater the intensity of the light, the greater is the number of photoelectrons emitted.

In the iconoscope (Figure 20-9), a thin sheet of mica has one face covered with a great many tiny droplets of silver. Each droplet is insulated from its neighbors and is coated with the photoelectric metal cesium. Each droplet, with its coating, is called an *element* and the entire surface of the mica sheet is called a *mosaic.* The rear of the mica sheet is coated with a metal film, called the *signal plate.* You can see that each element forms a tiny capacitor with the signal plate, the mica sheet acting as the dielectric and the signal plate being common for all the capacitors.

The side of the mica sheet that bears the elements (the *photo-sensitized* side) faces the front—that is, faces toward the object be-

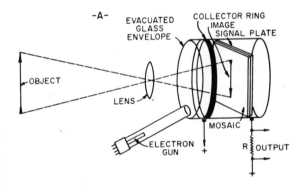

Fig. 20-9.

A. Iconoscope.
B. Commercial iconoscope.

Radio Corporation of America.

ing viewed or *televised*. An *electron gun* is so mounted that its beam can sweep across the surface of the mosaic. In front of the mosaic a metal ring, called the *collector ring,* is mounted. Electron gun, mosaic, signal plate, and collector ring are all mounted in a glass envelope from which the air has been evacuated.

As the image is focused on the mosaic, each light-sensitive element receives its portion of light from the picture. As light strikes each element, electrons are knocked off. The number of electrons emitted by each element is proportional to the intensity of the light striking it. The more intense the light, the more electrons are emitted. Thus bright spots of the picture, reflecting more intense light to the elements, cause more electrons to fly off. Darker spots of the picture cause fewer electrons to be emitted.

As each element loses an electron (which has a negative charge) it acquires a positive charge. Thus, bright spots of the picture cause their respective elements to acquire greater positive charges. The elements corresponding to the darker spots of the picture acquire lesser positive charges. Because the elements are insulated from each other, the electrical charges remain fixed and do not flow from one element to another. In this way light from the picture forms a sort of electrostatic image on the mosaic.

Note that the signal plate is connected to ground through resistor R. As an element is struck by a light ray, loses electrons, and acquires a positive charge, electrons are drawn up from the ground, through resistor R and on to a spot on the signal plate opposite the positively charged element. The more intense the light striking the element, the greater its positive charge and the greater the number of electrons on the signal plate opposite it. Thus, you see, light from the picture forms an electron image on the signal plate.

Now what would happen if the element were to lose its positive charge? The electrons on the signal plate opposite it, no longer attracted, would flow back through resistor R to ground. This flow constitutes an electric current, and consequently a voltage is developed across the resistor. The strength of this voltage depends upon the number of electrons flowing through the resistor. This, in turn, depends upon the intensity of the light striking the element. So you see that each spot of the picture can cause a voltage to be developed across the resistor R, and the strength of this voltage will be proportional to the brightness of that spot.

The positive charges on the elements are neutralized by the electrons of the beam generated by the electron gun. The electron beam is moved in a horizontal line (usually by means of an electromagnetic deflection system) from element to element, scanning the mosaic from left to right somewhat as your eyes scan a line in this book. When the beam reaches the end of a line it quickly returns to the left side of the mosaic, and, at the same time, drops to the next line which it then proceeds to scan. This continues until the beam reaches the bottom of the mosaic. It then is moved to the top and the entire process is repeated. In this way the beam touches every element of the mosaic.

As the beam moves from element to element, neutralizing the positive charge on each in turn, a varying voltage, varying in proportion to the charges, is developed across the resistor. And since these charges vary in proportion to the light and dark spots of the picture, the voltage across the resistor, too, will vary in proportion to these light and dark spots. Thus the picture has been converted into a varying voltage. If we amplify the varying voltage across resistor R and use it to modulate a carrier current, we have, in effect, our television signal.

As the light rays strike the light-sensitive elements of the mosaic, electrons are emitted. These electrons are attracted to the positively charged collector ring in the envelope in front of the mosaic and thus are drawn out of the envelope, and so out of the way.

In the television receiver, the cathode-ray tube is used as a reproducer. By means of proper voltages applied to the deflection system of the tube (which usually is of the electromagnetic, rather than the electrostatic, type) the electron beam is made to sweep across the surface of the screen in step with the sweep of the beam of the iconoscope. After the modulated wave has been received, amplified, and demodulated, the varying voltage that carries the intelligence is fed to the control electrode, or grid, of the tube. This electrode, you will recall, varies the density of the beam, varying in this way the intensity of the light produced on the screen.

For example, if at one instant the beam of the iconoscope discharges an element that has received a large positive charge owing to the fact that a bright light has fallen on it, a large current flows from the signal plate to the modulator of the transmitter. At the receiving end, the beam of the cathode-ray tube is at a position on the screen corresponding to the position of the beam in the iconoscope. The large voltage appearing at the control grid causes a bright spot to appear on the screen. Dark and bright spots appear on the cathode-ray screen in step with the dark and bright spots of the scene at the transmitting studio. Since these spots constitute the scene, the scene is reproduced on the receiving screen.

These spots merge to produce the scene because of two factors. One is the persistence of human vision. The eye sees a light for a fraction of a second after the light has disappeared. In this way, we get an overlapping of spots which blend to give us the scene. Similar to this is the persistence of glow which the chemicals on the cathode-ray screen possess. The glow persists for a fraction of a second after the electron stream has moved to the next spot. Once again the spots merge to produce the scene. If successive scenes are produced rapidly enough, we get the illusion of motion.

Generally, we associate television with home entertainment. But we gradually are learning to use this marvelous instrument for other purposes. For example, an engineer, seated in a control room, is able to keep an eye on the operations in all parts of a large factory by means of a number of television sets suitably located. In such an application, the television signals may be sent to the television receivers in the control room through cables, rather than by radio waves. Department stores may use a similar installation to display merchandise on sale in the various departments to customers gathered in a central hall.

Television may also be used to convey a picture of what is happening in a place where it is too dangerous for a human observer to be. For example, a suitably protected transmitter located inside a blast furnace permits a distant observer to see what occurs in the furnace. Television may be used to observe what is happening behind the protective walls of a chamber where an experiment in atomic fission is being performed. Again, a transmitter can be lowered to the bottom of the ocean and report the scene it sees to an observer on the surface or even many miles away.

Television is particularly useful in the field of education. It can be used to enable students located in all parts of the country to observe important experiments being performed at some of our great research centers. In the field of surgery, large numbers of doctors may obtain close-up views of important operations as they are performed. This latter application is greatly enhanced by the development of color television.

To understand how color television operates, consider the fact that we can reproduce any color by combining red, blue, and green in suitable proportions. Thus we need three distinct television systems, one for each color.

One camera, operating behind a red filter, picks up the red portions of the scene being televised and impresses the image it picks up upon its iconoscope. The rest of the process is the same as previously described, except that only the red portions of the scene are being transmitted. The receiving system, too, is the same, except that the phosphors of the cathode-ray tube are of a type that glow red when struck by the electron beam.

Similarly, we have a blue camera with its transmitter and receiver, and a green camera with its transmitter and receiver. At the receiving end, then, we have a red cathode-ray tube that reproduces the red portions of the scene, a blue cathode-ray tube that reproduces the blue portions of the scene, and a green cathode-ray tube that reproduces the green portions. If we superimpose the images of all three tubes upon each other, we can reproduce the scene in its original colors.

In a practical color television system we do not use three cameras, but a triple camera, each portion of which picks up one color. Also, we do not use three transmitters, but combine the signal information of all three cameras into a single modulated radio wave.

At the receiver, a single three-color picture tube is employed. The inner face of this tube is covered with thousands of groups of tiny phosphor dots. Each group consists of one phosphor dot that glows red when struck by an electron beam, one that glows blue, and one that glows green. The tube contains three electron guns—one whose beam strikes only red phosphor dots, one whose beam strikes only blue phosphor dots, and one whose beam strikes only green phosphor dots. These guns operate together and are so arranged that their beams can strike only one group of phosphor dots at a time.

At the receiver the signal information is separated into its red, blue, and green components. Each portion is fed to its own electron gun. Thus, as the beams from the three guns sweep the face of the tube, the various red, blue, and green phosphor dots glow with an intensity depending upon the signal information being fed to these guns. Since the phosphor dots are very small, the eye does not see a mass of colored dots but, rather, the dots blend together to form a picture of the scene in its original colors.

C. Radar *

Radar—R A dio Detection And Ranging—is one of the outstanding electronic developments in recent years. Essentially, it is a device for detecting objects at a considerable distance and for determining the object's direction and the distance between it and the radar station. Developed for war purposes, radar was quickly adapted to peaceful needs, especially in the field of navigation.

A consideration of the actual circuits employed in radar equipment is beyond the scope of this book. Instead, the general basic principles will be presented.

Assume that an airplane is flying high above the earth on a dark night. A searchlight station on the ground sends out a narrow beam of light. When this beam strikes the airplane, light is reflected back from the surface of the plane to the eyes of an observer stationed near the searchlight. The plane is seen, or *detected.*

With radar, a narrow radio beam is used instead of the light beam. This invisible beam, striking the plane, is reflected back to a radio receiver located near the transmitter and thus the plane is detected.

Thus far, the radio beam acts as the light beam. However, whereas clouds or fog render the light beam inoperative, the radio beam easily penetrates these obstacles. Further, the light beam is visible; the radio beam is invisible and the plane may be detected even though its occupants may not be aware of the fact.

It is not enough to detect the plane. We must know how far away it is, and how high up, and its bearing (that is, its compass position in relation to the observer). The searchlight permits only an approximation of the answers to these questions since it affords no accurate information concerning the distance of the plane from the observer.

With radar equipment, however, we are able to measure the time it takes the radio beam to travel from the transmitter to the plane and back again to the receiver. Knowing the speed at which the

---

* Reprinted from Abraham Marcus, *Physics for Modern Times* (New York: Prentice-Hall, Inc., 1952).

radio beam travels (approximately 186,000 miles per second), it is relatively easy to calculate the distance between the plane and the observer at the radar station. (Timing is accomplished by the use of *R-C* circuits as explained in Chapter 9, Subdivision D, 2.)

Because of the enormous speed of the radio wave, the time intervals are very small—in the order of *microseconds* (a microsecond is one-millionth of a second). The cathode-ray tube is used to measure these small intervals of time.

Assume that, at the instant the transmitter sends its radio beam at the target, the electron stream in the cathode-ray tube is set moving horizontally at a rate that will make the trace move across the face of the tube one inch per 100 microseconds. Further assume that the target is such a distance away from the transmitter that the radio wave, traveling at the rate of about 328 yards per microsecond, requires 100 microseconds to reach it. Since the reflected wave will require the same time to reach the receiver, the round trip will consume 200 microseconds.

During this interval, the trace on the face of the cathode-ray tube will have traveled two inches. If we had some method for marking the trace so that it would record the instant the radio wave was sent out and the instant it was received, we would then be able to tell the time required for the round trip (in microseconds) by measuring the distance (in inches) between the two marks.

The radio wave is sent out as a short *pulse*, or *burst*, of energy, rather than as a continuous wave. The duration of this pulse usually is only about one microsecond (abbreviated μs). Part of this pulse is sent to the vertical deflection system of the cathode-ray tube, and its effect is to produce a sharp bump, or *pip*, on the trace. When the reflected pulse is received, it, too, goes to the vertical deflection system of the tube. Thus a second pip appears on the trace (Figure 20-10).

In the 200 microseconds required for the radio pulse to reach the target and be reflected back to the receiver, the trace will have traveled two inches. Thus the two pips will appear two inches apart. By means of a scale printed on the face of the cathode-ray tube, we can translate the distance between the two pips of the trace into distance between the target and the radar station. Since the radio pulse travels at the rate of 328 yards per microsecond, it will require one microsecond for the pulse to reach a target 164 yards away and

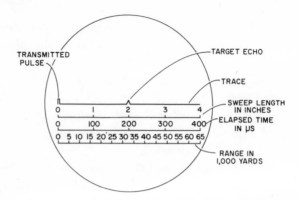

Fig. 20-10. Trace on the face of cathode-ray tube, showing pips.

be reflected back to the radar station. Thus, in our example, the distance between the two pips is two inches, the elapsed time for the round trip is 200 μs, and the distance between the radar station and the target is 32,800 yards (164 × 200).

The radio pulses may be sent out several hundred times per second. Since the sweep circuit of the cathode-ray tube is synchronized to start with each transmitted pulse, all the traces will coincide, producing the effect of a single trace.

Also, since the duration of each pulse is extremely brief and the time between pulses relatively great, the average power consumed is small. Thus, small tubes and other components may be employed, even though the power of each pulse is large.

The radio beam must be narrow so that it may be directed toward a particular spot, just as is the light beam of the searchlight. This requires special antenna arrays. To make the equipment portable and to allow the beam to be rotated easily, the antenna array must be quite small. This necessitates the use of very high frequencies— thousands of megacycles. Because of these high frequencies, radar operates on line-of-sight transmission, similar to light beams.

For peacetime use, radar equipment may be mounted on ships, airplanes, or other vehicles to detect obstacles that normally would not be seen because of darkness or fog.

1. IFF

It is not enough to detect a target by radar. Before opening fire on it, one should know whether the target is friendly or hostile.

RCA Educational Services.

Fig. 20-11. Radar antenna, mounted in the nose of an airplane.

To establish this identification, auxiliary apparatus has been developed for use with radar. This apparatus is known as *Identification—Friend or Foe (IFF)*.

Essentially, it consists of an automatic receiver and transmitter set which is carried by all friendly craft. When the target is detected by radar, a special coded signal, at a frequency other than the radar frequency, is transmitted. This challenging signal, when it is received by the receiver aboard the friendly craft, causes its transmitter to send out automatically a coded reply which is received by the receiver of the challenging station. If there is no reply, or if the reply is not in the code previously agreed upon, the craft is assumed to be hostile.

The cathode-ray tube is used here, too. If the reply to the challenge is the proper one, a pip appears on the screen. If there is no pip, the craft is presumed to be hostile. In some installations, the reply signal is superimposed on the radar screen through suitable circuits. In this way it changes the echoing pip produced by the target and thus identifies it as friendly.

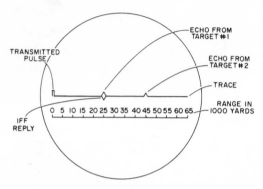

Fig. 20-12. Trace, showing the two targets. One, the nearest, is friendly, as indicated by IFF reply.

In Figure 20-12 there appears a radar screen which contains a trace showing two pips, and hence two targets, at different distances from the radar station. The nearest target (No. 1) is friendly, as shown by the downward pip appearing beneath the original pip. This downward pip is produced by the answer to the IFF challenge. The furthest target (No. 2) contains no downward pip and thus is assumed to be hostile.

For peacetime use, the automatic receiver and transmitter may be placed at definite, known points on the ground to serve as beacons for aircraft. As an airplane flies overhead, it might send out a challenging signal. The nearest beacon then would reply. The reply of each beacon would be coded differently for purposes of identification. Since the pilot would know the locations of these beacons from his maps, he thus would know his position.

2. PPI RADAR

More wonderful than the ordinary radar is the *PPI* radar (derived from Plan Position Indicator). With this instrument a radio beam is sent out and brings back a picture of the area surrounding the station.

Assume that a ship containing this apparatus is located near a shore (Figure 20-13A). The radar antennas are located at the top of a mast and are rotated so that they point at, or *scan*, the horizon. Below deck, and connected to the antennas, is the radar equipment.

The cathode-ray tube employed is of a special type whereby the electron beam sweeps from the center of the tube's face, along a radius to the periphery, and back to the center (Figure 20-13B).

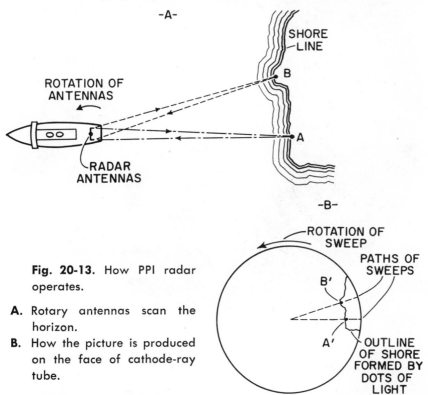

Fig. 20-13. How PPI radar operates.

A. Rotary antennas scan the horizon.

B. How the picture is produced on the face of cathode-ray tube.

In addition, the electron beam can be rotated around this center. The rotation of this electron beam is synchronized with the rotation of the radar antennas.

As the radar beam is transmitted from the antenna to a point on the horizon, the electron beam of the tube starts from the center toward a corresponding point on the periphery of the tube's face. The trace produced is just too faint to be seen. If the radar beam strikes a reflecting object (A), the echo causes the trace to brighten and a bright spot appears at a corresponding point on the trace (A′). Both the antenna and electron beam move to the next angular position. The echo from point B produces a corresponding bright spot on the trace (B′).

RCA Educational Services.

Fig. 20-14.

Scanning radar beam may be reflected back from storm clouds, producing a weather picture on the radarscope. Above is such a picture as seen by the pilot of an airplane. The plane's position is in the center of concentric circles, each of which marks a distance of five miles. The plane is heading toward the top of the picture. It is approaching the tail of a major storm which extends nearly 15 miles to the left. Straight ahead and ten miles away are two imposing thunderheads. This information enables the pilot to decide whether to fly into the storm-free area at his right and return to course through the gap between thunderheads seen at the 15-mile circle, or to attempt to weave through non-turbulent areas of the storm ahead.

This continues until a whole series of bright spots, corresponding to the outline of the shore, has appeared on the screen of the tube. Since the screen of the cathode-ray tube is of the high-persistence type, the bright spots will remain for some time after the sweep has moved on to other angular positions. The result is a picture of the area surrounding the ship, whose position is indicated by the center of the screen.

D. Industrial applications

For many years, the electron tube was used primarily for communication. Today, however, industry, too, has put the tube to work. Its industrial applications are so numerous that there is no room here to discuss even a small portion of them. However, a few examples will be presented merely to give the student some indication of how the tube is employed.

1. POWER CONTROL

Tremendous quantities of direct current are consumed by the chemical, metallurgy, and railway industries. Since power generally is supplied in the a-c form, it must be rectified before it can be used. Motor-generator sets (an a-c motor turning a d-c generator) had been used for this purpose. Today, electron tubes are taking over this job.

We have seen that the electron tube is, essentially, a rectifier, since the flow of electrons through it follows a one-way path from cathode to anode (plate). The vacuum-type diode described in Chapter 18, Subdivision B, generally is employed where high voltages and relatively small currents are involved. Industry, however, usually requires large currents. Accordingly, gas-filled rectifiers are needed.

The thyratron, discussed in Chapter 18, Subdivision C, is such a tube. Further, by controlling the point in the positive half-cycle where the grid voltage rises above the critical grid voltage, the power output may be controlled.

One method for controlling the thyratron is illustrated in Figure 20-15. The voltage on the grid is controlled by the setting of potentiometer R_1 across the grid battery. Alternating anode voltage is

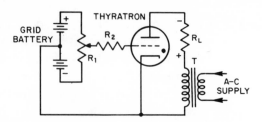

Fig. 20-15. Circuit of one method for controlling the thyratron.

applied by means of transformer T. R_2 is a resistor that limits the flow of grid current. R_L is the load.

When potentiometer R_1 is adjusted to its midpoint, the grid voltage is zero. The resulting action is illustrated graphically in Figure 20-16A. As the anode voltage becomes positive, current starts flowing, the grid loses its control, and current flows for the full positive half-cycle. The duration of current flow is indicated by the heavy portion of the anode-voltage curve.

As the slider of R_1 is moved toward the negative end of the potentiometer, the grid bias becomes negative. The resulting action is illustrated in Figure 20-16B. The grid-bias line crosses the critical grid-voltage curve at point No. 1 and current starts flowing through the tube at that instant of the positive half-cycle which corresponds to point No. 1 (point A).

Current flows for the remainder of the half-cycle. Note that the duration of the current flow (as shown by the heavy portion of the curve) is less than in the previous case. Thus the average current output of the thyratron is less.

In Figure 20-16C we see the graphic representation of what happens when the slider of R_1 is adjusted to make the grid bias more negative. The grid-bias line crosses the critical grid-voltage curve at point No. 2 and current starts flowing at point B of the anode-voltage curve. The duration of current flow is still less, and so is the average current output of the tube.

When the current requirements are not too great, the thyratron may be used. Where very large currents are required, mercury-pool rectifiers usually are employed. The *ignitron*, illustrated in Figure 20-17, is one such tube in common use.

Its cathode consists of a pool of mercury. The anode is a graphite cylinder. The envelope may be a glass bulb, but where very large currents are handled it may consist of an air-tight steel tank

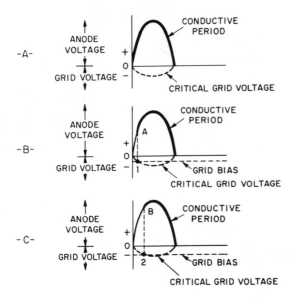

Fig. 20-16. Graphs indicating the flow of current through the thyratron during the positive half-cycle of the anode voltage. (The heavy portion of the curves indicates the period of current flow.)
  A. Flow at zero grid bias.
  B. Flow when small negative bias is placed on the grid.
  C. Flow when larger negative bias is placed on the grid.

from which the air has been evacuated, surrounded by a water jacket to dissipate the heat produced. Electron emission from the mercury-pool cathode is started by a spark between the mercury pool and an auxilliary electrode called the *igniter*. This spark produces a hot *cathode spot* on the surface of the mercury and it is from this spot that the electrons are emitted.

Electron emission takes place only when the anode is positive—that is, during the positive half-cycle of the alternating current. During the negative half-cycle the cathode spot is extinguished. Accordingly, the igniter must produce a cathode spot during each positive half-cycle.

The basic circuit of the ignitron is shown in Figure 20-18. The main rectification circuit consists of the a-c input, the ignitron tube, and the d-c output to the load. The igniter circuit consists of the

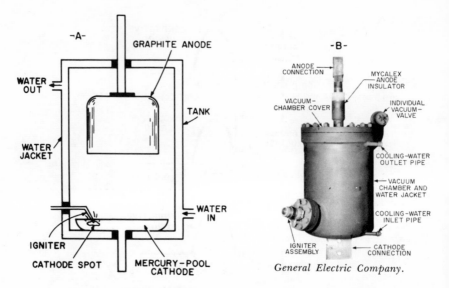

General Electric Company.

Fig. 20-17. A. Illustration of the construction of the ignitron.
B. Ignitron.

igniter and the small hot-filament diode rectifier with its step-down filament transformer. During the negative half-cycle of the a-c input the plate of the ignitron and the plate of the diode are both negative. Hence both tubes are inoperative.

During the positive half-cycle both plates are positive. Nevertheless, the ignitron is inoperative because there is, as yet, no electron emission from its cathode. On the other hand, as the plate of the diode becomes positive, current flows through that tube from its hot

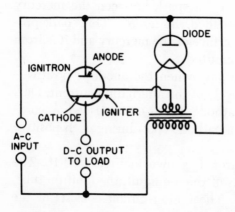

Fig. 20-18.

Basic circuit of ignitron.

filament. This flow of current places a positive charge on the igniter. This, in turn, produces the spark that establishes the cathode spot and electrons flow to the positive anode of the ignitron. Hence there is a flow of current through the ignitron during each positive half-cycle and a pulsating direct current is applied to the load.

The ignitron may be used as a controlled rectifier by substituting a controlled thyratron for the diode shown in Figure 20-18. Then, by controlling the point of the half-cycle at which the thyratron fires, we may control the firing point of the ignitron and, thus, its power output.

The controlled thyratron rectifier is widely used in motor-control and theatrical-lighting circuits. The controlled ignitron rectifier is employed extensively in resistance welding.

2. THE CATHODE-RAY OSCILLOSCOPE

In Chapter 18, Subdivision E, we discussed the cathode-ray tube. In this tube, you will recall, an electron gun at the narrow end of the evacuated funnel-shaped envelope shoots an extremely thin beam of electrons at the phosphor coating on the inside of the wide end. Where the electron beam strikes the phosphor, a spot of light is produced. The beam may be deflected up or down or from side to side by passing it through an electrostatic field produced by two sets of deflecting plates located inside the envelope. Or else the beam may be deflected by passing through a magnetic field produced by a set of external electromagnets. The path of light created by the tip of the electron beam moving over the phosphor coating is called the *trace* and may be viewed through the glass face of the tube.

The horizontal component, or sweep, of the trace is obtained by placing a sawtooth voltage upon the horizontal deflection system. (See Figure 18-25.) As this voltage rises steadily, the electron beam is deflected from the left-hand side of the screen to the right-hand side (looking at the wide face of the tube from the outside). When the voltage reaches its peak amplitude and drops rapidly to its lowest value, the beam quickly returns to the left-hand side of the tube. Then the entire cycle is repeated.

The voltage whose waveform is to be investigated is applied to the vertical deflection system. Thus, as the electron beam is being

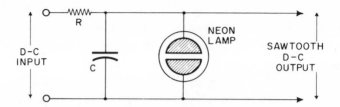

Fig. 20-19. Simple sawtooth oscillator using a neon lamp.

deflected from left to right under the influence of the horizontal sweep, it also is being moved up and down in step with the variations of the voltage being investigated. In this way the trace is spread over the face of the screen.

The device that generates the sawtooth voltage is called a *sawtooth, or sweep, oscillator.* The circuit of a simple type is shown in Figure 20-19. Here, direct current flowing through a resistor (R) charges a fixed capacitor (C). The voltage across this capacitor is applied to the horizontal deflection system of the cathode-ray tube. As the capacitor continues to charge, the voltage across it increases, and the electron beam continues to move from left to right.

Across this capacitor is a neon lamp (such as the "night light" illustrated in Figure 14-4). The lamp has no effect on the capacitor until a voltage high enough to ionize its gas (about 60 volts) is built up across the plates of the capacitor. When this voltage is reached, the gas within the lamp ionizes. The lamp becomes a conductor, instantly discharging the capacitor. The voltage across the capacitor, and, therefore, the voltage applied to the horizontal deflection system of the cathode-ray tube, drops to almost zero. This causes the electron beam to fly back to the left-hand side of the tube.

As the capacitor discharges, the neon gas in the lamp de-ionizes. Suddenly, the lamp becomes nonconductive and another cycle begins as the capacitor starts charging up again. The frequency of the saw-tooth voltage is determined by the length of time it takes to charge the capacitor to the ionizing point of the neon lamp. (See time constant of *R-C* circuits, Chapter 9, Subdivision D, 2.) By selecting proper values of capacitance and by making R variable, a sweep of any frequency from a few cycles up to many thousands per second may be obtained.

The cathode-ray tube with its sweep oscillator is called an *oscilloscope, or oscillograph.* The oscilloscope is, in reality, a voltmeter.

But it differs from the ordinary voltmeter is an important way. Because of the extremely light weight of the electron beam, it has practically no inertia. For this reason, the beam can be used to measure, by its deflection, *instantaneous* changes in voltage and give us a visual representation of these changes.

Practical oscilloscopes generally are supplied with horizontal and vertical amplifiers that are used to amplify the voltages applied to the horizontal and vertical deflection systems, respectively. Thus, very small voltages may be amplified to produce large traces on the screen.

The importance of the oscilloscope lies in the fact that we can devise comparatively simple electronic circuits to translate almost any quantity, quality, or property into changes in voltages. These changes are seen on the screen of the oscilloscope and we therefore can measure these quantities, qualities, or properties.

For example, we may determine the magnetic quality of a piece

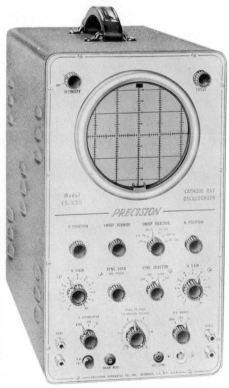

Fig. 20-20.

Cathode-ray oscilloscope.

Precision Apparatus Company.

of steel by measuring the voltage produced as it is moved through a coil of wire. Or we may measure the moisture content of a room by noting the changes in voltage when current flows through a moisture-absorbing substance placed in the room. Again, we may obtain pictures of sound waves as they strike the diaphragm of a microphone. The voltage changes produced are sent through the oscilloscope and the trace is viewed on the screen.

These are but a few of the many uses to which this device may be put. We cannot discuss here all these uses. Indeed, entire volumes have been written about this subject alone and hardly a day passes that a new application of the oscilloscope is not devised.

3. THE PHOTOELECTRIC RELAY

The phototube (see Chapter 12, Subdivision D) is widely used in industry to detect the presence or absence of light. Thus, in the burglar or fire alarm, the tube registers the fact that a beam of light focused on it is blocked out by the body of an intruder or obscured by the smoke from a fire. Conversely, in the automatic garage-door opener, the headlights of an automobile focused upon a normally-dark phototube start a motor that opens the door.

Because the current generated by the phototube is very small, its output generally is amplified until it is large enough to energize some device such as the electromagnetic relay which was discussed in Chapter 16, Subdivision A. In the circuit controlled by the relay the current may be large enough to ring a bell, light a lamp, or rotate a motor. The combination of phototube, amplifier, and electromagnetic relay is called a *photoelectric relay*.

The circuit of such a photoelectric relay is illustrated in Figure 20-21. In the absence of light, the phototube (V_1) offers a very high resistance, approaching infinity. When illuminated, however, its cathode emits electrons which are attracted to its positive anode, the tube becomes conductive, and its resistance drops to some low value.

Let us start with the phototube dark and therefore exhibiting a very high resistance. The values of the battery and cathode resistor (R_k) of the amplifier tube (V_2) are such that not enough plate current flows through the amplifier tube to energize the relay.

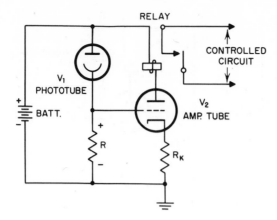

Fig. 20-21. Circuit of a forward-acting photoelectric relay.

As the phototube is illuminated, it becomes conductive and current flows from the battery, through resistor R and the phototube, and back to the battery. This current produces a voltage drop across R with the indicated polarity. As a result, the grid of V_2 becomes more positive (or, what is the same thing, less negative) with respect to its cathode, causing a flow of plate current sufficient to energize the coil of the relay.

Because the current flow through the phototube and R is only a few microamperes, the resistance of the latter must be quite large to produce a sufficient voltage drop across it. Values of R usually are in the order of megohms.

A photoelectric relay operating in this way is called *forward-acting*. It is used wherever a change from darkness to light is made to actuate some device. It is used, for example, in the automatic garage-door opener.

The photoelectric relay can also be constructed so that the relay is energized as a light beam shining on the phototube is interrupted or obscured. In this condition the relay is called *reverse-acting*. See Figure 20-22.

Let us start with the phototube illuminated. Note that the phototube and R act as a voltage divider across the battery. Because the phototube's resistance is low, the voltage drop across it, too, is low and with the indicated polarity. Because the resistance of R is very

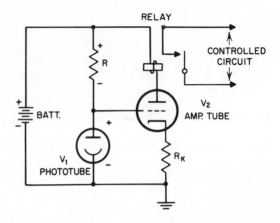

Fig. 20-22. Circuit of a reverse-acting photoelectric relay.

high, the voltage drop across it is much greater than that across the tube (note the indicated polarity).

The presence of its cathode resistor (R_k) makes the grid of the amplifier tube (V_2) quite negative with respect to its cathode. The voltage drop across the phototube tends to place a slight positive charge on this grid, but not large enough to overcome the negative charge placed there by the cathode resistor. Hence very little plate current flows, not enough to energize the relay.

When the phototube is darkened, its resistance becomes very high. The battery voltage now is divided so that a greater voltage drop appears across the phototube. The positive charge applied to the grid of V_2 is increased, the plate current rises, and the relay is energized.

Photoelectric relays of this type are widely used. For example, it may be employed as a safety device on industrial machines to stop the machine if the operator inadvertently places his hand in a dangerous area and interrupts the light beam in so doing.

QUESTIONS

Wherever possible, diagrams should be used to clarify the answers to these questions. These diagrams need not be elaborate, but they should be drawn neatly with the significant portions clearly labeled.

1. What are the three functions of the radio transmitter?
2. What are *a*) *audio* frequencies; *b*) *radio* frequencies?
3. Describe the waveform of the *carrier current.* What is meant by the *carrier wave?*
4. Explain how the modulated carrier current is obtained.
5. Draw the block diagram of a radio transmitter. Explain the functions of the component parts.
6. What are the three functions of the radio receiver?
7. Explain the function of the receiving antenna.
8. Explain how the receiver accepts signals from the desired station and rejects signals from all others.
9. Explain the action of the detector circuit.
10. Explain the function in a receiver of *a*) the radio-frequency amplifier; *b*) the audio-frequency amplifier.
11. What is the function of the loudspeaker? Explain its action.
12. Explain the basic principles of television.
13. Explain the function and operation of the *iconoscope* in the television transmitter.
14. Explain the function and operation of the *cathode-ray tube* in the television receiver.
15. Explain the basic principles of radar. How is the cathode-ray tube employed here?
16. Explain how the thyratron may be used as a controlled rectifier.
17. Describe the structure of the ignitron. Explain the function of each part.
18. Draw the basic circuit of the ignitron and explain its operation.
19. Explain how a thyratron may be used to control the d-c output of an ignitron.
20. List the essential portions of a cathode-ray oscilloscope. Explain the function of each portion.
21. Draw and explain the circuit of a forward-acting photoelectric relay.
22. Draw and explain the circuit of a reverse-acting photoelectric relay.

Appendix A

GLOSSARY OF ELECTRICAL TERMS, SYMBOLS, UNITS, AND ABBREVIATIONS

Term	Symbol	Unit	Abbreviation
alternating-current (as adjective)			a-c
ampere-turn	IN		
British thermal unit			Btu
calorie			cal
candlepower			cp
capacitance	C	farad	f
		microfarad	μf
		micromicrofarad	$\mu\mu$f
capacitive reactance	X_C	ohm	Ω
centimeter			cm
circular mils			cir mils
counter electromotive force	cemf	volt	v
cubic centimeter			cu cm or cm³
current	I	ampere	amp
		milliampere	ma
		microampere	μa
dielectric constant	K		
direct-current (as adjective)			d-c
electric energy		wattsecond (joule)	wsec
		watthour	whr
		kilowatthour	kwhr

482

Term	Symbol	Unit	Abbreviation
electric power	P	watt	w
		kilowatt	kw
		milliwatt	mw
		microwatt	μw
electromotive force (voltage, potential difference)	E or emf	volt	v
		kilovolt	kv
		millivolt	mv
		microvolt	μv
flux density (magnetic)	B	gauss	
foot-candle			ft-c
foot-pound			ft-lb
frequency	f	cycles per second	c or $\sim$
		kilocycles per second	kc
		megacycles per second	mc
frequency, resonant	fr	cycles per second	c or $\sim$
horsepower			hp
impedance	Z	ohm	Ω
inductance	L	henry	h
		millihenry	mh
		microhenry	μh
inductive reactance	X_L	ohm	Ω
kilovolt-ampere			kva
magnetic flux	ϕ	maxwell	
magnetomotive force	F	gilbert	
microsecond			μs
mutual inductance	M	henry	h
permeability (magnetic)	μ		
phase angle	θ	degree	°
power factor			pf
reactance	X	ohm	Ω
reluctance (magnetic)	$\mathcal{R}$		
resistance	R	ohm	Ω
		kilohm	KΩ
		megohm	MΩ
revolutions per minute			rpm
revolutions per second			rps
root mean square			rms
specific gravity			sp gr
square centimeter			sq cm or cm^2

Appendix B

GLOSSARY OF ELECTRICAL FORMULAS USED IN THIS BOOK

Ohm's law for d-c circuits

$$I = \frac{E}{R}; \; E = I \times R; \; R = \frac{E}{I}$$

Ohm's law for a-c circuits

$$I = \frac{E}{Z}; \; E = I \times Z; \; Z = \frac{E}{I}$$

I = current in *amperes* Z = impedance in *ohms*
E = electromotive force in *volts* R = resistance in *ohms*

Power in d-c circuits

$$P = I \times E; \; P = I^2 \times R; \; P = \frac{E^2}{R}$$

Power in a-c circuits

$$P = I \times E \times \text{pf}$$

P = power in *watts*
I = current in *amperes*
E = electromotive force in *volts*
R = resistance in *ohms*
pf = power factor in *per cent*

$$\text{Power factor} = \frac{\text{true power (as measured by wattmeter)}}{\text{apparent power (as measured by voltmeter and ammeter)}}$$

Heat produced by electric current

$$\text{Heat} = 0.24 \times I^2 \times R \times T$$

Heat = calories	R = resistance in *ohms*
I = current in *amperes*	T = time in *seconds*

1 wattsecond = 0.24 calorie
1 British thermal unit = 252 calories = 1,050 wattseconds

Resistors in series

$$R_{\text{total}} = R_1 + R_2 + R_3 +, \text{ and so forth}$$

Resistors in parallel

$$\frac{1}{R_{\text{total}}} = \frac{1}{R_1} + \frac{1}{R_2} + \frac{1}{R_3} +, \text{ and so forth}$$

R = resistance in *ohms*

Inductors in series (no interaction of fields)

$$L_{\text{total}} = L_1 + L_2 + L_3 +, \text{ and so forth}$$

Inductors in parallel (no interaction of fields)

$$\frac{1}{L_{\text{total}}} = \frac{1}{L_1} + \frac{1}{L_2} + \frac{1}{L_3} +, \text{ and so forth}$$

Inductors in series (fields aiding)

$$L_{\text{total}} = L_1 + L_2 + 2M$$

Inductors in parallel (fields aiding)

$$\frac{1}{L_{\text{total}}} = \frac{1}{L_1 + M} + \frac{1}{L_2 + M}$$

Inductors in series (fields bucking)

$$L_{\text{total}} = L_1 + L_2 - 2M$$

Inductors in parallel (fields bucking)

$$\frac{1}{L_{\text{total}}} = \frac{1}{L_1 - M} + \frac{1}{L_2 - M}$$

L = inductance in *henrys*
M = mutual inductance in *henrys*

Capacitors in series

$$\frac{1}{C_{\text{total}}} = \frac{1}{C_1} + \frac{1}{C_2} + \frac{1}{C_3} +, \text{ and so forth}$$

Capacitors in parallel

$$C_{\text{total}} = C_1 + C_2 + C_3 +, \text{ and so forth.}$$

$C =$ capacitance in *farads*

Capacitance of a capacitor

$$C = \frac{0.0885 \times K \times A}{T}$$

$C =$ capacitance in $\mu\mu f$
$K =$ dielectric constant
$A =$ area of plate in contact with one side of the dielectric, in *square centimeters*
$T =$ thickness of dielectric in *centimeters*

Inductive reactance

$$X_L = 2\pi f L$$

X_L $=$ inductive reactance in *ohms*
f $=$ frequency in *cycles per second*
L $=$ inductance in *henrys*
2π $= 6.28$

$$X_L = \frac{E}{I}; \quad I = \frac{E}{X_L}; \quad E = I \times X_L$$

$X_L =$ inductive reactance in *ohms*
$I =$ current in *amperes*
$E =$ electromotive force in *volts*

Capacitive reactance

$$X_C = \frac{1}{2\pi f C}$$

$X_C =$ capacitive reactance in *ohms*
$f =$ frequency in cycles *per second*
$C =$ capacitance in *farads*
$2\pi = 6.28$

$$X_C = \frac{E}{I}; \quad I = \frac{E}{X_C}; \quad E = I \times X_C$$

$X_C =$ capacitive reactance in *ohms*
$I =$ current in *amperes*
$E =$ electromotive force in *volts*

Reactance and impedance

$$X_{\text{total}} = X_L - X_C$$

$X_{\text{total}} =$ total reactance in *ohms*. If it be positive, the reactance is inductive. If it be negative, the reactance is capacitive.
$X_L =$ inductive reactance in *ohms*
$X_C =$ capacitive reactance in *ohms*

$$Z = \sqrt{R^2 + X_L{}^2}$$

$$Z = \sqrt{R^2 + X_C{}^2}$$

$$Z = \sqrt{R^2 + (X_L - X_C)^2}$$

Z = impedance in *ohms*
R = resistance in *ohms*
X_L = inductive reactance in *ohms*
X_C = capacitive reactance in *ohms*

Resonant frequency

$$f_r = \frac{1}{2\pi \sqrt{L \times C}}$$

f_r = resonant frequency in cycles *per second*
L = inductance in *henrys*
C = capacitance in *farads*
$2\pi = 6.28$

Values for alternating current with sinusoidal waveform

Average current (or voltage) = 0.636 × maximum current (or voltage)
Effective (rms) current (or voltage) = 0.707 × maximum current (or voltage)
Maximum current (or voltage) = 1.41 × effective current (or voltage)

Generator

$$f = \frac{\text{sets of poles} \times \text{speed}}{60}$$

f = frequency in *cycles per second*
speed = revolutions per minute

$$\text{Efficiency (per cent)} = \frac{\text{power output}}{\text{power input}} \times 100$$

$$\text{Voltage regulation} = \frac{\text{Voltage at no load} - \text{Voltage at full load}}{\text{Voltage at full load}} \times 100$$
(per cent)

1 kilowatt = 0.746 horsepower

Motor

$$\text{Speed} = \frac{f \times 120}{\text{poles per phase}}$$

f = frequency in *cycles per second*
speed = revolutions per minute

$$\text{Efficiency (per cent)} = \frac{\text{power output}}{\text{power input}} \times 100$$

1 horsepower = 550 foot-pounds per second

Transformer

$$\frac{E_p}{E_s} = \frac{N_p}{N_s}$$

$$\frac{I_p}{I_s} = \frac{N_s}{N_p}$$

E_p = primary voltage
E_s = secondary voltage
I_p = primary current
I_s = secondary current
N_p = number of turns in primary
N_s = number of turns in secondary

Appendix C

STANDARD ANNEALED COPPER WIRE TABLE *

American Wire Gage (B & S)

Gage No.	Diameter in mils[†] (d)	Area in circular mils (d^2)	Ohms per 1000 feet	Pounds per 1000 feet	Feet per ohm	Feet per pound
0000	460.0	211,600	0.04901	640.5	20,400	1.561
000	409.6	167,800	0.06180	507.9	16,180	1.968
00	364.8	133,100	0.07793	402.8	12,830	2.482
0	324.9	105,500	0.09827	319.5	10,180	3.130
1	289.3	83,690	0.1239	253.3	8,070	3.947
2	257.6	66,370	0.1563	200.9	6,400	4.977
3	229.4	52,640	0.1970	159.3	5,075	6.276
4	204.3	41,740	0.2485	126.4	4,025	7.914
5	181.9	33,100	0.3133	100.2	3,192	9.980
6	162.0	26,250	0.3951	79.46	2,531	12.58
7	144.3	20,820	0.4982	63.02	2,007	15.87
8	128.5	16,510	0.6282	49.98	1,592	20.01
9	114.4	13,090	0.7921	39.63	1,262	25.23
10	101.9	10,380	0.9989	31.43	1,001	31.82
11	90.74	8,234	1.260	24.92	794.0	40.12
12	80.81	6,530	1.588	19.77	629.6	50.59
13	71.96	5,178	2.003	15.68	499.3	63.80
14	64.08	4,107	2.525	12.43	396.0	80.44
15	57.07	3,257	3.184	9.858	314.0	101.40

Gage No.	Diameter in mils† (d)	Area in circular mils (d²)	Ohms per 1000 feet	Pounds per 1000 feet	Feet per ohm	Feet per pound
16	50.82	2,583	4.016	7.818	249.0	127.9
17	45.26	2,048	5.064	6.200	197.5	161.3
18	40.30	1,624	6.385	4.917	156.6	203.4
19	35.89	1,288	8.051	3.899	124.2	256.5
20	31.96	1,022	10.15	3.092	98.50	323.4
21	28.46	810.1	12.80	2.452	78.11	407.8
22	25.35	642.4	16.14	1.945	61.95	514.2
23	22.57	509.5	20.36	1.542	49.13	648.4
24	20.10	404.0	25.67	1.223	38.96	817.7
25	17.90	320.4	32.37	0.9699	30.90	1,031
26	15.94	254.1	40.81	0.7692	24.50	1,300
27	14.20	201.5	51.47	0.6100	19.43	1,639
28	12.64	159.8	64.90	0.4837	15.41	2,067
29	11.26	126.7	81.83	0.3836	12.22	2,607
30	10.03	100.5	103.2	0.3042	9.691	3,287
31	8.928	79.70	130.1	0.2413	7.685	4,145
32	7.950	63.21	164.1	0.1913	6.095	5,227
33	7.080	50.13	206.9	0.1517	4.833	6,591
34	6.305	39.75	260.9	0.1203	3.833	8,310
35	5.615	31.52	329.0	0.09542	3.040	10,480
36	5.000	25.00	414.8	0.07568	2.411	13,210
37	4.453	19.83	523.1	0.06001	1.912	16,660
38	3.965	15.72	659.6	0.04759	1.516	21,010
39	3.531	12.47	831.8	0.03774	1.202	26,500
40	3.145	9.888	1049	0.02993	0.9534	33,410

* Circular No. 31, Bureau of Standards.
† All measurements taken at 20°C (68°F).

Appendix D

HOW TO WRITE LARGE NUMBERS

It sometimes becomes necessary to use numbers that are so large (or so small) they become awkward to handle. We have several methods for dealing with such numbers. One is to use a series of prefixes which signifies certain numerical quantities.

The prefix *meg-* or *mega-* means a million (1,000,000).
The prefix *kilo-* means a thousand (1,000).
The prefix *milli- means a thousandth* (1/1,000).
The prefix *micro-* means a millionth (1/1,000,000).

Using this system, a *kilowatt* means a thousand watts, and a *milliwatt* means a thousandth of a watt. Similarly, a *megohm* is equal to a million ohms, and a *microfarad* is equal to a millionth of a farad. Sometimes the symbol μ (the Greek letter "mu") is used instead of *micro-*. Thus a microfarad might appear as μf (the symbol f stands for *farad*). Similarly, a micromicrofarad (one millionth of a microfarad) might appear as $\mu\mu$f.

Another method used for writing large numbers is a sort of mathematical shorthand. For example, multiply 10 by 10. The result is 100. Since 100 is formed by *two* 10's multiplied together, we express 100 as 10^2. Similarly, 1,000 is formed by *three* 10's multiplied together. It may be expressed, therefore, as 10^3. Using this system, a million (1,000,000) becomes 10^6. If we wish to express the number 5,000,000, we may do so simply by writing 5×10^6 (that is, five times 10^6).

The small figure following the 10 is called the *exponent* and indicates the number of 10's that are multiplied together. Thus, in the case of 10^6, 6 is the exponent. If we wish to indicate 1/1,000,000, we may write $1/10^6$. Another method is to write 10^{-6}. The figure "−6" is called the *negative exponent*. Thus, 1,000 may be expressed as 10^3 and 1/1,000 may be expressed as $1/10^3$ or 10^{-3}.

Appendix E

MATHEMATICAL TABLE OF SQUARES AND SQUARE ROOTS

No.	Square	Square root	No.	Square	Square root	No.	Square	Square root	No.	Square	Square root
1	1	1.000	26	676	5.0990	51	2601	7.1414	76	5776	8.7178
2	4	1.414	27	729	5.1962	52	2704	7.2111	77	5929	8.7750
3	9	1.732	28	784	5.2915	53	2809	7.2801	78	6084	8.8318
4	16	2.000	29	841	5.3852	54	2916	7.3485	79	6241	8.8882
5	25	2.236	30	900	5.4772	55	3025	7.4162	80	6400	8.9443
6	36	2.449	31	961	5.5678	56	3136	7.4833	81	6561	9.0000
7	49	2.646	32	1024	5.6569	57	3249	7.5498	82	6724	9.0554
8	64	2.828	33	1089	5.7446	58	3364	7.6158	83	6889	9.1104
9	81	3.000	34	1156	5.8310	59	3481	7.6811	84	7056	9.1652
10	100	3.162	35	1225	5.9161	60	3600	7.7460	85	7225	9.2195
11	121	3.3166	36	1296	6.0000	61	3721	7.8102	86	7396	9.2736
12	144	3.4641	37	1369	6.0828	62	3844	7.8740	87	7569	9.3274
13	169	3.6056	38	1444	6.1644	63	3969	7.9373	88	7744	9.3808
14	196	3.7417	39	1521	6.2450	64	4096	8.0000	89	7921	9.4340
15	225	3.8730	40	1600	6.3246	65	4225	8.0623	90	8100	9.4868
16	256	4.0000	41	1681	6.4031	66	4356	8.1240	91	8281	9.5394
17	289	4.1231	42	1764	6.4807	67	4489	8.1854	92	8464	9.5917
18	324	4.2426	43	1849	6.5574	68	4624	8.2462	93	8649	9.6437
19	361	4.3589	44	1936	6.6332	69	4761	8.3066	94	8836	9.6954
20	400	4.4721	45	2025	6.7082	70	4900	8.3666	95	9025	9.7468
21	441	4.5826	46	2116	6.7823	71	5041	8.4261	96	9216	9.7980
22	484	4.6904	47	2209	6.8557	72	5184	8.4853	97	9409	9.8489
23	529	4.7958	48	2304	6.9282	73	5329	8.5440	98	9604	9.8995
24	576	4.8990	49	2401	7.0000	74	5476	8.6023	99	9801	9.9499
25	625	5.0000	50	2500	7.0711	75	5625	8.6603	100	10000	10.0000

Appendix F

DECIMAL EQUIVALENTS OF FRACTIONS

		1/64	0.015625			33/64	0.515625
	1/32		0.031250		17/32		0.531250
		3/64	0.046875			35/64	0.546875
1/16			0.062500	9/16			0.562500
		5/64	0.078125			37/64	0.578125
	3/32		0.093750		19/32		0.593750
		7/64	0.109375			39/64	0.609375
1/8			0.125000	5/8			0.625000
		9/64	0.140625			41/64	0.640625
	5/32		0.156250		21/32		0.656250
		11/64	0.171875			43/64	0.671875
3/16			0.187500	11/16			0.687500
		13/64	0.203125			45/64	0.703125
	7/32		0.218750		23/32		0.718750
		15/64	0.234375			47/64	0.734375
1/4			0.250000	3/4			0.750000
		17/64	0.265625			49/64	0.765625
	9/32		0.281250		25/32		0.781250
		19/64	0.296875			51/64	0.796875
5/16			0.312500	13/16			0.812500
		21/64	0.328125			53/64	0.828125
	11/32		0.343750		27/32		0.843750
		23/64	0.359375			55/64	0.859375
3/8			0.375000	7/8			0.875000
		25/64	0.390625			57/64	0.890625
	13/32		0.406250		29/32		0.906250
		27/64	0.421875			59/64	0.921875
7/16			0.437500	15/16			0.937500
		29/64	0.453125			61/64	0.953125
	15/32		0.468750		31/32		0.968750
		31/64	0.484375			63/64	0.984375
1/2			0.500000	1			1.000000

Appendix G

TABLES OF MEASUREMENT

TABLES OF LENGTH

English System

12 inches	= 1 foot
3 feet	= 1 yard
1,760 yards	} = 1 mile (statute)
5,280 feet	
1.15 statute miles	= 1 knot (nautical mile)

Metric System

10 millimeters	= 1 centimeter
100 centimeters	} = 1 meter
1,000 millimeters	
1,000 meters	= 1 kilometer

1 centimeter = 0.394 inch
1 inch = 2.54 centimeters
1 yard = 0.91 meter
1 mile = 1.60 kilometers

TABLES OF AREA

English System

144 square inches	= 1 square foot
9 square feet	= 1 square yard
4,840 square yards	= acre
640 acres	= 1 square mile

Metric System

100 square millimeters	= 1 square centimeter
10,000 square centimeters	} = 1 square meter
1,000,000 square millimeters	
1,000,000 square meters	= 1 square kilometer

1 square centimeter = 0.155 square inch
1 square inch = 6.452 square centimeters
1 square yard = 0.83 square meter

TABLES OF VOLUME

English System

1,728 cubic inches = 1 cubic foot
27 cubic feet   = 1 cubic yard
128 cubic feet   = 1 cord

Metric System

1,000 cubic   = 1 cubic centimeter
millimeters
1,000 cubic   = 1 cubic decimeter
centimeters
1,000 cubic   = 1 cubic meter
decimeters

1 cubic centimeter = 0.061 cubic inch
1 cubic inch   = 16.387 cubic centimeters

TABLES OF WEIGHT

English System

7,000 grains }
16 ounces   } = 1 pound
2,000 pounds = 1 ton
2,240 pounds = 1 long ton

Metric System

1,000 milligrams   = 1 gram
1,000 grams   }
1,000,000 milligrams } = 1 kilogram
1,000 kilograms   = 1 metric ton

1 gram = 0.035 ounce
1 ounce = 28.349 grams
1 pound = { 453.6 grams
          { 0.453 kilogram

Appendix H

GRAPHIC SYMBOLS FOR ELECTRICAL DIAGRAMS

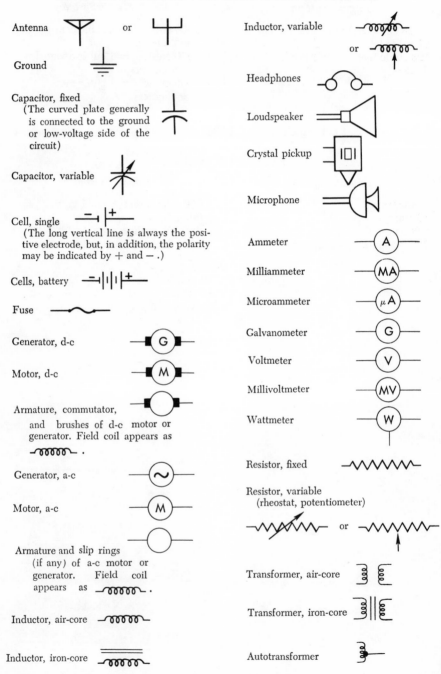

Antenna   or

Ground

Capacitor, fixed
(The curved plate generally
is connected to the ground
or low-voltage side of the
circuit)

Capacitor, variable

Cell, single
(The long vertical line is always the positive electrode, but, in addition, the polarity
may be indicated by + and − .)

Cells, battery

Fuse

Generator, d-c

Motor, d-c

Armature, commutator,
and brushes of d-c motor or
generator. Field coil appears as
.

Generator, a-c

Motor, a-c

Armature and slip rings
(if any) of a-c motor or
generator. Field coil
appears as   .

Inductor, air-core

Inductor, iron-core

Inductor, variable

or

Headphones

Loudspeaker

Crystal pickup

Microphone

Ammeter

Milliammeter

Microammeter

Galvanometer

Voltmeter

Millivoltmeter

Wattmeter

Resistor, fixed

Resistor, variable
(rheostat, potentiometer)

or

Transformer, air-core

Transformer, iron-core

Autotransformer

Switch, single-pole, single-throw

Switch, single-pole, double-throw

Switch, double-pole, single-throw

Switch, double-pole, double-throw

Switch, rotary, single-pole, 5-position

Wires connected

Wires not connected

Crystal diode; metallic rectifier
(arrowhead indicates forward direction)

Transistor

Electron tube, portions of:

Heater; directly heated filament

Cathode, indirectly heated

Grid

Plate or anode

Diode, vacuum-type   or

Diode, gas-filled   or

Ignitron

Triode, vacuum-type

Thyratron

Pentode

Phototube
(the curved element
is the emitter)

Cathode-ray tube, with electrostatic deflection system

Cathode-ray tube, for electromagnetic deflection system
(deflecting coils appear outside the tube
symbol)

Index